SYMBOLS FOR USE ON DRAWINGS:

TL — True Length

EV — Edge View

TS — True Size

— Parallel

— Perpendicular

— Piercing point of line and surface

SYMBOLS FOR INSTRUCTOR'S CORRECTIONS:

C — Show construction

D — Show dimensions; show given or required data

I — Improve form or spacing

H — Too heavy

NH — Not heavy enough

ND — Not dark enough

SL — Sharpen pencil or compass lead

— Error in encircled area

DESCRIPTIVE
GEOMETRY

Frontispiece. Many geometric forms are present in the Orthoflow Catalytic Cracking Unit at Tidewater's Delaware Refinery. *Courtesy Tidewater Oil Co., New York.*

DESCRIPTIVE GEOMETRY

SECOND EDITION

E. G. PARÉ
PROFESSOR OF MECHANICAL ENGINEERING
STATE COLLEGE OF WASHINGTON

R. O. LOVING
I. L. HILL
PROFESSORS OF TECHNICAL DRAWING
ILLINOIS INSTITUTE OF TECHNOLOGY

THE MACMILLAN COMPANY · NEW YORK

SECOND EDITION © THE MACMILLAN COMPANY 1959

ALL RIGHTS RESERVED. NO PART OF THIS BOOK MAY BE REPRODUCED OR UTILIZED IN ANY FORM OR BY ANY MEANS, ELECTRONIC OR ME-CHANICAL, INCLUDING PHOTOCOPYING, RECORDING OR BY ANY INFOR-MATION STORAGE AND RETRIEVAL SYSTEM, WITHOUT PERMISSION IN WRITING FROM THE PUBLISHER.

SEVENTH PRINTING 1965

LIBRARY OF CONGRESS CATALOG CARD NUMBER: 59–5109

PREVIOUS EDITION COPYRIGHT 1952 BY THE MACMILLAN COMPANY

THE MACMILLAN COMPANY, NEW YORK
BRETT-MACMILLAN LTD., GALT, ONTARIO

PRINTED IN THE UNITED STATES OF AMERICA

PREFACE

IN THIS TEXT the authors have endeavored to fulfill the need for a descriptive geometry textbook in which fundamentals are presented in the same pedagogically sound units of work as are usually introduced in laboratory periods. By division of the text material into relatively short, homogeneous chapters, convenient textbook reference is available to students. This simplified organization follows that of the authors' *Descriptive Geometry Worksheets,* Series A, B, and C, in which new principles are introduced in order of need and difficulty.

Solution illustrations throughout the text have been broken into the necessary steps to make the construction easy to follow. Considerable care has been exercised to provide solutions in pictorial form whenever they can be used to aid visualization. Emphasis is focused on those applications which serve to illuminate fundamentals and to introduce new engineering experiences.

Conveniently located at the end of each chapter are abstract and practical laboratory problems based on the text material of the chapter unit. Chapter 24 contains ideal review material and many problems, the solutions of which entail several principles. For convenience of students and instructors, problems are given in layout form exactly as they are to be reproduced on the drawing paper.

In this revision, the authors have refined and expanded the text and have revised and added illustrations to improve clarity and readability wherever the need has been indicated. In addition, some 10 per cent of the problem material has been either revised or replaced, and new problems have been added to the extent of more than 25 per cent. Also, a special effort has been made to place illustrations as close to pertinent text passages as possible. We believe the resulting convenience is more important than having all pages exactly the same length.

The authors gratefully acknowledge the helpful comments and suggestions offered by Professors Philip Chaikin, W. M. Christman, Jr., B. M. Green, F. A. Heacock, L. O. Johnson, A. H. Knebel, F. C. Morris, Gustav Rook, Irwin Wladaver, and others. Particularly, thanks are due Professor H. C. Spencer for his continual assistance and encouragement.

E. G. PARÉ
R. O. LOVING
I. L. HILL

CONTENTS

CHAPTER 1 ORTHOGRAPHIC PROJECTION   1

CHAPTER 2 PRIMARY AUXILIARY VIEWS   22

CHAPTER 3 LINES   37

CHAPTER 4 PLANES   56

CHAPTER 5 SUCCESSIVE AUXILIARY VIEWS   64

CHAPTER 6 PIERCING POINTS   80

CHAPTER 7 INTERSECTION OF PLANES   88

CHAPTER 8 ANGLE BETWEEN PLANES   95

CHAPTER 9 PARALLELISM   104

CHAPTER 10 PERPENDICULARITY   111

CHAPTER 11 ANGLE BETWEEN LINE AND OBLIQUE PLANE   129

CHAPTER 12 MINING AND CIVIL ENGINEERING PROBLEMS   136

CHAPTER 13 REVOLUTION   149

CHAPTER 14 CONCURRENT VECTORS   164

CHAPTER 15 PLANE TANGENCIES   176

CHAPTER 16 INTERSECTIONS OF PLANES WITH SOLIDS   190

CHAPTER 17 DEVELOPMENTS   201

CHAPTER 18 INTERSECTIONS OF SURFACES   226

CHAPTER 19 SHADES AND SHADOWS   252

CHAPTER 20 PICTORIAL PROJECTIONS   261

CHAPTER 21 CONICS   283

CHAPTER 22 MAP PROJECTION   288

CHAPTER 23   SPHERICAL TRIANGLES   299

CHAPTER 24   REVIEW   308

APPENDIX I.   GRAPHICAL ACCURACY   323

APPENDIX II.   GEOMETRIC CONSTRUCTIONS   329

APPENDIX III.   CLASSIFICATION OF GEOMETRIC FORMS   336

INDEX   343

NOTATION   Inside front cover

SYMBOLS FOR STUDENT AND INSTRUCTOR   Fly leaf inside front cover

TABLE OF NATURAL TANGENTS   Inside back cover

DESCRIPTIVE
GEOMETRY

ORTHOGRAPHIC PROJECTION

CHAPTER 1

ONE OF MAN'S most effective methods for communicating ideas is through the medium of illustrations or drawings. In accordance with the idea to be conveyed, the illustration or drawing may be an artist's painting, a photographer's print, an engineer's pictorial or multiview sketch, or a draftsman's carefully executed technical drawing. The pictorial type of drawing gives a rapid but superficial presentation of the subject. It remains for the technical drawing based on the principles of *orthographic projection* [1] to provide the completeness of detail necessary for the design and construction of a machine part or an architectural structure.

1.1 GRAPHIC SOLUTIONS

In addition to the communication of ideas, the principles of orthographic projection may be used for the solution of many engineering problems. Graphic solutions may be effectively employed when the required accuracy of the results falls within the limits of accuracy of the graphic method or of the original data, especially since a large proportion of the empirical data used in engineering calculations is considerably less precise than graphic methods. (See Appendix I for a discussion of graphical accuracy.)

The authors are partial to the idea that the student should treat his problem solutions as if they were engineering reports. His drawings should in this light always be absolutely clear and understandable without any oral explanation on his part. To accomplish this, the minimum amount of lettering should include the following:

(a) Identification in all views of isolated or unconnected points and end points of isolated lines.
(b) Identification of important construction points.
(c) Identification in all views of at least one prominent point on planes or solid objects.

---

[1] See Art. 1.5 for a definition of orthographic projection.

1

(d) A clear indication by dimensions or notes of the uses of all given data and of the sources of all required data.

(e) Identification of all *folding lines* employed in the problem solution (Art. 1.10).

1.2 DESCRIPTIVE GEOMETRY

Descriptive geometry is the science of graphic representation and solution of space problems. The fundamentals of descriptive geometry are based on the principles of orthographic projection—the same principles employed in a basic course in technical drawing. In descriptive geometry the theory of orthographic projection is applied to the drawing-board representation and solution of engineering problems more advanced than those usually encountered in an elementary course in engineering or technical drawing.

The majority of the problems investigated in this course will require solutions which are not obtainable in the three principal views of orthographic drawing: front, top, and side views. For this reason many of the solutions will employ one or more auxiliary views or revolution. Although most problems presented in engineering drawing courses are derived from the field of machine drawing, the problems included in a well-designed descriptive geometry course are selected from all the engineering sciences: civil, aeronautical, mechanical, chemical, electrical, architectural, and others.

Descriptive geometry is a versatile tool which the prospective engineer should learn to use broadly and skillfully. It is a means by which the well-trained engineer can effect great savings of time and economy of effort. The problems presented in this text have a careful balance of theoretical and practical applications so that the student will not only be fully trained in the fundamentals but will also be introduced to the extensive practical scope of this graphic method.

1.3 PROJECTIONS

In order to represent an object by a line drawing on a plane, imaginary *projectors* emanating from various points on the object are extended until they pierce a *picture plane* or *projection plane*. The projectors may be thought of as *visual rays* extending from the object to an observer. The various piercing points are then connected with lines to form a *view* of the object.

Two common types of projection are *perspective* projection, Fig. 1–1, and *orthographic* projection, Fig. 1–2.

1.4 PERSPECTIVE PROJECTION

The basic theory of perspective projection is illustrated in Fig. 1–1. The projectors emanate from points on the object and converge to an observer whose position is designated as the *station point*. The intersections of the

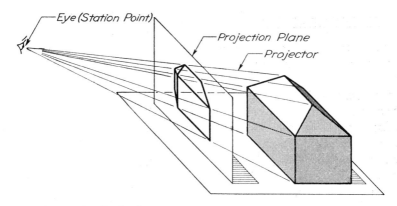

Fig. 1–1. Perspective Projection

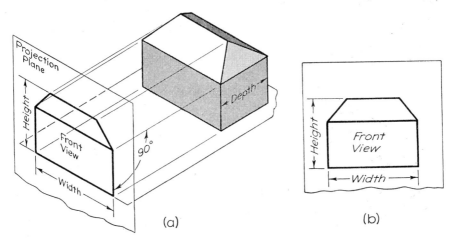

Fig. 1–2. Orthographic Projection

projectors with the projection plane provide the framework for the pictorial of the house, closely resembling that which would be seen by an observer actually looking at the house from the same station point. The size of the pictorial will vary as the relative positions of the eye, the projection plane, and the object are altered.

Although perspective projection produces a realistic pictorial view of an object, its distortion of angles and distances prevents its meeting the exacting requirements demanded of a technical drawing. Perspective projection is used primarily by architects and commercial artists to describe in a general way the physical external appearance of a structure or a product.[2]

---

[2] See Chapter 20 for a more thorough treatment of perspective projection, including methods of construction.

1.5 ORTHOGRAPHIC PROJECTION

Orthographic projection is a method of representing an object by a line drawing on a projection plane which is perpendicular to parallel projectors, Fig. 1–2.

In contrast with perspective projection, it is important to note that in orthographic projection the size of the view of the object will not vary with the distance between the object and the projection plane.

The object in space may be turned and tilted, a procedure which results in an *axonometric* pictorial having foreshortened edges.[3] This text is, however, primarily concerned with that class of orthographic projections called *multiview drawing* in which the main purpose is to obtain views of an object

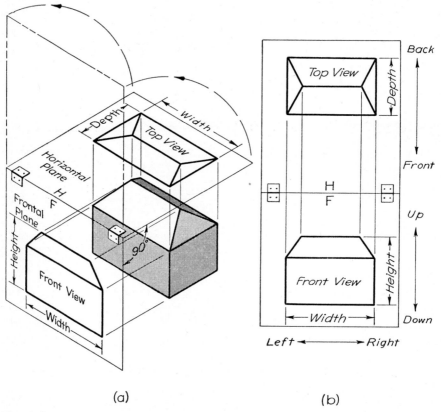

(a)   (b)

Fig. 1–3. Multiview Drawing

---

[3] See Chapter 20.

on which true measurements can be made. Therefore, in Fig. 1–2 the front face is oriented parallel to the projection plane so that the established view shows the true *width* and *height* of the house. It will be noted, however, that the *depth* dimension is not shown in this *front* view. Thus a single orthographic view in itself cannot fully describe an object. An additional view on a projection plane perpendicular to the first is needed to give the depth of the house. Figure 1–3(a) illustrates the projection of the house on two perpendicular planes. It will be noted that the width dimension appears in both views while the height appears only in the front view and the depth only in the top view.

Since it would indeed be inconvenient to carry about a drawing on planes at right angles to each other, a conventional means of showing several views on a single plane has been developed.

Figure 1–3(a) suggests the manner in which the *horizontal* projection plane (*H*) is rotated into the same plane as the front view (the *frontal* plane, *F*). Or it may be assumed that the frontal projection plane is rotated into the plane of the top view. Figure 1–3(b) shows these two views in the resulting conventional arrangement as they would be drawn on paper. Two such directly related views of an object are called *adjacent* views.

1.6   MULTIVIEW DRAWING

A multiview drawing is a systematic arrangement of orthographic views on a single plane (the drawing paper). The relationship of the views in the arrangement is based on the principle that *any two adjacent views lie on perpendicular planes of projection.* The two standard arrangements of views in general use are called *first-angle projection* and *third-angle projection.*

1.7   FIRST-ANGLE PROJECTION

In first-angle projection, Fig. 1–4(a), the object is placed in Quadrant I formed by the intersection of a horizontal and a frontal plane. The top view of the object is obtained by projecting from the object *downward* to the horizontal plane, and the front view is obtained by projecting from the object *backward* to the frontal plane. The horizontal plane is then rotated downward into the frontal plane, resulting in the arrangement of views in Fig. 1–4(b). Note that in first-angle projection the observer is always assumed to be looking *through the object* toward the projection plane. The resulting arrangement of six views is shown in Fig. 1–5.

First-angle projection is used by most foreign countries for all types of engineering drawings, and this arrangement of views is sometimes employed in the United States for architectural and structural drawings.

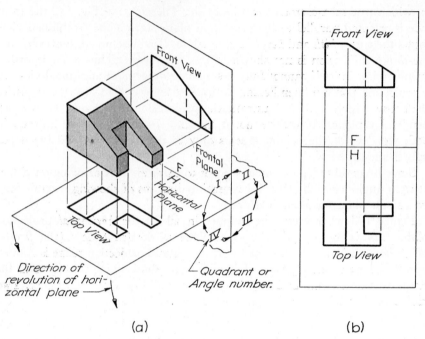

(a)   (b)

Fig. 1–4.   First-Angle Projection—Two Views

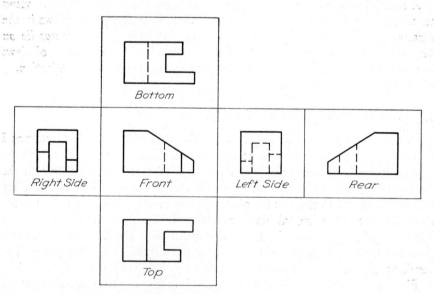

Fig. 1–5.   First-Angle Projection—Six Views

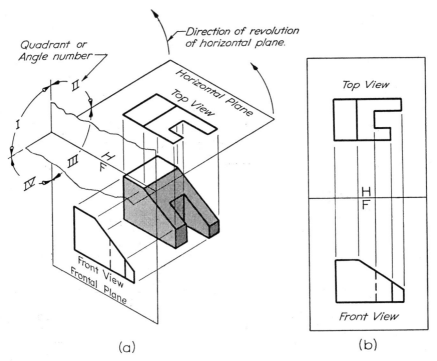

Fig. 1–6. Third-Angle Projection—Two Views

1.8 THIRD-ANGLE PROJECTION

In third-angle projection, Figs. 1–3 and 1–6(a), the object is placed in Quadrant III formed by the intersection of a horizontal and a frontal plane. The top view of the object is obtained by projection from the object *upward* to the horizontal plane, and the front view is obtained by projecting from the object *forward* to the frontal plane. The horizontal plane is then rotated upward into the frontal plane, resulting in the relative positions of views shown in Fig. 1–6(b). Note that the observer is always assumed to be looking *through the projection plane* toward the object. Compare this concept with that of first-angle projection.

Third-angle projection is used in the United States for practically all types of engineering drawings.

Of course a great many engineering drawings require more details than can be clearly indicated in two views only. A *right-side* (profile) view may be added by projecting from the object to a *profile* plane (*P*) as illustrated in

Fig. 1–7(a). The relative locations of the views on the drawing paper resulting from the rotation of the profile plane into the frontal plane is shown in Fig. 1–7(b). Another acceptable but less frequently used arrangement of these views may be obtained by rotating the profile plane into the horizontal plane, Fig. 1–8.

Occasionally it becomes desirable on an engineering drawing to use such views as a *left-side* view, a *bottom* view, or a *rear* view. These views, together with the top, front, and right-side views, constitute the six basic views, Fig. 1–9. These are the views that may be obtained by projecting from an object onto the faces of an enclosing rectangular "projection box."

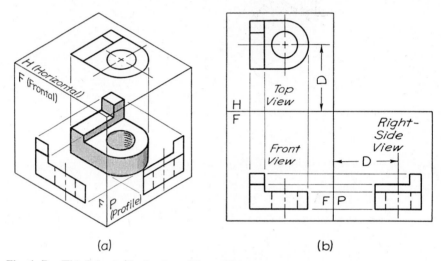

(a)   (b)

Fig. 1–7.   Third-Angle Projection—Three Views

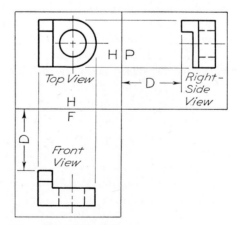

Fig. 1–8.   Alternate Position for Right-Side View

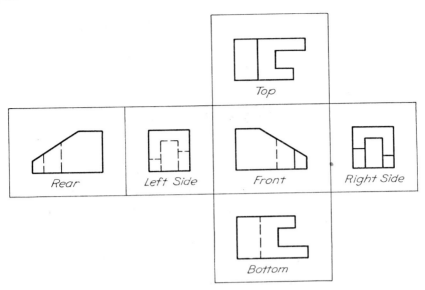

Fig. 1–9. Third-Angle Projection—Six Basic Views

1.9 VISUALIZATION

Until now, views have been defined as the result of projecting from an object onto a projection plane. This is the historically basic theory of descriptive geometry resulting in the internationally understood arrangements of views.

For purposes of visualization, however, most engineers find that a more direct approach is to consider that each view is an actual picture of the object as seen with a *line of sight* perpendicular to the corresponding projection plane.

To obtain a front view of an object, the observer imagines himself placed in front of the object, shifting position for each point so that the line of sight is always perpendicular to an imaginary frontal projection plane (F), Fig. 1–10(a).

To procure a top view, the object is considered stationary, and the observer imagines his position changed so that he is looking down on the object from a "bird's-eye view," Fig. 1–10(b).

Other views may be obtained in a similar manner, with the observer changing his position successively until a sufficient number of views is secured to describe adequately all the features of the object. For ease in construction and interpretation, the relative positions of these views on the drawing paper must always conform to the arrangement of views secured by third-angle projection.

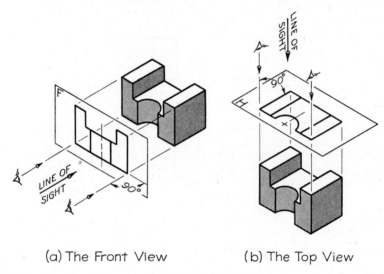

(a) The Front View   (b) The Top View

Fig. 1–10.   Obtaining Views by the Line-of-Sight Method

To read a technical drawing, or let us say to *visualize* an object from its given orthographic views, the observer should always consider the views to be the object itself and should always be acutely aware of the position occupied by the observer relative to the object observed. Thus, when reading the front view, the observer must be aware that he is facing the front of the object with his line of sight directed front to back. Hence, a glance at the front view discloses the height and width of the object, and in addition the location for the top, bottom, left-side, and right-side surfaces of the object. The observer must never forget that the line of sight for the top view is directed *downward* in space toward the object so that depth and width dimensions appear in the top view while height dimensions are not available in this view. These principles enable the observer to build up a mental three-dimensional outline, Fig. 1–11(a) and (b).

In Fig. 1–11(a), a circle is observed in the top view. A study of the corresponding lines that represent this feature in the front view shows that the circle represents a hole rather than a protruding boss. This feature is then added to the mental picture, Fig. 1–11(c). Other features are similarly checked in adjacent views until a complete mental picture of the object is developed, Fig. 1–11(d).

1.10   FOLDING LINES

Most technical drawings in industry do not include those lines between the views which represent the intersections of the projection planes (the lines marked H/F or F/P). However, since descriptive geometry construc-

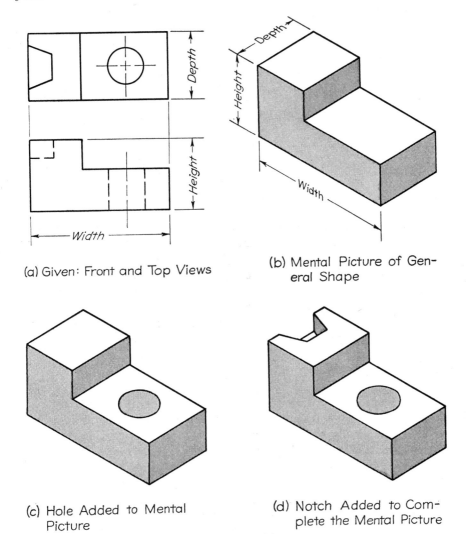

(a) Given: Front and Top Views

(b) Mental Picture of General Shape

(c) Hole Added to Mental Picture

(d) Notch Added to Complete the Mental Picture

Fig. 1–11. Visualization

tions often include abstract forms, such as points, lines, and planes, the inclusion of these lines will be useful as shown later.

The lines of intersection of the mutually perpendicular projection planes are referred to as *folding lines*. The folding line between the front and top views is labeled H/F as shown in Fig. 1–12(a) and (b), the F indicating the frontal plane and the H the horizontal plane. *It should be noted that when the front view is examined, this folding line represents the edge view of the horizontal plane, Fig. 1–12(b). When the top view is studied, the same folding line represents the edge view of the frontal plane.*

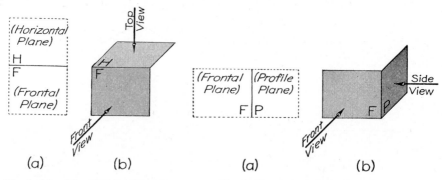

Fig. 1–12.   The H/F Folding Line   Fig. 1–13.   The F/P Folding Line

The folding line between the front and side views is labeled F/P as shown in Fig. 1–13(a) and (b), the P indicating the profile plane. When the front view is examined, this folding line represents the edge view of the profile plane; and when the side view is examined, the folding line represents the edge view of the frontal plane, Fig. 1–13(b).

The use of folding lines serves as a reminder that adjacent views lie in planes which were at right angles to each other in space before rotation into the plane of the paper.

1.11   VIEWS OF A POINT

Fundamentally a mental picture of an object is built up or read from given views by a point-by-point analysis: two points locating a line, lines defining surfaces, and finally surfaces combining to form objects. Consequently a logical starting place for a thorough investigation of the theory of descriptive geometry is an analysis of the nature of and relationship between views of a single, isolated point.

Theoretically a *point* has location only and no dimensions. For accuracy an isolated point is best indicated on the drawing by fine intersecting dashes, as shown in Fig. 1–14, rather than by a dot.

In Fig. 1–14 three views of a point B are shown. Since the top and profile views of any object lie in planes which are perpendicular to the frontal plane, the top and profile projections of point B are the same distance D from the frontal plane, Fig. 1–14(a). It follows that the projections of that point in the top and profile views must be the same distance D from the folding lines representing edge views of the frontal plane, Fig. 1–14(b).

Note that the point in *space* is designated by a capital letter (B) while each of its views is identified with the lower case letter plus the appropriate superscript: b^F, b^H, and b^P.[4]

---

[4] An illustration showing typical lettering and line weights is printed on the inside of the front cover.

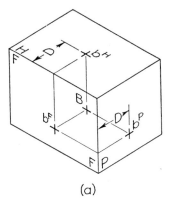

(a)

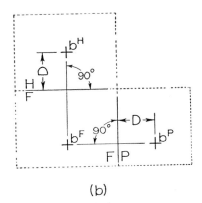

(b)

Fig. 1–14. Three Views of a Point

1.12 VIEWS OF A LINE

In geometry a *line* theoretically has no width. In practice, of course, lines are drawn with various widths according to established conventions. A line may be considered to consist of an infinite number of points. The position of a *straight* line is established by locating any two non-coincident points on the line. For drafting accuracy, points should be selected that are separated by an appreciable distance (Appendix I.2).

To obtain a view of a line, the views of the end points of the line may be established as illustrated in the following problem.

PROBLEM:

Add a profile view of a line *AB,* having given the top and front views, Fig. 1–15(a).

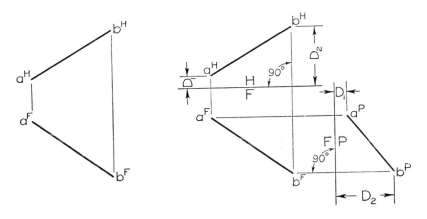

(a) Two Views Given   (b) Right-Side View Constructed

Fig. 1–15. Construction of a Third View of a Line

ANALYSIS:

A straight-line segment is established by locating its end points. The projections of the end points in the front and profile views will be at the same elevation. The projections of these points in the top and profile views will be the same distance behind the frontal plane.

GRAPHIC SOLUTION:

The folding line F/H is inserted between the top and front views and perpendicular to the projection lines between them, Fig. 1–15(b). The folding line F/P is added at any convenient distance to the right of the front view and perpendicular to the projection lines from the front view to the side view. The elevations of the points for the profile projection are obtained by extending horizontal projection lines from the front view to the profile view. The measurements D_1 and D_2, which represent the distances the points lie behind the frontal plane, are then transferred with dividers from the top view to the profile view. The line joining the projections of the two points is the required profile view of the line AB.

A similar procedure may be followed in a problem which requires the addition of a top view of a line having given the front and profile views. Drawing an additional view of a surface or solid object entails successive repetition of this procedure to locate all points and lines in turn.

1.13   VISIBILITY

An essential step in drawing an orthographic view is the correct determination of the visibility of the lines which make up the view. The *outline*

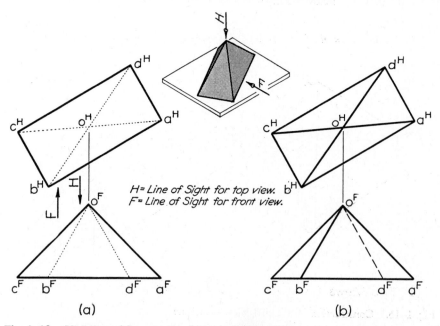

H= Line of Sight for top view.
F= Line of Sight for front view.

(a)   (b)

Fig. 1–16.   Visibility of Intersecting Lines in Principal Views

of a view will always be visible, but the lines within the outline may be visible or hidden, depending on the relative positions of those lines with respect to the line of sight.

Frequently the visibility of lines may be determined by inspection, such as those in Fig. 1–16(a). The screened lines in the top view will be visible or hidden, depending upon the visibility of point O from which all these lines emanate.

The line of sight for a top view is directed toward the object from above. Thus, on the drawing, if the front view is regarded as the object itself, the line of sight for the top view may be represented by an arrow pointing downward as indicatd by arrow H. Since o^F is the point nearest arrow H, point O must be visible in the top view. Therefore, the four edges $o^H a^H$, $o^H b^H$, $o^H c^H$, and $o^H d^H$ are visible in the top view, Fig. 1–16(b).

The line of sight for a front view is directed toward the front of the object. Thus, on the drawing, if the top view is now regarded as the object, the line of sight for the front view is represented by an arrow pointing toward the top view as indicated by arrow F, Fig. 1–16(a). Since edge $o^H b^H$ is nearest arrow F, $o^F b^F$ is visible, Fig. 1–16(b). Since edge $o^H d^H$ is behind the body of the object, $o^F d^F$ is hidden.

The determination of the visibility of non-intersecting lines, such as those illustrated by two rods AB and CD in Fig. 1–17(a), requires a more detailed study. Since the rods are non-intersecting, one of the rods must be above the other at the apparent point of crossing in the top view. Thus the apparent

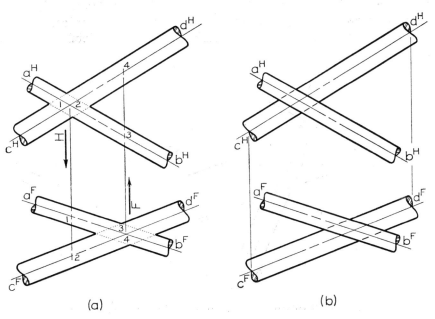

(a)   (b)

Fig. 1–17. Visibility of Non-Intersecting Rods in Principal Views

point of intersection of center lines $a^H b^H$ and $c^H d^H$ in the top view actually represents *two* points, one point on AB and the other point on CD. These are located on the respective center lines in the front view, where it can be observed that point 1 on $a^F b^F$ is at a higher elevation than point 2 on $c^F d^F$; that is, point 1 is nearer to line of sight H than is point 2. Since AB is thus higher than CD at this location, it is nearer to an observer looking downward at the object as indicated by line of sight H. Thus rod AB is completely visible in the top view and rod CD is hidden where it passes below AB, Fig. 1–17(b).

The apparent point of crossing in the front view, Fig. 1–17(a), also represents two points which are labeled 3 and 4 for convenience. These points are then located in the top view where it can be seen that point 3 on $a^H b^H$ is nearer an observer represented by the line of sight F than is point 4 on $c^H d^H$. Thus rod AB is completely visible in the front view and rod CD is hidden where it passes behind AB, Fig. 1–17(b).

The preceding discussion of visibility has been in terms of the top and front views. However, the visibility of lines in *any* two adjacent views may be determined by using the identical approach because any two adjacent views can be reoriented by turning the drawing paper or by shifting the view point so that the two views assume the relative positions of front and top views.

In the two successive views of Fig. 1–18, the apparent point of crossing of $e^1 g^1$ and $j^1 k^1$ in view 1 is labeled 3 and 4, and then these two points are located on the center lines in view 2. In third-angle projection *the line of sight for a view is always directed from that view toward the adjacent view.* Therefore the line of sight for view 1 in Fig. 1–18 is toward view 2 as indicated by arrow 1. Thus point 3 in view 2 is nearer the observer looking along arrow 1, and rod EG is completely visible in view 1. The visibility in view 2

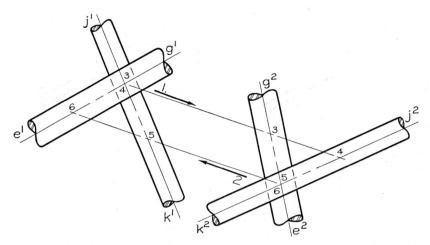

Fig. 1–18. Visibility of Non-Intersecting Rods in Any Two Adjacent Views

may be determined similarly by observing the positions of points 5 and 6 in view 1 in relation to the line of sight 2.

The foregoing principles may also be applied to the determination of the visibility of the interior lines in the views of the *tetrahedron* [5] in Fig. 1–19(a). The apparent point of crossing of $a^F b^F$ and $c^F e^F$ is labeled 1 and 2, and these points are located in view P. Since point 1 on $a^P b^P$ is nearer the observer (line of sight F), line AB is visible in the front view, Fig. 1–19(b). In similar fashion, observation of the relative positions of points 3 and 4 and line of sight P reveals that line AB is visible in the profile view.

In comparing Figs. 1–17, 1–18, and 1–19, it should be observed that the visibility must be determined independently for each view; that is, the visibility of one view is not a clue to the visibilty in the other view.

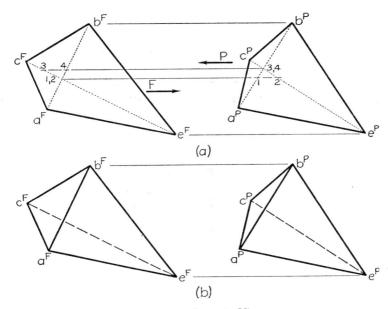

Fig. 1–19. Visibility of Non-Intersecting Lines in Views

1.14 PROBLEM LAYOUTS

Although this text contains some theoretical descriptive geometry problems, the emphasis is focused on those practical problems which serve both to inculcate the basic fundamentals and to introduce a variety of new engineering experiences.

At the end of each chapter, problem material will be found that is based on those principles previously introduced. Review Chapter 24 contains problems whose solutions entail a combination of principles.

[5] See Appendix III.1.

Each worksheet problem presented in this text is accompanied by a layout illustration. The layout dimensions are so stated and the space requirements of the solutions so planned that any conventional border on an 8½ x 11 in., 9 x 12 in., or similar sheet will prove satisfactory.

Some data are given exactly by location dimensions or by a coordinate system; others are purposely presented so that the student is required to plan the spacing. Coordinate dimensions are given in inches and are always to *full* scale, even if the scale of the problem itself is otherwise specified. It will be noted that the "origin" of all coordinate dimensions is the lower left corner of the working space. The first coordinate locates the views of the point from the left border. The second and third coordinates establish the respective positions of the front and top views of the point from the bottom border line of the working space. Figure 1–20(a) demonstrates the location of a point *A* and of point *N* of a line *MN* on a divided sheet; Fig. 1–20(b) shows the location of the views of point *C* of a solid on a full sheet.

The amount of lettering the student should include in his solution is, of course, at the discretion of his instructor (or see Art. 1.1). The notation in the illustrations throughout this book is shown in complete form for ease in correlation with the text material. A representative illustration is printed for reference on the inside of the front cover.

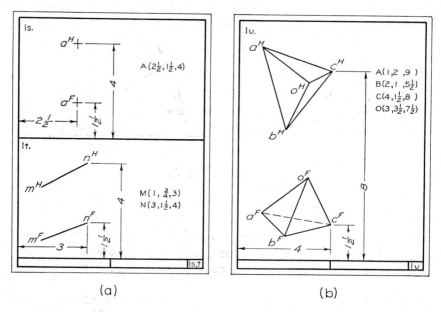

(a)   (b)

Fig. 1–20.   The Coordinate System

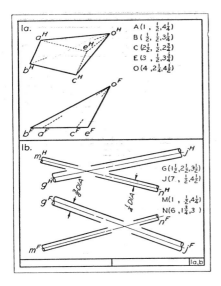

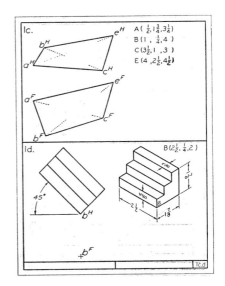

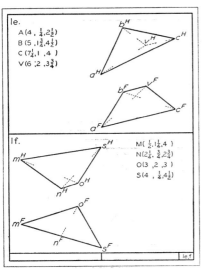

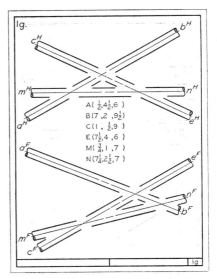

1a. Complete the visibility of the pyramid and add a right-side view.

1b. Show the correct visibility of the two non-intersecting rods.

1c. Complete the visibility of the tetrahedron and add a right-side view.

1d. Complete the front view and add a right-side view.

1e. Complete the visibility of the tetrahedron and add a left-side view.

1f. Complete the visibility of the tetrahedron and add a right-side view.

1g. Complete the visibility of the three non-intersecting ⅜-in. diameter rods.

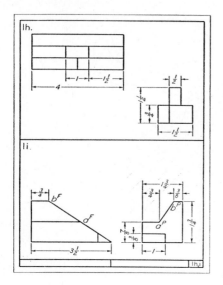

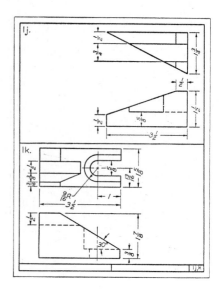

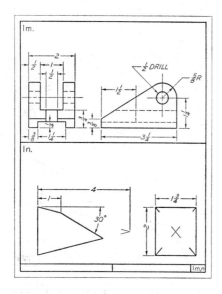

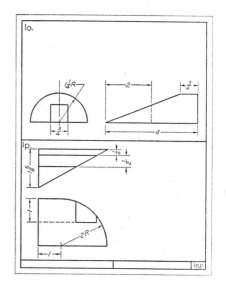

1h. Duplicate the given views and add a front view. Omit dimensions unless assigned.

1i. Duplicate the given views and add a top view. Label *A* and *B* in each view.

1j. Duplicate the given views and add a left-side view.

1k. Duplicate the given views and add a right-side view.

1m. Duplicate the given views and add a top view.

1n. Complete the given views of the truncated pyramid and add a top view.

1o. Duplicate the given views and add a top view.

1p. Duplicate the given views and add a right-side view.

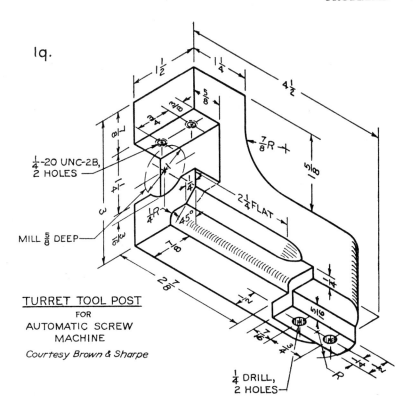

1q.

¼-20 UNC-2B, 2 HOLES

MILL ⅝ DEEP

⅞R

2¼FLAT

¼R

45°

⅞

TURRET TOOL POST

FOR

AUTOMATIC SCREW MACHINE

Courtesy Brown & Sharpe

¼ DRILL, 2 HOLES

1q. Draw the necessary views of the *turret tool post*. Omit dimensions unless assigned.

1r. Indicate whether the following statements are true or false. If assigned, provide written statements or sketches to justify your answers.

(a) A frontal plane appears edgewise in a top view.

(b) A top view shows the height and depth of an object.

(c) First-angle projection is obsolete everywhere.

(d) Third-angle projection pertains to the fact that three views of an object are used on the drawing.

(e) In a front view a profile plane appears edgewise.

(f) A folding line is the line of intersection of two adjacent projection planes.

(g) The visibility of the lines in a view is independent of the relationship of the lines in any other view.

(h) If a line is visible in a top view, it must also be visible in a profile view.

PRIMARY AUXILIARY VIEWS

ALTHOUGH THE ESSENTIAL details of most objects can be shown in front, top, and profile views, many of the more complex problems with which this text is concerned require for their solutions the use of *auxiliary* views. *An auxiliary view is a view projected on any plane other than one of the three principal planes of projection* (frontal, horizontal, or profile).

A *primary* auxiliary view is obtained by projection on a plane that is perpendicular to one of the three principal planes of projection and is inclined to the remaining two.

2.1 VIEWS PROJECTED FROM THE TOP VIEW

An *auxiliary elevation* view, illustrated pictorially in Fig. 2–1(a), is obtained by projection on a plane which is perpendicular to the horizontal plane of projection and inclined to the profile and frontal planes of projection. The procedure for constructing an auxiliary view is essentially the same as for drawing any additional basic view. This similarity should be particularly noted in the following example.

With the top and front views of the house drawn in conventional multi-view arrangement as in Fig. 2–1(b), the steps to obtain a profile view and an auxiliary elevation view follow:

Step 1. Establish the line of sight.

To draw any additional view, it is first necessary to establish that line of sight which will result in a view showing the desired information. In this case let it be assumed that the desired lines of sight are P (for a right-side view) and 1 (for an auxiliary elevation view) as indicated in Fig. 2–1(b). The projection lines for the new views are drawn parallel to the respective lines of sight, Fig. 2–1(c).

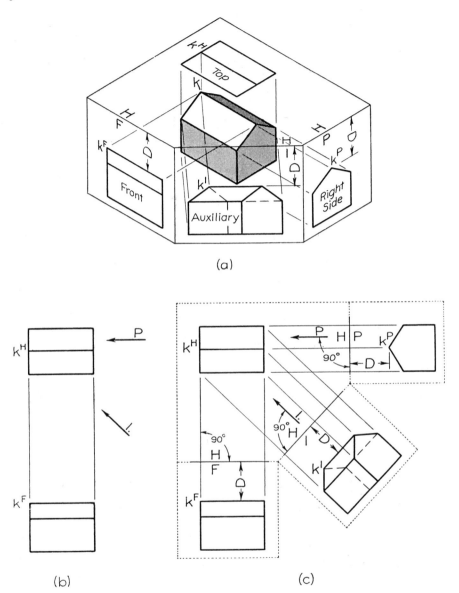

Fig. 2–1. Views Projected from the Top View

Step 2. Introduce the necessary folding lines.

One folding line H/F is drawn between the given views and perpendicular to the projection lines joining them.

Folding lines represent the edge views of projection planes, Art. 1–10. It is a fundamental principle of multiview projection that the plane of projection for a view must be perpendicular to the line of sight for that view. Consequently the remaining folding lines H/P and $H/1$ are drawn perpendicular to the established lines of sight P and 1, respectively, at a convenient distance from the top view.

Step 3.   Transfer distances to the new view.

Since in this case the front view, view P, and view 1 all lie on planes perpendicular to the horizontal projection plane, the corresponding points on these three views of the house lie the same distances below the horizontal plane. Therefore, the measurements to be transferred are obtained from the front view; for example, dimension D, which is the distance point K lies below the horizontal plane. These measurements are transferred as indicated to the corresponding projection lines in each of the new views.

Step 4.   Determine the visibility and complete the views.

The preceding four steps may be used to draw any number of additional auxiliary elevation views; for example, those obtained by the lines of sight 2 and 3 in Fig. 2–2. It should be noted as a general principle that *all views projected from a top view contain identical height dimensions.*

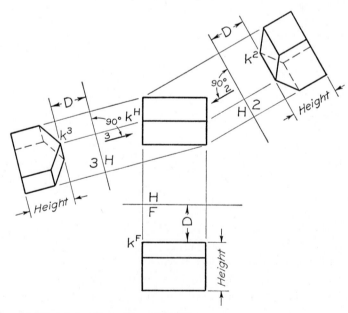

Fig. 2–2.   Additional Auxiliary Elevation Views

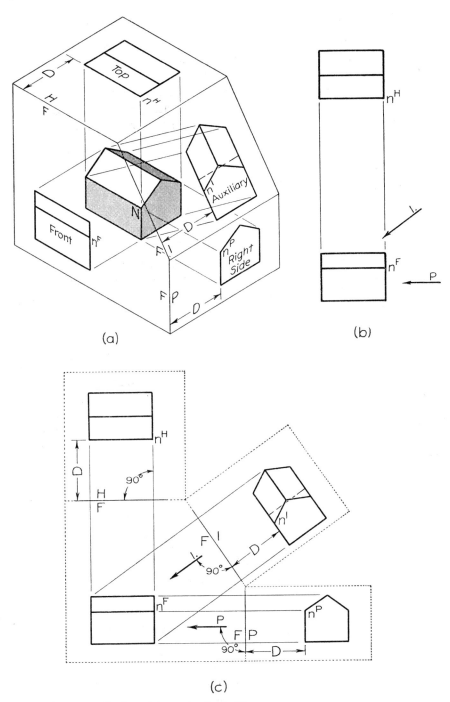

Fig. 2–3. Views Projected from the Front View

2.2   VIEWS PROJECTED FROM THE FRONT VIEW

Another related group of primary auxiliary views may be obtained by projection on planes perpendicular to the frontal plane and inclined to the horizontal and profile planes, Fig. 2–3(a).

The following steps are used to obtain the right-side view P and the auxiliary view 1 of the house, having given the top and front views, Fig. 2–3(b). It should be noted that the steps are the same as those used in constructing views projected from the top view.

Step 1.   Establish the line of sight.

In this case the lines of sight P and 1 are given, establishing the directions of the projection lines.

Step 2.   Introduce the necessary folding lines.

Folding line H/F is drawn between the given views and perpendicular to the projection lines joining them, Fig. 2–3(c). The other folding lines F/P and $F/1$ are drawn perpendicular to the established lines of sight P and 1, respectively, at a convenient distance from the front view.

Step 3.   Transfer distances to the new view.

Since in this case the top view, view P, and view 1 all lie on planes perpendicular to the frontal projection plane, the corresponding points on these three views of the house lie the same distances behind the frontal plane. Therefore the measurements to be transferred are obtained from the top view; for example, dimension D, which is the distance point N lies behind the frontal plane. These measurements are transferred as indicated to the corresponding projection lines in each of the new views.

Step 4.   Determine the visibility and complete the views.

These preceding same four steps may be used to draw any number of additional auxiliary views projected from the front view; for example, those obtained by the lines of sight 2 and 3, Fig. 2–4. *All views projected from a front view contain common depth dimensions.*

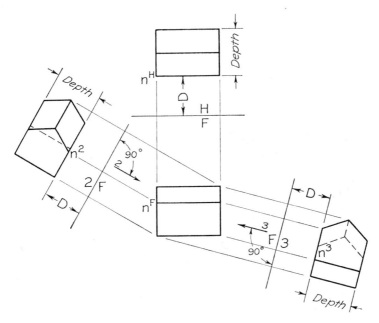

Fig. 2–4. Additional Auxiliary Views Projected from the Front View

2.3 VIEWS PROJECTED FROM THE SIDE VIEW

Still another related group of primary auxiliary views may be obtained by projection on planes perpendicular to the profile plane and inclined to the horizontal and frontal planes, Fig. 2–5(a).

The following steps are used to obtain the auxiliary view 1 of the house having given the front and side views, Fig. 2–5(b). The steps used are the same as those for constructing views projected from the top or front views.

Step 1. Establish the line of sight.

In this case the line of sight 1 is given, establishing the direction of the projection lines.

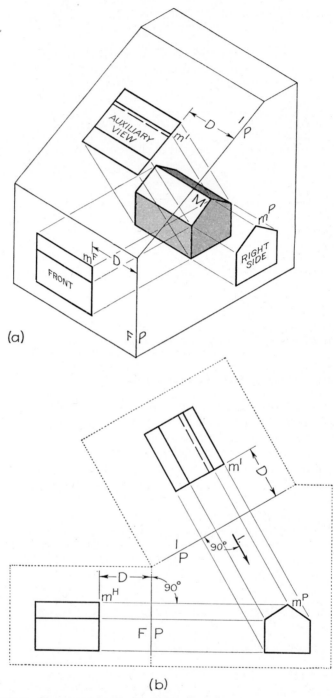

Fig. 2–5. Views Projected from the Side View

Step 2.   Introduce the necessary folding lines.

One folding line *F/P* is drawn between the given views and perpendicular to the projection lines joining them. The other folding line *P/1* is drawn perpendicular to the established line of sight 1 at a convenient distance from the side view.

Step 3.   Transfer distances to the new view.

Since in this case the front view and view 1 both lie on planes perpendicular to the profile projection plane, the corresponding points on these two views of the house lie the same distances to the left of the profile plane. Therefore the measurements to be transferred are obtained from the front view; for example, dimension *D*, which is the distance point *M* lies to the left of the profile plane. The measurements are transferred as indicated to the corresponding projection lines in the new view.

Step 4.   Determine the visibility and complete the view.

The preceding four steps may be used to draw any number of additional auxiliary views projected from the profile view; for example, those obtained by the lines of sight 2 and 3 in Fig. 2–6. *All views projected from a side view contain common width dimensions.*

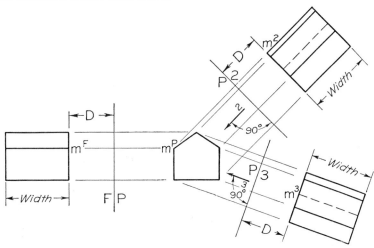

Fig. 2–6.   Additional Auxiliary Views Projected from the Side View

2.4   NORMAL VIEW OF A PLANE WITH EDGE VIEW GIVEN

The preceding discussion in this chapter has dealt with the basic mechanics of drawing primary auxiliary views. The following material is concerned with one of the most frequent applications of such views.

A plane will be shown in its true size and shape, TS, *in a view for which the line of sight is normal* (perpendicular) *to that plane.* For example, let it be assumed that in Fig. 2–7(a) a view is required showing the true size and shape of surface $ABCE$. The line of sight H for the required view must then be perpendicular to the surface $ABCE$ as shown pictorially in Fig. 2–7(b). Since the *edge view*, EV, of surface $ABCE$ shows as the horizontal line a^F–c^F in the front view, the line of sight H appears perpendicular to a^F–c^F, Fig. 2–7(c). Folding lines F/H and F/P and transfer distances such as D are then used to construct the required true size and shape view of $ABCE$. The resulting top view $a^H b^H c^H e^H$ is called a *partial* top view, since only the surface $ABCE$ is shown. The complete top view is drawn in Fig. 2–7(d).

It should be noted in Fig. 2–7(c) that a second line of sight H_1 is also normal to an edge view, e^P–b^P, of the surface $ABCE$. The required normal view could therefore be positioned above arrow H_1 instead of above arrow H.

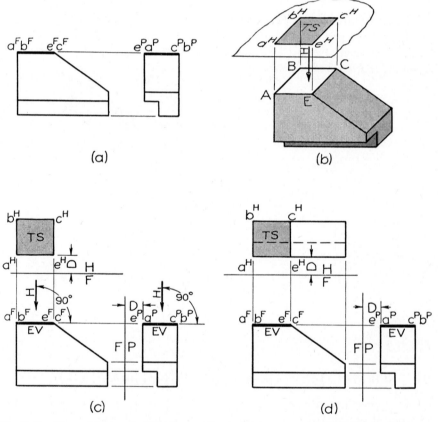

Fig. 2–7. Normal View of a Horizontal Plane Surface with Edge View Given

A normal view of surface $CEGJ$, Fig. 2–8(a), may be obtained by following the same basic procedure as in the preceding example. Line of sight 1 is established perpendicular to the edge view of surface $CEGJ$, represented by line c^F–g^F, Fig. 2–8(c). The resulting view in Fig. 2–8(c) is a partial auxiliary view showing the true size and shape of the surface. The remaining points on the object may be projected to this view to obtain the complete auxiliary view, Fig. 2–8(d).

In practice only the essential features of each view are included unless ambiguity would result from the omission of the remainder of the view. Note in Fig. 2–9, which is a working drawing from industry, that both the auxiliary view and the bottom view are partial views. Elliptical curves and a great many hidden lines are omitted in these views, since their inclusion would merely create confusion without in any way clarifying the shape description.

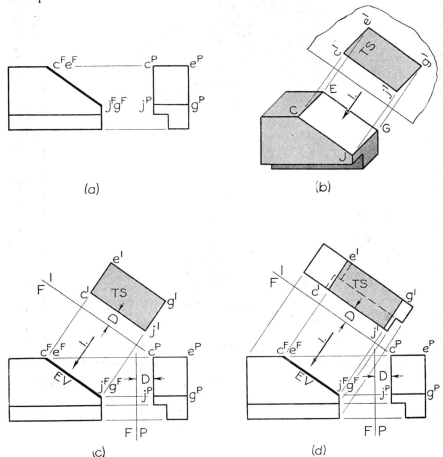

Fig. 2–8. Normal View of an Inclined Plane Surface with Edge View Given

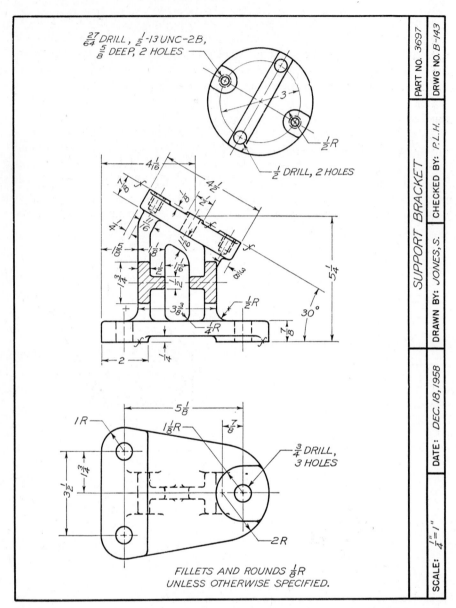

Fig. 2–9. An Industrial Working Drawing Employing a Primary Auxiliary View

2.5 PLOTTING A CURVE BY PROJECTION

Since circles and cylinders are among the most common geometrical shapes in industrial design, it frequently occurs that a circular feature is viewed obliquely, appearing elliptical in the resulting view. This is likely to occur in the construction of auxiliary views. It may also happen that a cylindrical or other curved shape is cut, or *truncated,* in an inclined direction, resulting in an elliptical or other noncircular line of intersection. The construction of such a curve entails the location of a series of appropriately spaced points along the curve, Fig. 2–10. It should be noted that the principles involved in locating the points are in no way different from those used in constructing any other portions of the views. Thus, the points may be located by transferring distances from the folding line F/P to the corresponding projection lines in the auxiliary view 1.

If, as in Fig. 2–10, the object is symmetrical, it may be more convenient to establish first the axis of symmetry, center line XX. A single distance D_1 may then be used to locate four points in turn, as indicated for points 1, 2, 3, and 4. Repetition of this process rapidly establishes enough points for the drawing of a smooth curve.

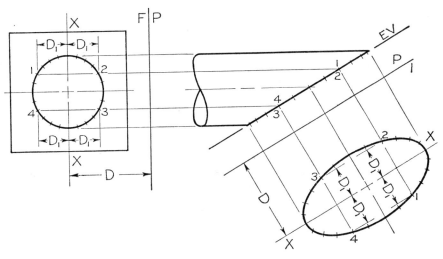

Fig. 2–10. Plotting a Curve in a Primary Auxiliary View

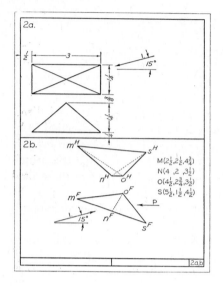

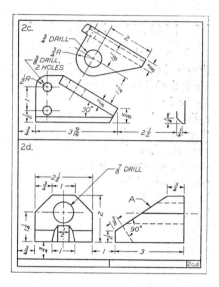

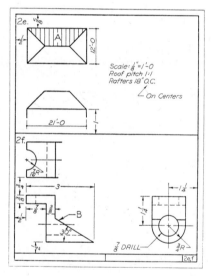

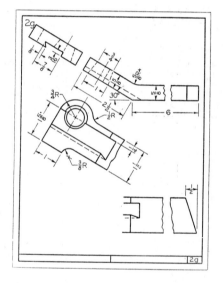

2a. Add the auxiliary view of the pyramid as indicated by arrow 1.

2b. Complete the visibility of the tetrahedron and add views P and 1.

2c. Complete the right-side view of the *angle bracket*.

2d. Draw a partial auxiliary view that shows the true size of surface A of the *locating slide.*

2e. Add the views necessary to show the true size of roof plane A and the true lengths of the rafters.

2f. Draw a partial auxiliary view showing the true shape of surface B and complete the top view.

2g. Complete the front view of the *tool holder.*

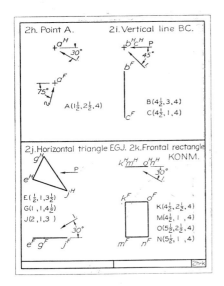

2h. Point A.   2i. Vertical line BC.

$A(1\frac{1}{2}, 2\frac{1}{2}, 4)$

$B(4\frac{1}{2}, 3, 4)$
$C(4\frac{1}{2}, 1, 4)$

2j. Horizontal triangle EGJ. 2k. Frontal rectangle KONM.

$E(\frac{1}{2}, 1, 3\frac{1}{2})$
$G(1, 1, 4\frac{1}{2})$
$J(2, 1, 3)$

$K(4\frac{1}{2}, 2\frac{1}{2}, 4)$
$M(4\frac{1}{2}, 1, 4)$
$O(5\frac{1}{2}, 2\frac{1}{2}, 4)$
$N(5\frac{1}{2}, 1, 4)$

2h-k

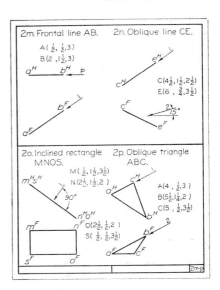

2m. Frontal line AB.   2n. Oblique line CE.

$A(\frac{1}{2}, \frac{1}{2}, 3)$
$B(2, 1\frac{1}{2}, 3)$

$C(4\frac{1}{2}, 1\frac{1}{2}, 2\frac{1}{2})$
$E(6, \frac{3}{4}, 3\frac{1}{2})$

2o. Inclined rectangle MNOS.   2p. Oblique triangle ABC.

$M(\frac{1}{2}, 1\frac{1}{2}, 3\frac{1}{2})$
$N(2\frac{1}{2}, 1\frac{1}{2}, 2)$
$O(2\frac{1}{2}, \frac{1}{2}, 2)$
$S(\frac{1}{2}, \frac{1}{2}, 3\frac{1}{2})$

$A(4, \frac{1}{2}, 3)$
$B(5\frac{1}{2}, 1\frac{1}{4}, 2)$
$C(5, \frac{1}{2}, 3\frac{1}{2})$

2m-p

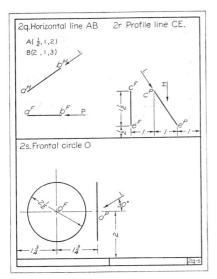

2q. Horizontal line AB   2r. Profile line CE.

$A(\frac{1}{2}, 1, 2)$
$B(2, 1, 3)$

2s. Frontal circle O

2q-s

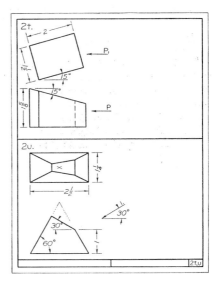

2t.

2u.

2t,u

2h, i, j, k, m, n, o, p, q, r, s, t, and **u.** Draw the view or views indicated by the line-of-sight arrows.

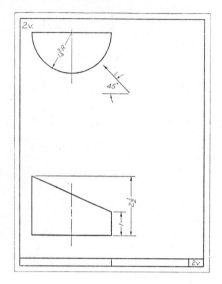

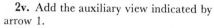

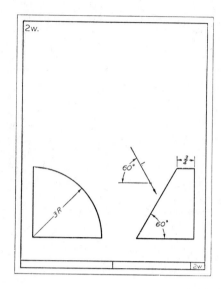

2v. Add the auxiliary view indicated by arrow 1.

2w. Add the auxiliary view indicated by arrow 1.

2x. Indicate whether the following statements are true or false. If assigned, provide a written statement or sketch to justify the answers.

(a) All views projected from a top view contain common height dimensions.

(b) An auxiliary view cannot show a line as a point.

(c) An auxiliary view may be used to show the true size of a plane surface.

(d) Projectors for an auxiliary view are always drawn at 30°, 60°, or 45° with the horizontal.

(e) A circle always appears true shape in an auxiliary view.

(f) The folding line for a new view is always perpendicular to the projection lines for the new view.

CHAPTER 3	LINES

THE TERM LINE is generally used to designate a *straight* line unless otherwise specified. Theoretically a line is of indefinite length, but frequently the term implies a definite line *segment* when the conditions of the problem make this obvious.

3.1 TRUE LENGTH OF A LINE

A line is shown in true length (TL) when the line of sight is normal (perpendicular) to the line. For example, in Fig. 3–1 the lines of sight F and H for the front and top views are each perpendicular to edge AB of the rectangular block. The front and top views $a^F b^F$ and $a^H b^H$ are therefore each true length.

In orthographic projection a view of a line cannot be longer than the line itself. Any line of sight not normal to a line results in a view which is shorter than true length. For example, in Fig. 3–1(b) line of sight 1, which is not normal to edge AB of the solid, results in the *foreshortened* view $a^1 b^1$. Similarly in Fig. 3–1(c), which shows AB as an individual line, view $a^1 b^1$ is foreshortened.

3.2 PRINCIPAL LINES

Lines that lie in or parallel to a principal plane of projection (frontal, horizontal, or profile) are called *principal lines*. Such lines are widely used in descriptive geometry and are designated according to the planes to which they are parallel.

A *frontal line* lies in or parallel to a frontal plane. Figure 3–2(a) and (b) illustrates a frontal line AB as an edge of a solid object. Figure 3–2(c) shows the same line AB independently. Note that the top view is parallel to folding

37

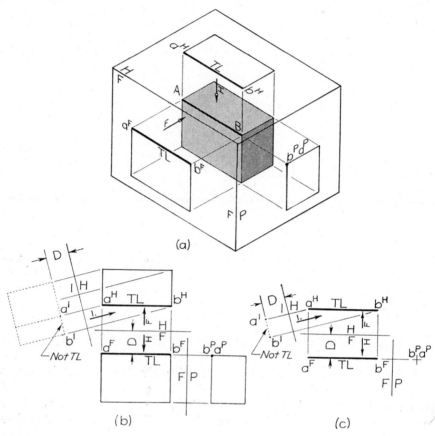

Fig. 3–1. True Length of a Line

line H/F and is therefore a horizontal line on the drawing paper. This is the characteristic by which any frontal line is easily recognized. Since the line of sight for the front view is perpendicular to line AB, the front view $a^F b^F$ is true length.

It will be noted that the front view also shows the horizontal and profile projection planes in edge view.[1] *The true angle between any line and any*

---

[1] See Art. 1.9.

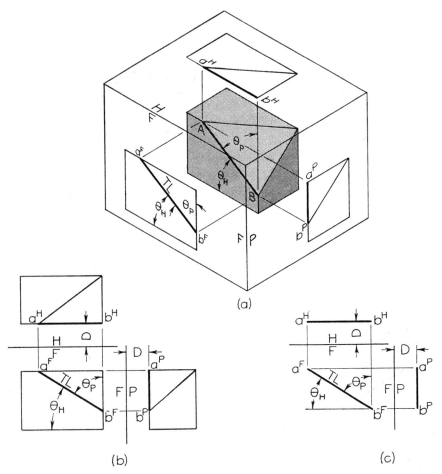

Fig. 3–2. Principal Lines—The Frontal Line

plane appears in any view that shows simultaneously the line in true length and the plane in edge view. Hence, as indicated in Fig. 3–2, the true angles θ_H and θ_P between line AB and the horizontal and profile planes, respectively, may be measured in the front view.

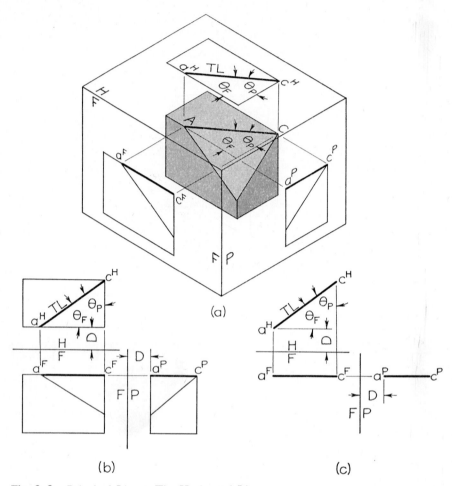

Fig. 3–3. Principal Lines—The Horizontal Line

A *horizontal line* lies in or parallel to a horizontal plane. Figure 3–3 illustrates a horizontal line AC as an edge of a solid object, (a) and (b), and as an independent line, (c). Horizontal lines are also called *level lines*.

The distinguishing characteristic of a horizontal line is that its front view is parallel to the H/F folding line and therefore appears horizontal on the drawing paper. Since the line of sight for the top view is normal to a horizontal line, the top view $a^H c^H$ is true length. The top view also shows the frontal and profile projection planes in edge view. Hence the true angles, θ_F and θ_P, respectively, between line AC and these planes are shown in the top view as indicated.

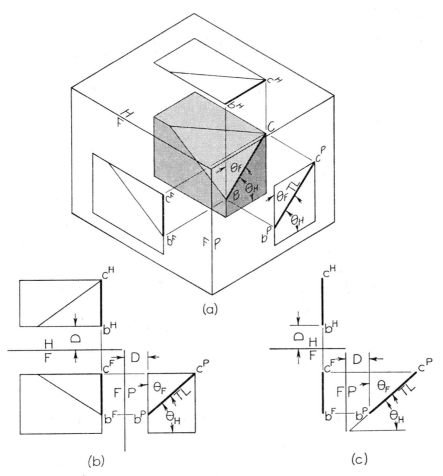

Fig. 3–4. Principal Lines—The Profile Line

A *profile line* lies in or parallel to a profile plane. Figure 3–4 illustrates a profile line *BC* as an edge of a solid object and as an independent line.

The distinguishing characteristic of a profile line is that its front view is parallel to the F/P folding line and appears vertical on the drawing paper. Since the line of sight for the profile view is normal to a profile line, the profile view $b^P c^P$ is true length. The profile view also shows the frontal and horizontal projection planes in edge view. Therefore the true angles, θ_F and θ_H, respectively, between the line *BC* and these planes are shown in the profile view.

3.3   TRUE LENGTH OF AN OBLIQUE LINE

An *oblique* line is one that is not parallel to any of the principal planes of projection: horizontal, frontal, and profile. This being the case, none of the lines of sight for the principal views is perpendicular to an oblique line, and therefore these views of the line are foreshortened. For example, note in Fig. 3–5 the foreshortened front and top views of a pencil placed in an oblique position.

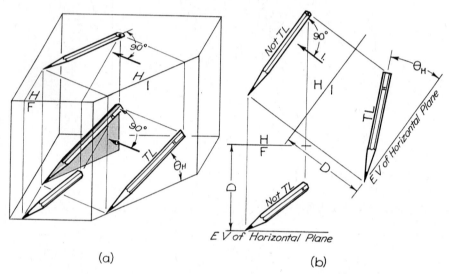

(a)   (b)

Fig. 3–5.   True Length of an Oblique Line and Its Angle with a Horizontal Plane

In order to find the true length of an oblique line—the pencil—an additional view must be constructed with the line of sight perpendicular to the oblique line. For example, if a horizontal line of sight is assumed perpendicular to the pencil, as shown by the pictorial arrow in Fig. 3–5(a), the top view of this arrow appears perpendicular to the top view of the pencil. The resulting auxiliary elevation view shows the true length of the pencil, Fig. 3–5(a) and (b). It may be noted that *a line is shown true length in a particular view when the adjacent view of the line is parallel to the folding line between the two views.*

In this same auxiliary elevation view, the horizontal plane upon which the pencil point is resting shows in edge view and parallel to folding line $H/1$. The student should take particular note that *any auxiliary elevation shows all horizontal planes in edge view and parallel to the folding line between that auxiliary view and the top view.* Since in the auxiliary elevation view of Fig. 3–5 the line is shown true length and the horizontal plane in edge view, the true angle θ_H between the two is shown as indicated.

The true length of an oblique line may be found just as readily by assuming a frontal line of sight perpendicular to the line as indicated pictorially in Fig. 3–6(a). In this case the line of sight appears perpendicular to the front view of the pencil, as shown by arrow 1. The resulting auxiliary view, projected from the front view, shows the true length of the pencil, Fig. 3–6(b).

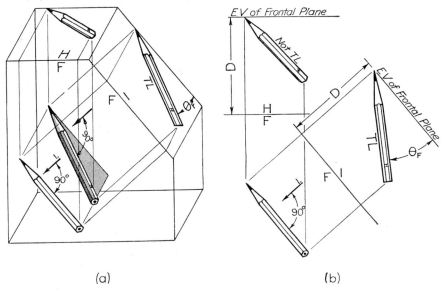

(a)   (b)

Fig. 3–6. True Length of an Oblique Line and Its Angle with a Frontal Plane

In this auxiliary view the frontal plane against which the pencil point is resting shows in edge view and parallel to folding line $F/1$. It should be observed that *any auxiliary view projected from the front view shows all frontal planes in edge view and parallel to the folding line between the auxiliary view and the front view.* With the pencil now in true length and the frontal plane in edge view, the true angle θ_F between them is shown.

The true length of an oblique line may be shown by still another type of primary auxiliary view. If a line of sight parallel to the profile plane is assumed perpendicular to an oblique pencil, as shown pictorially in Fig. 3–7(a), the line of sight appears in the side view as arrow 1 perpendicular to the side view of the pencil. The profile plane touching the pencil point shows in the resulting auxiliary view as a line parallel to the folding line $P/1$. *Any auxiliary view projected from a side view shows all profile planes in edge view and parallel to the folding line between the auxiliary view and the side view.* With the pencil now in true length and the profile plane in edge view, the true angle θ_P between them is shown.

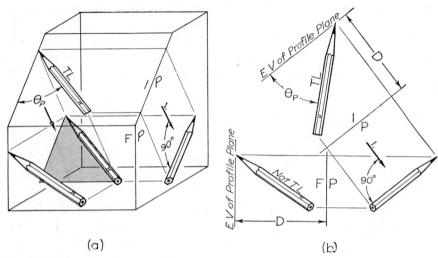

Fig. 3–7.   True Length of an Oblique Line and Its Angle with a Profile Plane

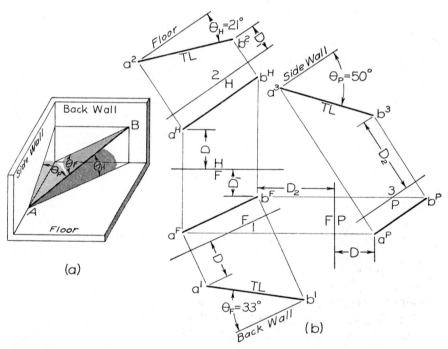

Fig. 3–8.   Comparison of the Separate Constructions for θ_H, θ_F, and θ_P

In summary of the material just discussed, Fig. 3–8 shows the true length of an oblique line *AB* obtained by each of the three types of primary auxiliary views. Although each auxiliary view shows the line in true length, the *true angle* between the line and *one* and *only one* of the principal planes of projection appears in any particular view. The student should specifically note, Fig. 3–8(b), that no pair of these angles is either complementary or supplementary. Hence, a *separate auxiliary view must be drawn to obtain each of the angles* θ_H, θ_F, and θ_P.

3.4 BEARING, SLOPE, AND GRADE

On the drawing paper a line is represented by its projections on at least two planes of projection. In engineering practice, however, the position of a line in space is often described by its *bearing* and *slope,* or by its *bearing* and *grade.*

Bearing is a term used to describe the direction or course of a line on the earth's surface. For practical purposes small portions of the earth's surface are usually regarded as planes; a map of such a portion is then merely a top view. Hence the bearing of a line is the angular relationship of the top view of the line with respect to due north or south, expressed in degrees. North is assumed to be directed toward the top of the drawing unless specifically given otherwise.

In Fig. 3–9 line *AB,* implying "*A* toward *B,*" has a bearing of S 55° E; or it could be stated that line *BA* (*B* toward *A*) has a bearing of N 55° W. In this system it is customary to make the specified angle less than 90°, selecting north or south accordingly as the base direction. It should be noted that lines *AB,* A_1B_1, A_2B_2, and A_3B_3 all have the same bearing since their top views coincide. In other words, the bearing of a line specifies the direction

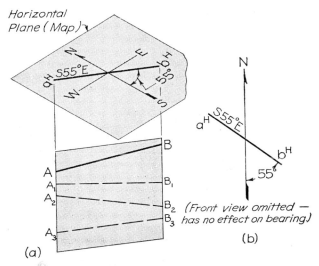

(a)

(b)

Fig. 3–9. Bearing

of its top view and is in no way affected by the angle between the line and the horizontal plane.

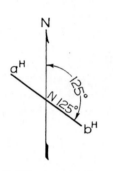

Fig. 3–10.   Azimuth Bearing

Another method of specifying the direction of the top view of a line is by *azimuth bearing*, which finds its greatest use in navigation and civil engineering. The azimuth bearing of a line is the *clockwise departure* in degrees of the top view of the line from a base direction, usually north. Figure 3–10 shows line *AB* again, with an azimuth bearing of N 125°.

The *slope* of a line may be defined as the angle in degrees that a line makes with a horizontal plane. This is the same angle as that designated as θ_H in Arts. 3.2 and 3.3, in which it was pointed out that the angle must be measured in a view which shows the horizontal plane in edge view and the line in true length.

Example: Bearing, Slope, and True Length

PROBLEM, Fig. 3–11:

A 250-ft segment *AB* of a power line has a bearing of N 60° E and a downward slope of 20° from the given point *A*, Fig. 3–11(a). Complete the front and top views.

ANALYSIS:

The bearing of a line establishes the direction of its top view. The slope of a line (θ_H) and the true length will be seen in an auxiliary view having a line of sight normal to the top view of the line.

GRAPHIC SOLUTION:

A construction line of indefinite length is drawn from a^H at the given bearing N 60° E, Fig. 3–11(a). The line of sight 1 is positioned normal to this construction line. Point a^1 in the auxiliary view is established by the conventional use of folding lines and transfer distance *D*. Since this view will show the true slope of the line, the 20° angle may be set off in the auxiliary view as indicated. The direction "downward" is away from the folding line $H/1$, as it can be seen in the front view that any point lower than *A* will be at a greater distance than a^F from the H/F folding line. With a construction line having a 20° downward slope now established, the true length of 250 ft is set off to scale from a^1 to b^1. Point b^H is then located, Fig. 3–11(b), by returning to the top view along a projection line perpendicular to the folding line $H/1$. The transfer distance D_1 is set off along a vertical projector from b^H to establish b^F.

The *grade* of a line is another means of describing the inclination of a line with respect to a horizontal plane. Grade is given by the following expression:

$$\text{Per cent grade} = \frac{\text{vertical rise}}{\text{horizontal run}} \times 100$$

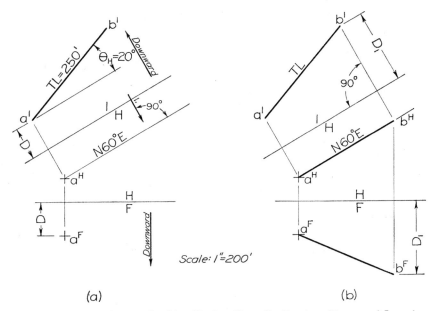

(a)   (b)

Fig. 3–11. Locating Views of a Line Having Given Its Bearing, Slope, and Length

These terms are illustrated pictorially in Fig. 3–12. It will be noted that the grade is the tangent of θ_H, multiplied by 100.

For the special case of a frontal line, the true slope is seen in its front view, and hence the rise and run may be measured as shown in Fig. 3–13. For ease in calculation the run is set off as 100 units of an appropriate size. An engineers scale is convenient for such measurements, since 10 main (numbered) divisions on each of its scales contain 100 subdivisions. The "50-scale" is appropriate for many of the problems in this text. With the corresponding rise measured in the same units, the per cent grade is obtained directly without calculations.

For the general case of an oblique line, Fig. 3–14, the true slope is not shown in the front view. If an auxiliary elevation view showing the true length of the line is drawn as indicated, the true slope will be seen and the

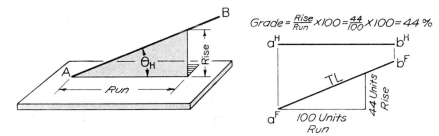

$$Grade = \frac{Rise}{Run} \times 100 = \frac{44}{100} \times 100 = 44\%$$

Fig. 3–12. Per Cent Grade   **Fig. 3–13.** Grade of a Frontal Line

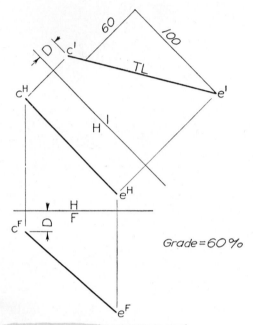

Fig. 3–14.   Grade of an Oblique Line

Grade = 60 %

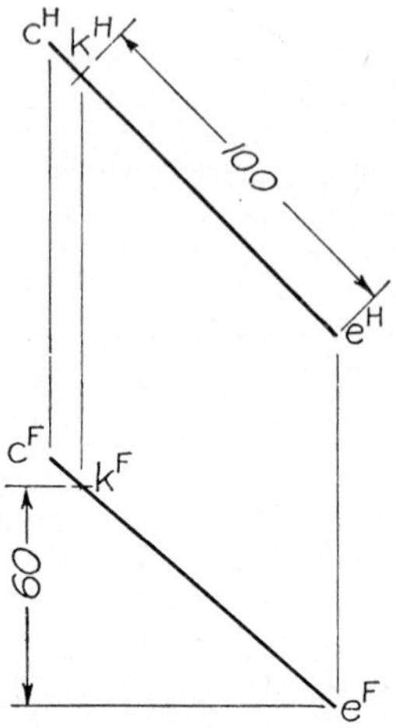

Fig. 3–15.   Grade Measured in the Front and Top Views

grade calculation may be made. The horizontal run (100 units) must be set off parallel to folding line $H/1$ in order to be horizontal *in space*. The corresponding rise (60 units) must then be measured in a direction perpendicular to $H/1$ in order to be vertical in space.

Actually, the grade of an oblique line may be obtained from the front and top views without additional views. Horizontal distances such as the run may always be measured on a map or top view. Hence the run of 100 units may be set off along the top view as shown in Fig. 3–15, thus establishing k^H. Vertical distances such as the rise appear in any elevation view. Therefore the rise appears in the front view as the difference in elevation (60 units) between e^F and k^F.

In some engineering fields inclinations are specified in other ways peculiar to the particular field. In Fig. 3–16 some of these are illustrated: (a) *batter*, (b) *slope* of a beam, (c) *slope* on an earth dam, and (d) *pitch* of a roof.

3.5   POINTS ON LINES

If a point is on a line (in space), the views of the point appear on the corresponding views of the line. Any two successive views of a point must lie on a projection line perpendicular to the folding line between the two views. Consequently, if a point is known to be on a line, it may usually be located in successive views of the line by simple projection as illustrated for point C in Fig. 3–17. The exception occurs when the views of the line are perpen-

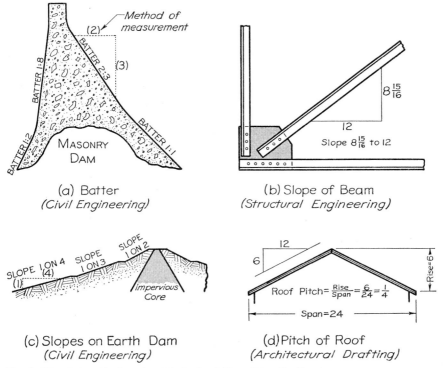

(a) Batter
(Civil Engineering)

(b) Slope of Beam
(Structural Engineering)

(c) Slopes on Earth Dam
(Civil Engineering)

(d) Pitch of Roof
(Architectural Drafting)

Fig. 3–16.   Other Engineering Methods of Describing Inclination

dicular to the folding line, Fig. 3–18(a). In this case, the top view of the
given point X cannot be determined by direct projection. An additional view
is drawn for which the folding line is
not perpendicular to the given views
of the line, Fig. 3–18(b). Point X is
projected to this new view, and the
transfer distance D_1 is used to locate
the required view x^H, Fig. 3–18(c).

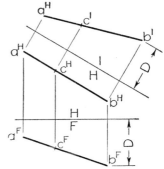

If given views are nearly perpendicular to the folding line between them,
projection from one to the other may
be quite inaccurate, in which case the
preceding procedure is recommended,
Appendix I.2.

Fig. 3–17.   Point on a Line

Points on lines may also be determined by spatial relations. A point may be
said to be above or below, in front of or behind, or to the right or to the left
of another point. These directions are oriented as indicated in Fig. 3–19(a).
A specific illustration appears in Fig. 3–19(b), in which point X is on line
AB and ¼ in. behind A. Note that this description does not necessarily
imply that point X is *directly* behind A nor even that X is ¼ in. from A

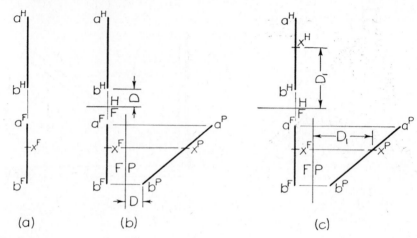

Fig. 3–18. Point on a Profile Line

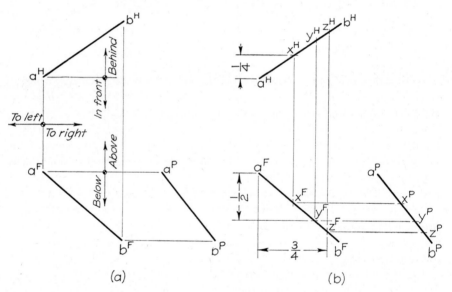

Fig. 3–19. Points on Line by Spatial Description

(true distance along *AB*). In this same problem point *Y* is on *AB* ½ in. below *A*, and point *Z* is on *AB* ¾ in. to the right of *A*.

Points dividing a line segment in a given ratio will divide any view of the line in the same ratio. See Fig. 3–20 in which the true-length auxiliary view of the line *GE* is divided into three equal segments. When the points *X* and *Y* are projected back to the profile and front views, it becomes evident that these views of the line are divided in this same ratio; and thus the division could have been made without the use of the auxiliary view. Of course, if the actual lengths of the segments are desired, the true-length view is necessary.

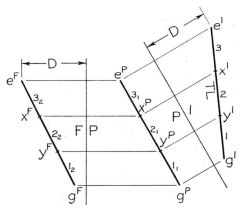

Fig. 3–20. Points Dividing a Line into Parts

Intersecting lines are lines that contain a common point.[2] In order for a point to be common to two lines, the views of the point must lie on a single projection line perpendicular to the folding line between any two adjacent views. In Fig. 3–21 points x^H and x^F lie on a common vertical projector. These are then views of a single point which is on both lines, and therefore the lines intersect. In any additional view, such as the side view in Fig. 3–21, the corresponding view of the common point X must still fall on the proper projection line.

In contrast, note that in Fig. 3–22 projection to the top view of the apparent point of crossing y^F in the front view results in *two* separate points, $y_1{}^H$ and $y_2{}^H$. Similarly, the projection of x^H to the front view results in two points, $x_1{}^F$ and $x_2{}^F$. From this it can be seen that the two lines do not have a

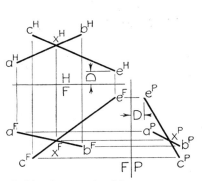

Fig. 3–21. Intersecting Lines

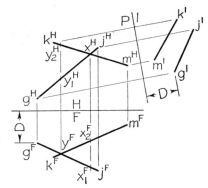

Fig. 3–22. Non-Intersecting Lines

[2] Parallel lines and perpendicular lines are discussed in Chapters 9 and 10, respectively.

single point in common and therefore are non-intersecting. This is further substantiated by the additional view, in which the line segments do not cross within the limits of the view as drawn.

Example: Intersecting Lines

PROBLEM, Fig. 3–23:

Complete the top view of the hoist frame, Fig. 3–23(a), having given the information that the braces CE and GE intersect AB at point E.

GRAPHIC SOLUTION:

Since the top view of point E cannot be obtained directly by projecting from e^F to the top view, the side view of the hoist frame is drawn, Fig. 3–23(b). Point e^P is located by extending a horizontal projection line from e^F to intersect $a^P b^P$. Transfer distance D then establishes e^H in the top view, and the view is completed as shown.

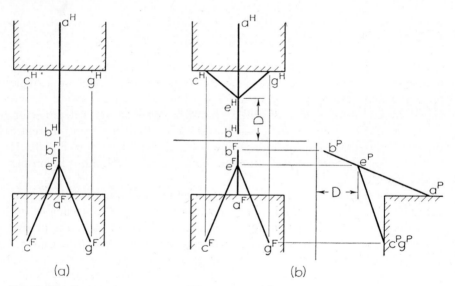

(a)   (b)

Fig. 3–23.   Intersecting Structural Members—Hoist Frame

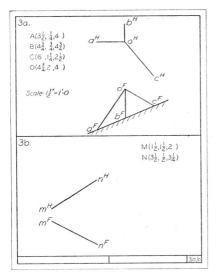

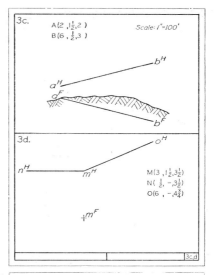

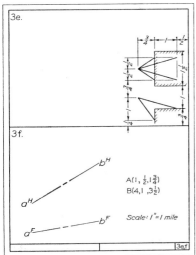

3a. Find the true lengths of the three members OA, OB, and OC.

3b. Determine the true length of MN and its true angles with horizontal and profile planes.

3c. Determine the bearing, length, and grade of shaft AB.

3d. MN has a down grade of 30%, and MO has a down grade of 40%. Complete the front views of these lines.

3e. Determine the angles between the members of the *support frame* and the surfaces to which they are attached.

3f. Determine the length and grade of highway AB. Find the views of a three-mile additional section BC that bears S 45° E on an 8 per cent down grade.

3g. An airplane at A, elevation 2000 ft, is flying at 120 mph air speed on a bearing of N 345° and is gaining altitude at the rate of 200 ft in 1000 ft. From A a ship is sighted at N 330° on a 35° angle of declination. Thirty seconds later the ship is sighted at N 260° on a 45° angle of declination. Determine the ship's course and its speed in knots.

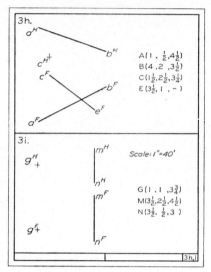

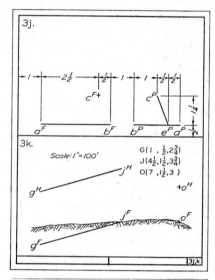

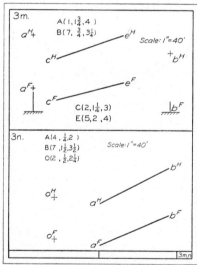

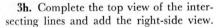

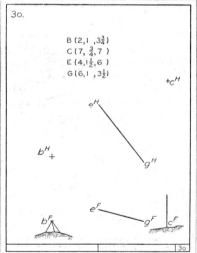

3h. Complete the top view of the intersecting lines and add the right-side view.

3i. Complete the views of line GK which intersects MN at a point 30 ft from point N.

3j. Complete the views of the intersecting lines AB and CE.

3k. Find the bearing, length, and grade of a shaft to be driven from point O to join tunnel GJ at a point 100 ft from J.

3m. A television antenna is at A and the base of a receiving antenna is at B. The maximum height of an obstruction is represented by line CE. What minimum height must be exceeded by the receiving antenna to provide a "line-of-sight" condition?

3n. Point S lies on line AB 40 ft behind point A in space. Determine the bearing, length, and grade of line OS.

3o. Determine the *vertical angle* (θ_H) for a transit telescope at B to sight a stadia rod at C, with the line of sight just clearing an obstruction whose maximum height is represented by EG.

3p. Indicate whether the following statements are true or false. If assigned, provide written statements or sketches to justify the answers.

(a) In an orthographic view a line can project longer or shorter than the line itself.

(b) A principal line appears true length in a front, top, or side view.

(c) The true slope of a line is always observed in a front view.

(d) A line may lie in only two principal planes at the same time.

(e) Two successive auxiliary views are needed to obtain the true length of an oblique line.

(f) Only one auxiliary view exists that produces the true-length view of a given line.

(g) A line must be true length before its bearing can be measured.

(h) The grade and angular slope of a line have the same numerical value.

(i) The grade of a line can be greater than 200 per cent.

(j) *Rise* is always measured perpendicular to a horizontal plane.

CHAPTER 4	PLANES

A PLANE IS a surface such that a straight line connecting *any* two points in that surface lies wholly within the surface. Any two lines in a plane must therefore either intersect or be parallel. The general term "plane" implies a plane indefinite in extent unless otherwise specified.

4.1 REPRESENTATION OF PLANES

A plane may be uniquely represented by two intersecting lines, Fig. 4–1(a). A plane may also be represented by two parallel lines, by three points not in a straight line, or by a point and a line, Fig. 4–1(b), (c), and (d). Multiview drawings of these representations are shown in Fig. 4–2(a), (b), (c), and (d), respectively. In graphical constructions involving planes, representations, (b), (c), and (d) are usually converted to (a) as suggested by the phantom lines.

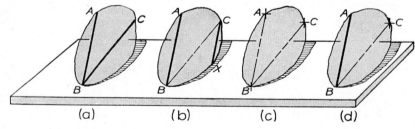

Fig. 4–1. Representation of a Plane in Space

4.2 POINTS AND LINES IN PLANES

If a line is known to be in a plane, any point on that line is in the plane. A line may be drawn in a plane by keeping it in contact with (intersecting) any two given lines in the plane. A line may also be located in a plane by

56

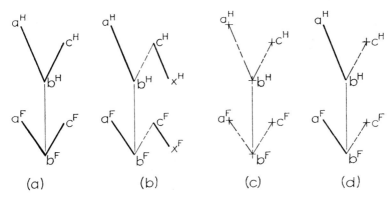

Fig. 4–2. Representation of a Plane in Multiview Projection

drawing the line through a known point in the plane and parallel to a line in the plane, Art. 9.1.

Example: Locating a Point in a Plane

PROBLEM, Fig. 4–3:

Having given the front and side views of a plane *MON* and the front view of a point *A* in the plane, determine the side view of the point.

ANALYSIS:

An infinite number of lines which contain the point may be drawn in the plane. Any convenient one may be selected, such as *XY*, Fig. 4–3(a). The views of the point must lie on the corresponding views of the line.

GRAPHIC SOLUTION:

A line $x^F y^F$ is drawn through a^F, representing the front view of line *XY* on the plane. The side views x^P and y^P of the contact points *X* and *Y* with the given lines of the plane are located by projection and line $x^P y^P$ is drawn. The intersection with $x^P y^P$ of a horizontal projection line from a^F locates a^P, the required side view of point *A*.

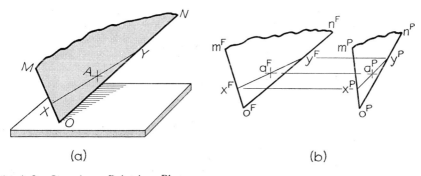

Fig. 4–3. Locating a Point in a Plane

4.3   LINES IN PLANES

The preceding ideas may also be applied to the location of the views of given lines lying in planes. For example, in Fig. 4–4(a) a five-sided plane figure $ABCEG$ is given with the front view incomplete. In the top view, Fig. 4–4(b), $a^H g^H$ is extended to intersect $b^H c^H$ at x^H. The front view of X is located by projection from x^H to $b^F c^F$, thus establishing $a^F x^F$. Projection from g^H locates g^F on $a^F x^F$, and the front view is then completed as shown.

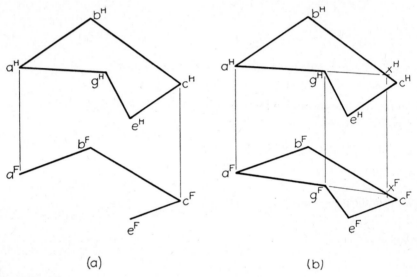

(a)   (b)

Fig. 4–4.   Oblique Lines on Plane

4.4   PRINCIPAL LINES IN PLANES

Many problems in descriptive geometry require the addition of frontal, horizontal, or profile lines in a plane.

In Fig. 4–5(a) the frontal line AF has been located in the plane ABC by first drawing its top view $a^H f^H$ parallel to folding line H/F. (In this particular case it is not actually necessary to draw folding line H/F because it is not used in the subsequent construction.) Since point F is the intersection of AF and BC, its front view f^F may be located by projecting to $b^F c^F$, thus establishing $a^F f^F$. Other frontal lines such as $A_1 F_1$ may be drawn on the given plane. Note that any such additional frontal line is parallel to AF. As a general principle *all frontal lines in the same plane are parallel* unless the plane itself is frontal, in which case all lines in the plane are frontal and are not necessarily parallel.

In a similar fashion a horizontal line, Fig. 4–5(b), may be located by drawing its front view in a horizontal position and determining its top view by projection. *All horizontal lines in the same plane are parallel,* unless the plane itself is horizontal, in which case all lines in the plane are horizontal and are not necessarily parallel.

In Fig. 4–5(c) profile line BP has been located in the plane ABC by first drawing either $b^F p^F$ or $b^H p^H$, each of which appears as a vertical line on the drawing paper, and then locating $b^P p^P$ by projection. *All profile lines in the same plane are parallel,* with the exception that profile lines in a profile plane are not necessarily parallel.

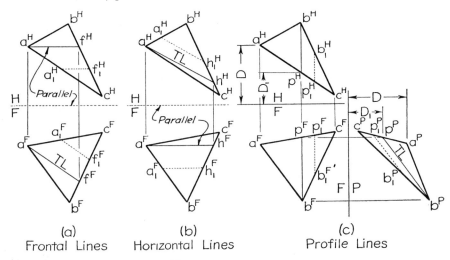

(a)	(b)	(c)
Frontal Lines	Horizontal Lines	Profile Lines

Fig. 4–5.   Principal Lines in a Plane

4.5   LOCUS

A *locus* is the path of a point, line, or curve moving in some specified manner. Or a locus can be thought of as the assemblage of all possible positions of a moving point, line, or curve. Thus the locus of points in a plane and at a specified distance from a given point is a circle, while the locus of points in space at a specified distance from a given point is a sphere. The concept of a locus appears in the solution of the example problem of Art. 4.6.

4.6   SPACE ANALYSIS

The student may have noted in several previous example problems that the explanation was divided into two general parts, designated as *analysis* and *graphical solution*. The analysis is usually a *space* analysis in which a logical procedure is formulated for the solution of the problem *in space*—as if dealing with a three-dimensional model. The graphical solution then consists of the representation of these steps on the drawing board in terms of multiview projection.

In many cases it will be found desirable to outline the space analysis in written form before translating it to the drawing board solution. Such an analysis will require the student to consider carefully and to visualize in their logical order the fundamental steps necessary to reach the desired solution. A written analysis will also provide the student with a constant reminder of the successive constructions to apply to the solution of the problem. It will help prevent his rushing headlong into a graphic solution without his knowing where he is going or how he is going to get there.

Example: Application of Space Analysis

PROBLEM, Fig. 4–6:

In given plane *ABC* locate a point *K* which lies ¼ in. above horizontal line *AB* and ³⁄₁₆ in. in front of frontal line *AC*. Scale: full size.

SPACE ANALYSIS:

(a) *Establish a horizontal line HH in plane ABC and ¼ in. above line AB, Fig. 4–6(a).*

This line is the locus of all points in plane *ABC* which are ¼ in. above line *AB* in space. See Fig. 3–19(a).

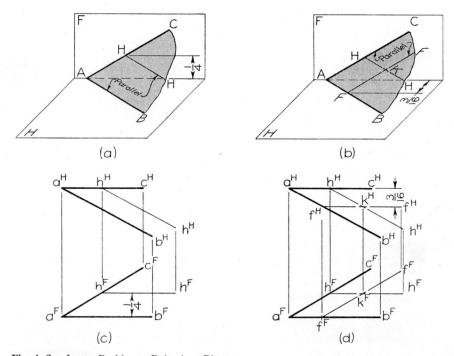

Fig. 4–6. Locus Problem—Point in a Plane

(b) *Establish a frontal line FF in plane ABC and* ³⁄₁₆ *in. in front of line AC, Fig. 4–6(b).*

This line is the locus of all points in plane *ABC* and ³⁄₁₆ in. in front of line *AC*.

(c) *The intersection of lines HH and FF is the required point K.*

Point *K* is the only point that fulfills all the specifications.

GRAPHIC SOLUTION:

In Fig. 4–6(c) the drawing board representation of analysis step (a) is shown. The remaining steps which complete the solution are shown in Fig. 4–6(d).

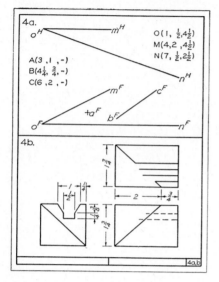

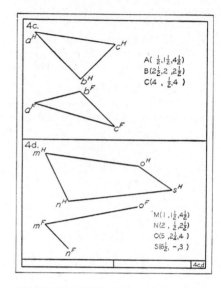

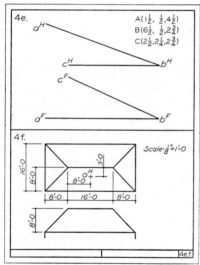

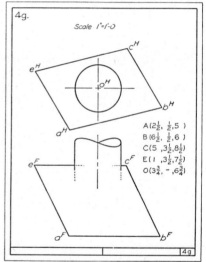

4a. Point A and line BC are in plane MON. Locate their top views.

4b. Complete the views of the *slotted block*.

4c. Add the side view of plane ABC. In the plane draw three views each of: (a) a frontal line through C; (b) a horizontal line through A; and (c) a profile line through B.

4d. Complete the front view of the plane figure $MNSO$.

4e. Locate a point P in plane ABC which lies 1 in. above line AB and ¾ in. behind line CB.

4f. Show the views of a hole in the roof plane cut for a 4 x 4 ft chimney centered at O.

4g. Complete the front view, including the opening in bulkhead $ABCE$ cut for the 2-ft diameter vertical vent.

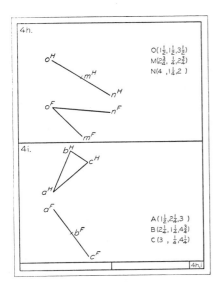

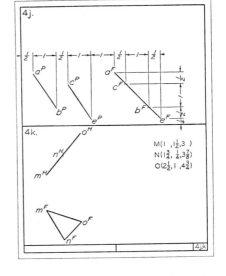

4h. Locate the views of a point in plane *MON* that is equidistant from the sides *ON* and *OM* and 2 in. from point *O*.

4i. Locate the views of a point in plane *ABC* that is equidistant from the three points.

4j. Locate the views of a point in plane *ABCE* that is equidistant from parallel lines *AB* and *CE* and that is equidistant from points *A* and *B*.

4k. Locate the center and plot the front view of a circle that passes through the points *M, N,* and *O*.

4m. Indicate whether the following statements are true or false. If assigned, provide written statements or sketches to justify the answers.

(a) An infinite number of planes can be passed through a single line.

(b) Any two horizontal lines determine a single plane.

(c) Only one plane can be passed through three points not in a straight line.

(d) Four points cannot lie in a single plane.

(e) Frontal lines in an oblique plane appear parallel in any principal view.

(f) Two lines in a plane must either intersect or be parallel.

(g) The lateral surface of a cylinder may be considered to be a plane surface, since the parallel elements of the cylinder lie wholly within the surface.

(h) The surface of a cone may be considered to be a plane surface, since the elements intersect at the vertex.

SUCCESSIVE AUXILIARY VIEWS

CHAPTER 5

A PRIMARY AUXILIARY VIEW is an auxiliary view obtained by projection from one of the six basic views. As was stated in Chapter 2, a primary auxiliary plane of projection is one that is perpendicular to one of three principal projection planes and inclined to the remaining two.

A *secondary* auxiliary view is one projected from a primary auxiliary view. Since any two adjacent views must lie on mutually perpendicular projection planes, the plane of projection for the secondary auxiliary view must be perpendicular to that of the primary auxiliary view. A secondary auxiliary view is used to obtain information available only in a view projected on a plane which is oblique to the principal planes.

In some instances it may be necessary to construct a third auxiliary view projected from a secondary auxiliary view. Theoretically it is possible to continue this chain of additional auxiliary views indefinitely, adding a fourth, a fifth, etc. In general terms, auxiliary views in such a series are called *successive* auxiliary views.

5.1 CONSTRUCTION OF SUCCESSIVE AUXILIARY VIEWS

As an illustration of the mechanics of drawing successive auxiliary views, Fig. 5–1 shows the construction of two additional views of a point A, given the top and front views and successive lines of sight 1 and 2.

In Fig. 5–1(a) the auxiliary elevation indicated by line of sight 1 has been drawn, using the conventional procedure, Art. 2.1. Since the auxiliary plane and the frontal plane are perpendicular to the horizontal plane, views a^1 and a^F lie the same distance D below the horizontal plane as shown in the pictorial, Fig. 5–1(a). In the multiview drawing, view a^1 is therefore located by transferring the distance D from the front view as indicated.

With the primary auxiliary view a^1 completed, the secondary auxiliary view indicated by line of sight 2, Fig. 5–1(a) and (b), may be drawn as follows, using the conventional steps listed in Arts. 2.1, 2.2, and 2.3:

64

Step 1.   Establish the line of sight.

In this case the line of sight is given as arrow 2, Fig. 5–1(b). In practical applications the line of sight is established according to the information desired.

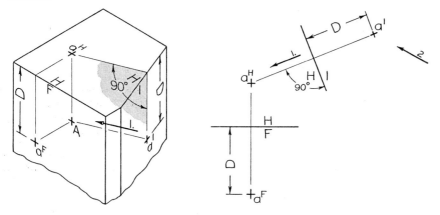

(a) The Primary Auxiliary View

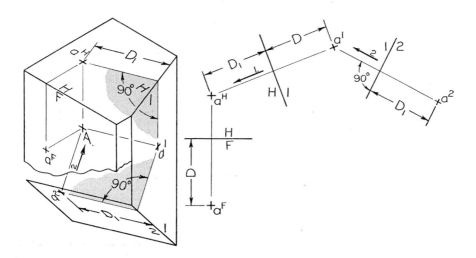

(b) The Secondary Auxiliary View

Fig. 5–1. Successive Auxiliary Views of a Point

Step 2.   Introduce the necessary folding lines.

One of the necessary folding lines is $H/1$. The other folding line $1/2$ is drawn perpendicular to the line of sight 2 at a convenient distance from view 1.

Step 3.   Transfer distance(s) to the new view.

In this case, the top view and the new view 2 both lie on planes perpendicular to the projection plane of view 1. Consequently views a^2 and a^H lie the same distance from the plane of view 1. The distance to be transferred is then D_1, which is the distance point A lies from the plane of view 1.

Step 4.   Complete the view.

Additional successive auxiliary views may be obtained by repeated application of the preceding steps, since in any chain of three successive views the two "outside" views both lie on projection planes that are perpendicular to the plane of the central view. In Fig. 5–2 a third auxiliary view a^3 has been constructed for a given line of sight 3. Theoretically a fourth auxiliary view a^4 could then be added, then a fifth view a^5, and so on in an endless chain. Practically speaking, very few descriptive geometry problems require more than two successive auxiliary views in their solutions.

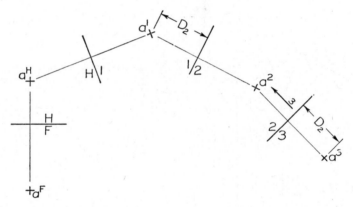

Fig. 5–2.   Additional Successive Auxiliary Views of a Point

5.2   POINT VIEW OF A LINE

A fundamental operation, which may require as many as two successive auxiliary views, is the construction of a view showing a given line as a point.

A line will appear as a point in any view for which the line of sight is parallel to the line in space.

In Fig. 5–3 line AB is shown in true length in the front view. Therefore line of sight 1, being parallel to $a^F b^F$, is parallel to line AB in space. The resulting auxiliary view $a^1 b^1$ is a point view of line AB. In contrast, line of sight P, while parallel to $a^H b^H$, is not parallel to line AB in space since $a^H b^H$ is not true length. View P consequently cannot show line AB in point view, as is proven by the resulting view $a^P b^P$.

In order to produce a point view of a line, the line of sight must be *parallel to a true-length view of the line*. If no given view of the line is true length, it is necessary to construct a true-length view before a point view can be obtained.

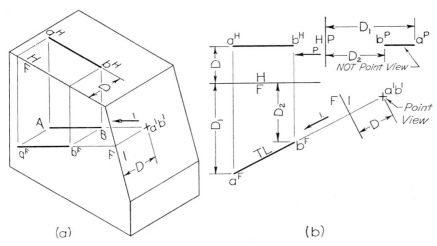

Fig. 5–3. Point View of a Frontal Line

In Fig. 5–4(a) let it be assumed that the front and top views of an oblique line *EG* are given, with a point view required. Neither $e^F g^F$ nor $e^H g^H$ is true length. Therefore, the first step is to construct a true-length auxiliary view. In this case the line of sight is selected perpendicular to the top view, resulting in the desired true-length view $e^1 g^1$.

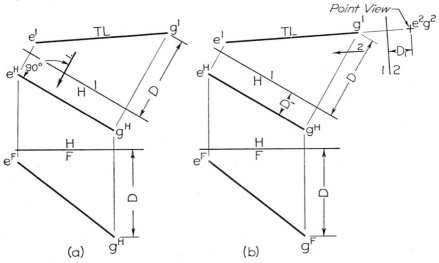

Fig. 5–4. Point View of an Oblique Line

Line of sight 2 is then established parallel to the view e^1g^1, Fig. 5–4(b). The resulting view e^2g^2 is the required point view of EG. Note that the distance D_1 is the same for any point on e^Hg^H.

The point view of a line is used as an intermediate step in a number of descriptive geometry constructions such as in Art. 5–3.[1] It may also be used to find the true distance from the line to some point in space as in the following "clearance" problem.

Example: True Distance from a Point to a Line (Point-View Method)

PROBLEM, Fig. 5–5:

Find the true clearance between the spherical tank with its center at point O and the cylindrical pipe with center line XY.

ANALYSIS:

If center line XY is viewed as a point, the true distance from XY to point O is observed and the desired clearance may be measured.

GRAPHIC SOLUTION:

Line of sight 1 is assumed perpendicular to x^Hy^H in order to obtain the true-length auxiliary view x^1y^1. Point O is also projected to this view, appearing as o^1. Line of

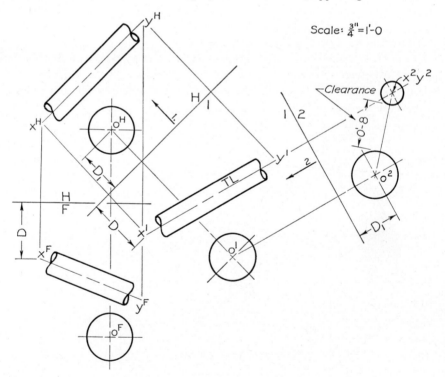

Fig. 5–5.   Application of Point View of a Line to a Clearance Problem

---
[1] See also Arts. 8.1, 10.4, and 13.2

sight 2 is then introduced parallel to x^1y^1 resulting in the point view x^2y^2 and the view o^2. This view also shows the true circular shape of the pipe. Since any view of the sphere is circular, the clearance between the two may be measured in view 2 as indicated.

5.3 EDGE VIEW OF A PLANE

Graphical representations of many engineering situations require the construction of views showing plane surfaces in *edge view* (EV).

A plane will appear in edge view in any view for which the line of sight is parallel to the plane. If the line of sight is to be parallel to the plane, it must be parallel to a line in the plane, thus producing a point view of that line. Consequently it may be said that a plane will appear in edge view in any view in which a line in the plane appears as a point; that is, *a plane will appear in edge view in any view for which the line of sight is parallel to a true-length line in the adjacent view.*

Since the line of sight F in Fig. 5–6(b) is parallel to the true-length view a^Hb^H, the front view shows line AB as a point and surface $ABCE$ in edge view. In this instance, line EC is also shown in point view since it appears true length in the top view.

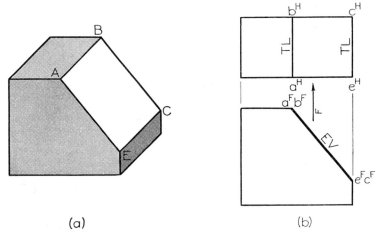

(a)   (b)

Fig. 5–6.   Edge View of a Plane Surface

In the case of the oblique plane $ABEC$ of Fig. 5–7(b), line CE is horizontal and shows true length in the top view. Line of sight 1 is therefore assumed parallel to c^He^H, resulting in the edge view b^1–c^1.

It is also possible to construct an edge view of the plane $ABEC$ by projection from the front view, Fig. 5–7(c). To do this, it is necessary to have a line in the plane appearing true length in the front view. Since none of the four edges of the surface meets this requirement, a frontal line AF is intro-

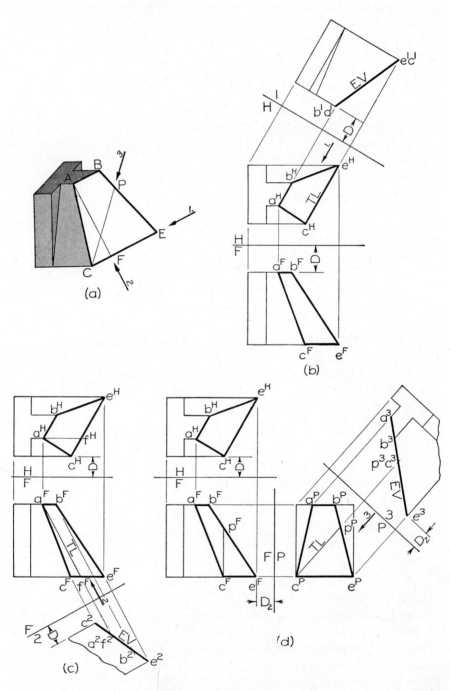

Fig. 5–7. Edge Views of an Oblique Plane Surface

duced in the plane. Line of sight 2 is then assumed parallel to the true-length front view $a^F f^F$, resulting in the edge view c^2-e^2.

In similar fashion, Fig. 5–7(d), a profile line *CP* may be added to the plane. After the side view is drawn, line of sight 3 is assumed parallel to the true-length view $c^P p^P$. The auxiliary view thus obtained, a^3-e^3, is again an edge view of the same surface *ABEC*.

5.4 NORMAL VIEW OF A PLANE

A *normal* or *true size-and-shape* (TS) view of a plane is obtained in any view for which the line of sight is perpendicular to the plane. On the drawing paper this line of sight will appear perpendicular to the edge view of the plane.

Therefore, in obtaining a normal view of an oblique plane such as plane *ABCE* in Fig. 5–8(a), the first step is to construct an edge view of this plane by the method of Art. 5.3. A horizontal line *EH* is added to the plane and the line of sight 1 is established parallel to the true-length view $e^H h^H$. The primary auxiliary view a^1-c^1 is an edge view as shown.

A second line of sight 2 is then introduced perpendicular to a^1-c^1, Fig. 5–8(b). Since this line of sight is perpendicular to the plane *ABCE*, the secondary auxiliary view $a^2 b^2 c^2 e^2$ is the required normal view.

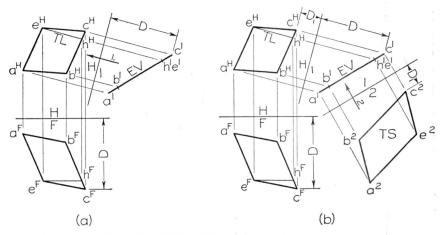

(a)   (b)

Fig. 5–8. Normal View of an Oblique Plane

In practice, normal views of plane surfaces are used to provide true size-and-shape views so that they may be properly dimensioned and clearly described to the shop man or other user of the drawing, Fig. 5–9.

Normal views are also used in the solution of space problems involving plane geometry constructions, such as (1) finding the shortest distance from a point to a line (plane method), (2) measuring the angle between two

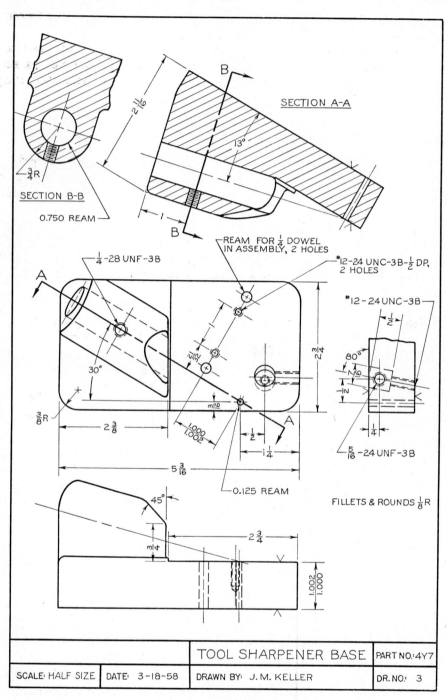

Fig. 5–9. An Industrial Drawing Employing Successive Auxiliary Views

intersecting lines, (3) constructing the bisector of an angle, (4) inscribing a circle in a triangle, and many others.

Example: A Plane Geometry Construction in an Oblique Plane

PROBLEM, Fig. 5–10:

Find the front and top views of a 10-ft radius bend joining two pipes represented by their intersecting center lines BA and BC, Fig. 5–10(a).

ANALYSIS:

The arc of the required bend must lie in the plane ABC. Its true circular shape will therefore show in a normal view of this plane.

GRAPHIC SOLUTION:

To the given front and top views of ABC, a frontal line BF is added as shown, Fig. 5–10(a). (Note the addition of the line AC to secure point F.) Since $b^F f^F$ is true length, auxiliary view 1 showing plane ABC in edge view may now be drawn as indicated. Line of sight 2 is established perpendicular to the edge view of the plane, and the normal view $a^2 b^2 c^2$ is constructed. In this view the center of the 10-ft radius arc is located such that the arc is tangent to lines $b^2 a^2$ and $b^2 c^2$, Appendix II.10. The points of tangency are indicated as t^2 and t_1^2.

Conveniently spaced intermediate points 1, 2, and 3 are now assumed on the arc in view 2, Fig. 5–10(b). These points plus t^2 and t_1^2 are projected to the edge view of the plane in view 1. They are then projected to the front view and located by means of transfer distances such as D_2.

The points are now established in the top view by projecting upward from the front view and transferring distances such as D_3 from view 1. The front and top views are completed by fairing smooth curves through the points.

Frequently elliptical views of a circle in an oblique plane may be more conveniently drawn by establishing the major and minor axes and then employing the *trammel* method,[2] an *ellipse template*, or the *Ellipsograph*.

Figures 5–11 and 5–12 illustrate two methods by which the major and minor axes of such elliptical views may be found. Both methods are based on the facts that the major axis in any view must always be that diameter of the circle which appears true length in that view, and that the minor axis is perpendicular to the major axis. In Fig. 5–11, a frontal line FF is drawn

---

[2] Appendix II.6.

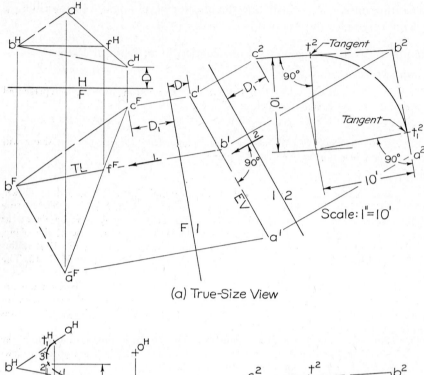

(a) True-Size View

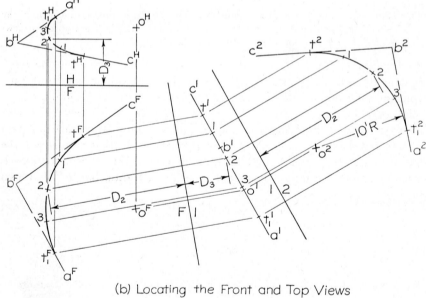

(b) Locating the Front and Top Views

Fig. 5–10.   Drawing a Circular Arc in an Oblique Plane

through the center point O, establishing the direction of true-length lines in the front view. The major axis $s^F s^F$ is then set off as shown, equal to the diameter of the circle as given. Auxiliary view 1, showing the edge view of the plane of the circle, is then constructed. Along this edge view the diameter of the circle is set off, establishing points n^1 which when projected to the front view determine the end points of the minor axis, n^F and n^F.

In similar fashion the major axis $y^H y^H$ in the top view lies on a true-length line through o^H. Auxiliary view 2 is then employed to secure the end points x^H and x^H of the minor axis in the top view. It should be noted that the axes in the front view and in the top view are projections of two entirely different pairs of diameters of the circle.

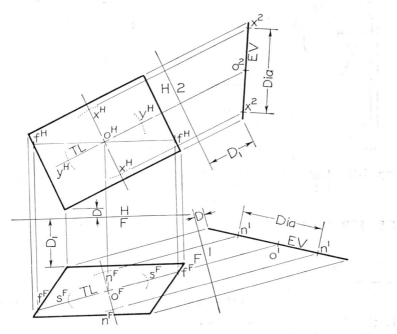

Fig. 5–11. Finding the Axes of the Elliptical Views of a Circle in an Oblique Plane

In Fig. 5–12 the major axis $y^H y^H$ and minor axis $x^H x^H$ in the top view and major axis $s^F s^F$ in the front view have all been established as in Fig. 5–11. As an alternate method, minor axis $n^F n^F$ is obtained as follows: Its direction is known to be at right angles to $s^F s^F$, and when extended, it intersects lines of the given plane at points 1 and 2. These points are projected to the top view, to view 1, and finally to normal view 2, establishing line 1,2 in these views. In view 2, line 1,2 intersects the circle at points n^2. These points are returned to view 1 to locate points n^1 from which transfer distances such as D are used to establish points n^F on line 1,2 in the front view.

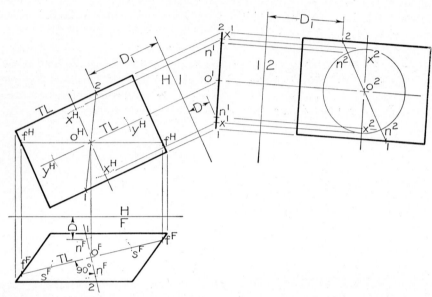

Fig. 5–12.   Finding the Axes of the Elliptical Views of a Circle in an Oblique Plane (Alternate Method)

5.5 SUMMARY OF USES OF ADDITIONAL VIEWS

Use	Position of Line of Sight	
	In space	*On multiview drawing*
1. True length of line (TL)	Perpendicular to line	Perpendicular to any view of the line or directed toward a point view of the line
2. Point view of line	Parallel to line	Parallel to true-length view of line
3. Edge view of plane (EV)	Parallel to plane	Parallel to true-length view of line in plane or directed toward a true-size view of the plane
4. Normal or true-size view of plane (TS)	Perpendicular to plane	Perpendicular to edge view of plane

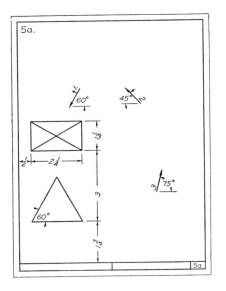

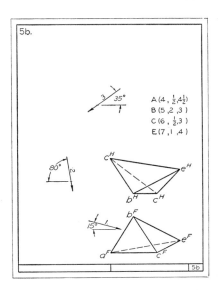

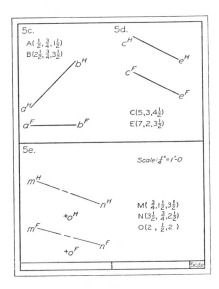

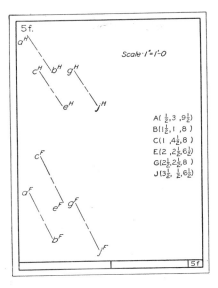

5a, b. Draw the successive auxiliary views indicated by arrows 1, 2, and 3 at the specified positions or as assigned.

5c. Obtain a point view of line *AB*.

5d. Obtain a point view of line *CE*.

5e. Determine the clearance between a 2-ft diameter cylinder located by its center line *MN* and a 3-ft diameter sphere with its center at *O*.

5f. Determine the minimum clearance between three 6-in. diameter pipes having the given center lines.

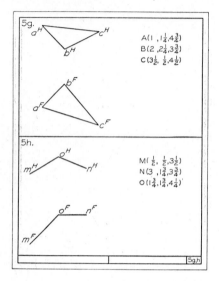

5g.

A(1, $1\frac{1}{4}$, $4\frac{3}{4}$)
B(2, $2\frac{1}{4}$, $3\frac{3}{4}$)
C($3\frac{1}{2}$, $\frac{1}{2}$, $4\frac{1}{2}$)

5h.

M($\frac{1}{2}$, $\frac{1}{2}$, $3\frac{1}{2}$)
N(3, $1\frac{1}{4}$, $3\frac{3}{4}$)
O($1\frac{3}{4}$, $1\frac{3}{4}$, $4\frac{1}{4}$)

5g,h

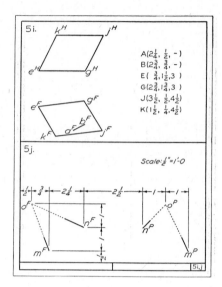

5i.

A($2\frac{1}{4}$, $\frac{1}{2}$, $-$)
B($2\frac{3}{4}$, $\frac{3}{4}$, $-$)
E($\frac{3}{4}$, $1\frac{1}{2}$, 3)
G($2\frac{3}{4}$, $1\frac{3}{4}$, 3)
J($3\frac{1}{2}$, $\frac{1}{2}$, $4\frac{1}{2}$)
K($1\frac{1}{2}$, $\frac{1}{4}$, $4\frac{1}{2}$)

5j.

Scale:$\frac{1}{2}$"=1'-0

5i,j

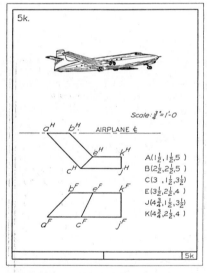

5k.

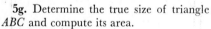

Scale:$\frac{3}{4}$"=1'-0

AIRPLANE ₵

A($1\frac{1}{2}$, $1\frac{1}{2}$, 5)
B($2\frac{1}{2}$, $2\frac{1}{2}$, 5)
C(3, $1\frac{1}{2}$, $3\frac{1}{2}$)
E($3\frac{1}{2}$, $2\frac{1}{2}$, 4)
J($4\frac{3}{4}$, $1\frac{1}{2}$, $3\frac{1}{2}$)
K($4\frac{3}{4}$, $2\frac{1}{2}$, 4)

5k

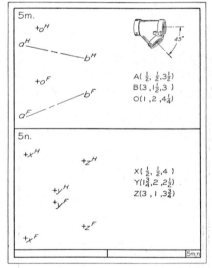

5m.

45°

A($\frac{1}{2}$, $\frac{1}{2}$, $3\frac{1}{2}$)
B(3, $1\frac{1}{2}$, 3)
O(1, 2, $4\frac{1}{4}$)

5n.

X($\frac{1}{2}$, $\frac{1}{2}$, 4)
Y($1\frac{1}{4}$, 2, $2\frac{1}{2}$)
Z(3, 1, $3\frac{3}{4}$)

5m,n

5g. Determine the true size of triangle *ABC* and compute its area.

5h. Find the true size of the angle formed by the structural members intersecting at *O* so that a gusset plate may be correctly cut.

5i. Line *AB* is one side of a regular hexagon lying in plane *EGJK*. Complete the views.

5j. Locate the views of the center of a 3-ft diameter pulley oriented to carry a belt from *M* to *N* around the turn near *O*.

If assigned, also plot the views of the pulley, neglecting thickness.

5k. Determine the true sizes of the airplane windshield *ABCE* and the side glass *CEJK* so that correct patterns may be cut. Compute the glass areas involved, neglecting waste.

5m. Locate the views of a branch pipe line from *O* to connect with the main line *AB* with a standard 45° Y-fitting.

5n. Find the views of the center of a circle passing through points *X*, *Y*, and *Z*.

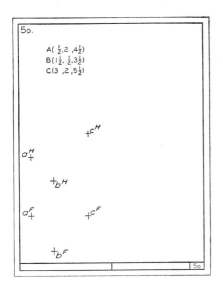

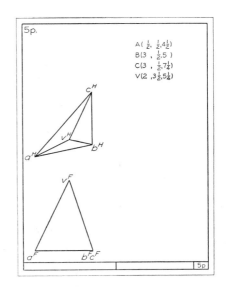

5o. Locate the circle that passes through points *A*, *B*, and *C*. Plot the front and top views of the circle and indicate the major and minor axes in these views.

5p. Determine which of the two planes *ABV* and *BCV* has the greater area. Show calculations.

5q. Indicate whether the following statements are true or false. If assigned, provide written explanations or sketches to justify the answers.

(a) No more than two successive auxiliary views are essential to obtain a normal view of a plane surface.

(b) Two successive projection planes are always at right angles.

(c) A point on the lateral surface of a cylinder always appears true distance from the center line of the cylinder.

(d) Any view of a sphere appears as a true circle.

(e) The true diameter of a circle is available in any view of the circle.

(f) The true length of any line in a plane is available in an edge view of the plane.

(g) In order to obtain a point view of a line, a line of sight may be selected parallel to any view of the line.

(h) The true angle between two lines is observed in a view which shows either one of the lines in true length.

CHAPTER 6

PIERCING POINTS

UNLESS A LINE is in or parallel to a plane, it must intersect the plane. This intersection point, called a *piercing point,* may be within the limits of the line segment or plane as given, or it may be necessary to extend one or both, in which case the piercing point can be considered imaginary. Such a point may prove useful in certain constructions. A line or a plane is considered indefinite in extent unless specific information to the contrary is available.

6.1 PIERCING POINT—AUXILIARY-VIEW METHOD

In Fig. 6–1(a) let it be required to find by means of an auxiliary view the piercing point in plane *ABC* of line *EG*. The intersection of a given line with a given plane is a point common to both. An edge view of a plane contains

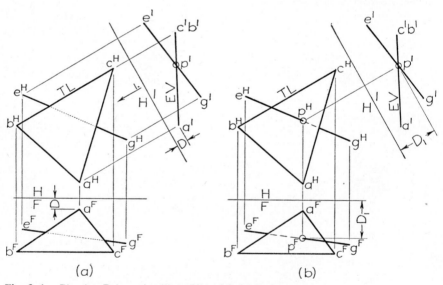

(a)   (b)

Fig. 6–1.   Piercing Point—Auxiliary-View Method

80

all points in the plane. Therefore, in a view which shows the given plane in edge view, the point at which the given line intersects the edge view of the plane is the point common to both—the piercing point.

In Fig. 6–1(a), line BC appears true length in the top view. Line of sight 1 is therefore assumed parallel to $b^H c^H$, the result being the edge view $a^1 c^1 b^1$. In this auxiliary view the piercing point p^1 appears as the intersection of $e^1 g^1$ and the edge view of the plane, $a^1 c^1 b^1$.

The top and front views of piercing point P, Fig. 6–1(b), are found by projecting from p^1 to $e^H g^H$ to establish p^H and thence to the front view to establish p^F. The accuracy of the location of p^F may be checked by the distance D_1 as indicated. The visibility of line EG in the front and top views is then determined to complete the drawing.[1]

Alternate Solution. The piercing point may be also determined by an edge view of the plane projected from the front view. This is not a different method but merely an alternate manner of applying the same method. In Fig. 6–2 frontal line BF is added to procure a true-length line in the front view of the plane, and the views of the piercing point are found in a manner similar to that of Fig. 6–1.

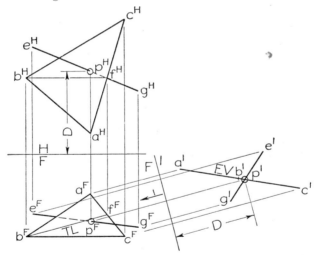

Fig. 6–2. Piercing Point—Auxiliary-View Method (Alternate Solution)

6.2 PIERCING POINT—TWO-VIEW METHOD

The piercing point of line EG with plane ABC, may be found using only the given views as follows, Fig. 6–3(a):

(a) Any convenient cutting plane containing line EG is introduced, Fig. 6–3(b). A cutting plane perpendicular to one of the principal planes is convenient because it appears in edge view in a principal view. This simplifies the following step.

---

[1] See Art. 1.13.

(b) The line of intersection 1,2 between this cutting plane and plane *ABC* is determined.

(c) Since lines *EG* and 1,2 both lie in the cutting plane, they intersect, locating point *P*.

(d) Since line 1,2 also lies in plane *ABC*, point *P* is the required piercing point of line *EG* with the plane *ABC*.

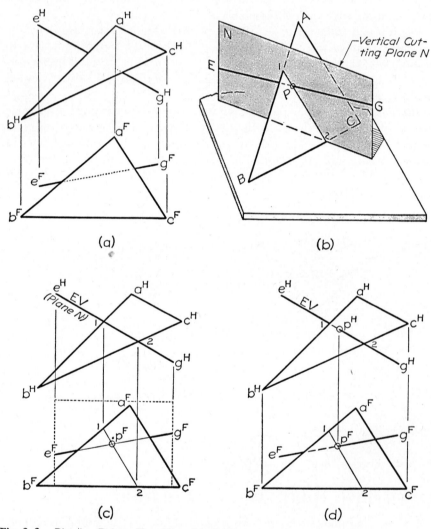

Fig. 6–3. Piercing Point—Two-View Method

In the multiview construction, Fig. 6–3(c), a vertical cutting plane N containing EG is introduced, with its top view an edge view containing $e^H g^H$. The line of intersection 1,2 of the cutting plane and plane ABC coincides with the cutting plane in the top view. Since line 1,2 lies in plane ABC, its front view is located by projection of points 1 and 2 to the corresponding lines of the plane in the front view. The intersection of 1,2 and $e^F g^F$ locates the front view p^F of the piercing point.

The top view of point P is determined by a projection line from p^F, Fig. 6–3(d). The determination of the visibility of line EG, if desired, completes the solution.

Alternate Solution. The foregoing problem may also be solved by introducing a cutting plane M which contains line EG and appears in edge view in the front view, Fig. 6–4. Its line of intersection 3,4 with plane ABC when projected to the top view determines p^H, the top view of the piercing point. A vertical projection line from p^H then locates p^F, and the solution is completed as in the preceding example.

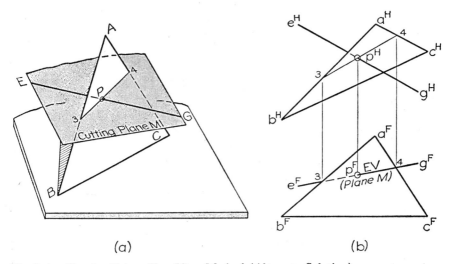

(a)   (b)

Fig. 6–4.   Piercing Point—Two-View Method (Alternate Solution)

A Special Case. In Fig. 6–5 the two-view method is shown applied to a vertical line and an oblique plane. Since the top view of the given vertical line XY is a point view, any cutting plane containing the line appears in edge view in the top view. A cutting plane M is selected which produces a line of intersection 1,2 meeting $x^F y^F$ (extended) at an angle large enough to establish p^F accurately. The top view p^H coincides with $x^H y^H$. In this case the piercing point may be considered imaginary, although it can be of use in subsequent constructions.

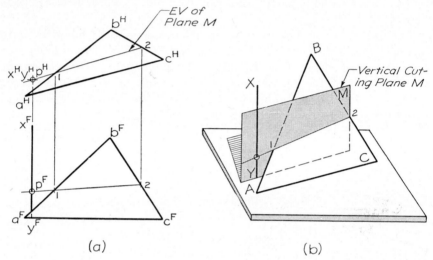

(a)   (b)

Fig. 6–5.   Piercing Point of a Vertical Line and an Oblique Plane—Two-View Method

6.3   COMPARISON OF AUXILIARY-VIEW AND TWO-VIEW METHODS

While the two-view method has the advantage of brief construction and minimum space requirements, the auxiliary-view method is often the easier of the two methods for the beginning student to comprehend. The auxiliary-view method is also frequently advantageous when several lines pierce the same plane. See, for instance, Art. 16.4.

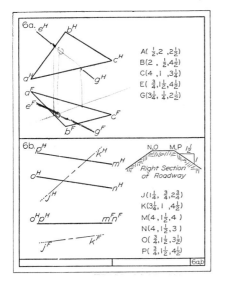

A($\frac{1}{2}$,2 ,2$\frac{1}{2}$)
B(2 , $\frac{1}{2}$,4$\frac{1}{2}$)
C(4 ,1 ,3$\frac{1}{4}$)
E($\frac{3}{4}$,1$\frac{1}{2}$,4$\frac{1}{2}$)
G(3$\frac{1}{4}$, $\frac{1}{4}$,2$\frac{1}{2}$)

6b.

N,O   M,P 1$\frac{1}{4}$
Right Section
of Roadway

J(1$\frac{1}{4}$, $\frac{3}{4}$,2$\frac{3}{4}$)
K(3$\frac{1}{4}$,1 ,4$\frac{1}{2}$)
M(4 ,1$\frac{1}{2}$,4)
N(4 ,1$\frac{1}{2}$,3)
O($\frac{3}{4}$,1$\frac{1}{2}$,3$\frac{1}{2}$)
P($\frac{3}{4}$,1$\frac{1}{2}$,4$\frac{1}{2}$)

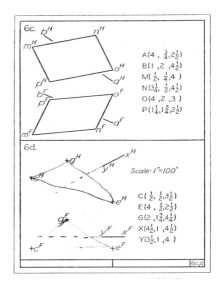

6c.

A(4 , $\frac{3}{4}$,2$\frac{1}{2}$)
B(1 ,2 ,4$\frac{1}{2}$)
M($\frac{1}{2}$, $\frac{1}{4}$,4)
N(3$\frac{1}{4}$, $\frac{1}{2}$,4$\frac{1}{2}$)
O(4 ,2 ,3)
P(1$\frac{1}{4}$,1$\frac{3}{4}$,2$\frac{1}{2}$)

6d.

Scale: 1"=100'

C($\frac{1}{2}$, $\frac{1}{2}$,3$\frac{1}{2}$)
E(4 , $\frac{1}{2}$,2$\frac{1}{2}$)
G(2 ,1$\frac{3}{4}$,4$\frac{1}{4}$)
X(4$\frac{1}{2}$,1 ,4$\frac{1}{2}$)
Y(3$\frac{1}{2}$,1 ,4)

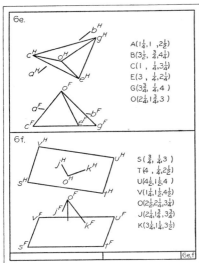

6e.

A(1$\frac{1}{4}$,1 ,2$\frac{1}{2}$)
B(3$\frac{1}{2}$, $\frac{3}{4}$,4$\frac{1}{4}$)
C(1 , $\frac{1}{4}$,3$\frac{1}{4}$)
E(3 , $\frac{1}{4}$,2$\frac{1}{4}$)
G(3$\frac{3}{4}$, $\frac{1}{4}$,4)
O(2$\frac{1}{4}$,1$\frac{3}{4}$,3)

6f.

S($\frac{3}{4}$, $\frac{1}{4}$,3)
T(4 , $\frac{1}{4}$,2$\frac{1}{2}$)
U(4$\frac{1}{2}$,1$\frac{1}{2}$,4)
V(1$\frac{1}{4}$,1$\frac{1}{2}$,4$\frac{1}{2}$)
O(2$\frac{1}{2}$,2$\frac{1}{4}$,3$\frac{1}{4}$)
J(2$\frac{1}{4}$,1$\frac{3}{4}$,3$\frac{3}{4}$)
K(3$\frac{1}{4}$,1$\frac{1}{4}$,3$\frac{1}{2}$)

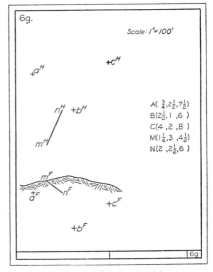

6g.

Scale: 1"=100'

A($\frac{3}{4}$,2$\frac{1}{2}$,7$\frac{1}{2}$)
B(2$\frac{1}{2}$,1 ,6)
C(4 ,2 ,8)
M(1$\frac{1}{4}$,3 ,4$\frac{1}{2}$)
N(2 ,2$\frac{1}{2}$,6)

NOTE: In Problems 6a through 6g use the auxiliary-view method.

6a. Find the intersection of *EG* with the plane *ABC*. Show complete visibility.

6b. Locate the views of the points at which the center line *JK* of a culvert pierces the 1½ to 1 fill of the roadway embankment.

6c. Locate the intersection of control cable *AB* with the bulkhead *MNOP*.

6d. Find the true distance that tunnel *XY* must be extended from *Y* to meet an

ore vein determined by points *C, E,* and *G*.

6e. Show the intersection of *AB* and the pyramid. Omit that part of the line within the solid.

6f. Locate the intersection of a vertical mast at *O* and the guy wires *OJ* and *OK* with the roof plane *STUV*.

6g. Find the true length of the extension of inclined shaft *MN* needed to reach an ore vein determined by points *ABC*.

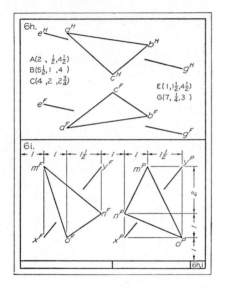

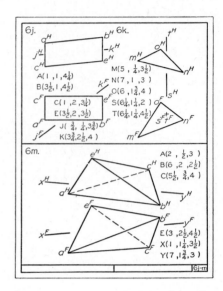

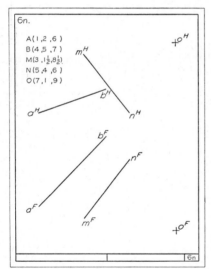

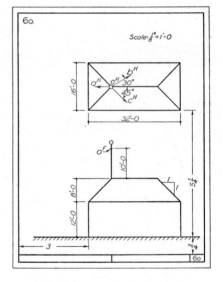

NOTE: In Problems 6h through 6o use the two-view method. Show visibility.

6h. Find the intersection of *EG* with the plane *ABC*.

6i. Find the intersection of *XY* with the plane *MNO*.

6j. Locate the intersection of *JK* with the plane *ABCE*.

6k. Locate the intersection of *ST* with the plane *MNO*.

6m. Find the piercing points of *XY* with the surfaces of the tetrahedron.

6n. Draw a line through point *O* and intersecting the skew lines *AB* and *MN*.

6o. Locate the intersections of guy wires *OA*, *OB*, and *OC* with the surfaces to which they are attached if each wire makes an angle of 30° with the vertical mast.

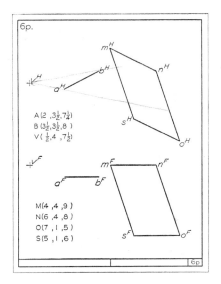

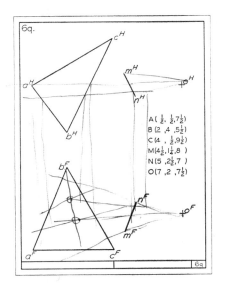

6p. Using V as a light source, determine the shadow of line AB on the plane $MNOS$.

6q. Using point O as a light source, determine that portion of the shadow of line MN that falls on plane ABC.

6r. Indicate whether the following statements are true or false. If assigned, provide written explanations or sketches to justify the answers.

(a) A straight line can intersect a plane surface at only one point.

(b) A straight line can intersect the surfaces of a regular prism at not more than two points including imaginary points.

(c) A line parallel to a plane surface does not intersect that surface.

(d) For the most convenient construction, a cutting plane used for finding the intersection of a line with a plane should be an edge-view cutting plane.

(e) The visibility of a line intersecting a limited plane surface changes at the piercing point of the line and plane.

(f) The intersection of a cutting plane with a plane surface is a single straight line.

INTERSECTION OF PLANES

CHAPTER 7

ANY TWO PLANES must either be parallel or be intersecting, even if the intersection falls beyond the limits of the planes as given. The intersection of two planes is a straight line common to the planes, and its position is therefore determined by any two points common to the planes. For graphical accuracy the two points should be separated by a reasonable distance.[1].

Since a plane is indefinite in extent unless otherwise specified, the line of intersection of two planes is, in general, of no definite length. It frequently occurs, however, that a given plane is bounded by a closed figure as in the case of a plane surface of a solid object, in which instance the plane may be regarded as limited. The line of intersection of such a plane and another plane would be limited correspondingly.

Points common to two planes may be found by any one of three general methods: the *auxiliary-view* method; the *two-view, piercing-point* method; or the *cutting-plane* method.

7.1 INTERSECTION OF TWO PLANES—AUXILIARY-VIEW METHOD

The point in which a line in one plane pierces another plane is a point common to the two planes. As was discussed in Art. 6.1, the point in which a line pierces a plane is shown in any view which shows the plane in edge view. Consequently, if it is required to find the line of intersection of two planes, any view showing one of the planes in edge view secures the piercing points of all lines of the other plane. Of course, if a line is parallel to a plane, it does not pierce the plane, or if a line is nearly parallel to the plane, the piercing point may fall outside the working area of the drawing. Any two available piercing points, if a sufficient distance apart for graphical accuracy, locate the required line of intersection.

For the two planes in Fig. 7–1(a), plane *EGJK* is arbitrarily selected to

---

[1] See Appendix I.

be shown in edge view. Horizontal line *JH* is added to plane *EGJK* as shown, and the desired edge view is projected from the top view. In the resulting view 1, the piercing points *X* and *Y* of lines *AB* and *BC*, respectively, appear as x^1 and y^1. The required line of intersection of the two planes passes through the points *X* and *Y* and therefore coincides with the edge view of plane *EGJK* in view 1.

The front and top views of line *XY* are located by projecting from x^1 and y^1 to $a^H b^H$ and $b^H c^H$ in the top view, and then to $a^F b^F$ and $b^F c^F$ in the front view, Fig. 7–1(b). In this problem the given planes are limited and the line of intersection may therefore be regarded as terminating at points *Y* and *Z*. The visibility of the remaining lines is then determined and the drawing completed as shown.

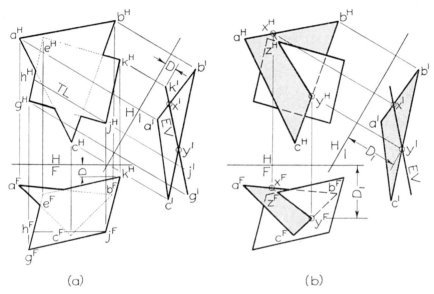

          (a)   (b)

Fig. 7–1. Intersection of Two Limited Planes—Auxiliary-View Method

7.2   INTERSECTION OF TWO PLANES—TWO-VIEW, PIERCING-POINT METHOD

Since the piercing point of a line in a plane may be determined by using only the two given views (Art. 6.2), the line of intersection of two planes may be located by applying this piercing-point method twice, or more if necessary for accuracy.

In Fig. 7–2(a) line *DE* of plane *DEG* is first selected as convenient for this method. Accordingly, an imaginary edge-view cutting plane is assumed coinciding with $d^F e^F$. Its line of intersection 1,2 with plane *ABC* is then located in the side view by projecting points 1 and 2 to lines $a^P c^P$ and $b^P c^P$, respectively. Since lines DE and 1,2 both lie in this plane, they are intersecting lines, and the point of intersection X, determined in the side view (x^P) and projected to the front view (x^F), is the piercing point of line DE in plane ABC. Point X is therefore common to the given planes ABC and DEG and is one point on the required line of intersection.

The foregoing process is repeated for some other line of either plane—in this example, line EG, Fig. 7–2(b). An edge-view cutting plane is assumed coinciding with $e^F g^F$ to secure a second point Y common to both planes. The views of the line of intersection pass through the respective projections of X and Y as shown. It will be noted that the given planes in this problem are not limited. Visibility is usually not considered in such cases, and the line of intersection may be drawn to any appropriate length.

If the two piercing points determined by the foregoing method are relatively close together, a third piercing point may be secured to assure the accurate location of the line of intersection. Since the line of intersection is common to the planes, it must intersect or be parallel to all lines in the planes. This fact may also be used to check the accuracy of the solution as suggested by intersection point 5 in Fig. 7–2(b).

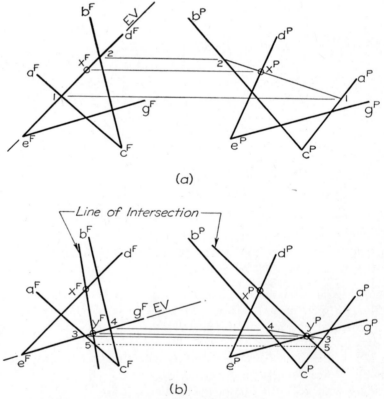

(a)

(b)

Fig. 7–2.   Intersection of Two Planes—Two-View, Piercing-Point Method

7.3   INTERSECTION OF TWO PLANES—CUTTING-PLANE METHOD

If two nonparallel planes are intersected by a third plane (not parallel to the intersection of the first two), the resulting lines of intersection meet at a point common to all three planes. Two or more such cutting planes may be employed to secure a corresponding number of points common to the two given planes, thus establishing the line of intersection of these two planes.

In Fig. 7–3(a) the front and top views of two planes are given, and it is required to find their line of intersection through the use of cutting planes according to the preceding principle.

For convenience, edge-view cutting planes are used. These may be horizontal, frontal, profile, or inclined planes, or any combination of these, whichever seems appropriate in a particular problem. In Fig. 7–3(b), two

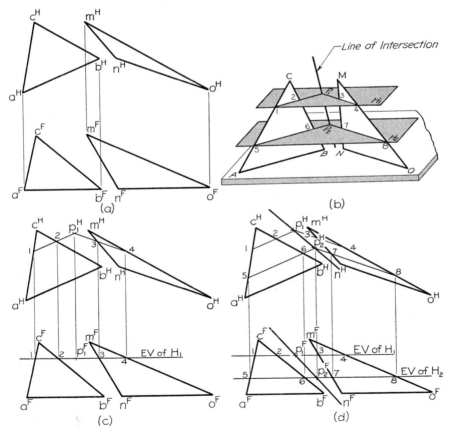

Fig. 7–3.   Intersection of Two Planes—Cutting-Plane Method

horizontal cutting planes used in the solution are shown in pictorial form. It will be noted that cutting plane H_1 intersects planes ABC and MNO in two lines which in turn intersect each other at point P_1 on the required line of intersection. This construction is shown in multiview form in Fig. 7–3(c). The horizontal cutting plane H_1 appears as a horizontal line in the front view. Lines 1,2 and 3,4 coincide with H_1 in this view, but when projected to the top view they intersect, when extended, at point p_1^H. A vertical projection line from p_1^H establishes p_1^F and completes the location of a point common to the two given planes.

In similar fashion a second horizontal cutting plane H_2, Fig. 7–3(b), intersects the given planes in lines which, when extended, locate point P_2 on the line of intersection of the given planes. This construction is shown in multiview form in Fig. 7–3(d). Lines drawn through p_1^F and p_2^F, and p_1^H and p_2^H, respectively, represent the front and top views of the line of intersection of the planes ABC and MNO.

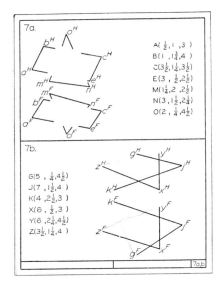

7a.

$A(\frac{1}{2},1,3)$
$B(1,1\frac{3}{4},4)$
$C(3\frac{1}{2},1\frac{1}{4},3\frac{1}{2})$
$E(3,\frac{1}{2},2\frac{1}{2})$
$M(1\frac{1}{4},2,2\frac{1}{2})$
$N(3,1\frac{1}{2},2\frac{1}{4})$
$O(2,\frac{1}{4},4\frac{1}{2})$

7b.

$G(5,\frac{1}{4},4\frac{1}{2})$
$J(7,1\frac{1}{2},4)$
$K(4,2\frac{1}{2},3)$
$X(6,\frac{1}{2},3)$
$Y(6,2\frac{1}{4},4\frac{1}{2})$
$Z(3\frac{1}{2},1\frac{1}{4},4)$

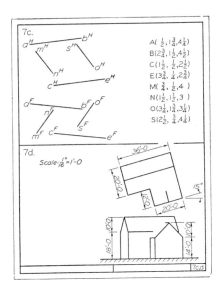

7c.

$A(\frac{1}{2},1\frac{3}{4},4\frac{1}{2})$
$B(2\frac{3}{4},1\frac{1}{2},4\frac{1}{2})$
$C(1\frac{1}{2},\frac{1}{2},2\frac{1}{2})$
$E(3\frac{3}{4},\frac{1}{4},2\frac{3}{4})$
$M(\frac{3}{4},\frac{1}{2},4)$
$N(1\frac{1}{2},1\frac{1}{2},3)$
$O(3\frac{1}{4},1\frac{3}{4},3\frac{1}{2})$
$S(2\frac{1}{2},\frac{3}{4},4\frac{1}{4})$

7d.

Scale $\frac{1}{8}"=1'-0$

36'-0

20'-0

/5°

/2'-0

20'-0

18'-0

10'-0

4'-0

10'-0

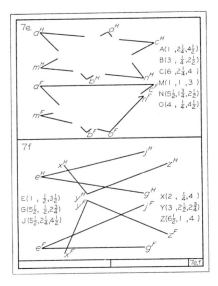

7e.

$A(1,2\frac{1}{4},4\frac{1}{2})$
$B(3,\frac{1}{4},2\frac{1}{2})$
$C(6,2\frac{1}{4},4)$
$M(1,1,3)$
$N(5\frac{1}{2},1\frac{3}{4},2\frac{1}{2})$
$O(4,\frac{1}{4},4\frac{1}{2})$

7f

$E(1,\frac{1}{2},3\frac{1}{2})$
$G(5\frac{1}{2},\frac{1}{2},2\frac{1}{2})$
$J(5\frac{1}{2},2\frac{1}{4},4\frac{1}{2})$

$X(2,\frac{1}{4},4)$
$Y(3,2\frac{1}{2},2\frac{3}{4})$
$Z(6\frac{1}{2},1,4)$

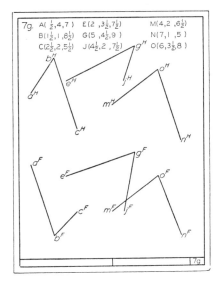

7g. $A(\frac{1}{2},4,7)$ $E(2,3\frac{1}{2},7\frac{1}{2})$ $M(4,2,6\frac{1}{2})$
$B(1\frac{1}{2},1,8\frac{1}{2})$ $G(5,4\frac{1}{2},9)$ $N(7,1,5)$
$C(2\frac{1}{2},2,5\frac{1}{2})$ $J(4\frac{1}{2},2,7\frac{1}{2})$ $O(6,3\frac{1}{2},8)$

7a. By the auxiliary-view method determine the intersection of the planes. Show visibility.

7b. Using the auxiliary-view method, locate the intersection of the planes.

7c. By the auxiliary-view method find the line of intersection of the planes determined by the sets of parallel lines.

7d. Complete the plan and elevation views.

7e. Find the intersection of the two planes. Show complete visibility.

7f. Find the line of intersection of the two planes.

7g. Locate the point common to the three given planes.

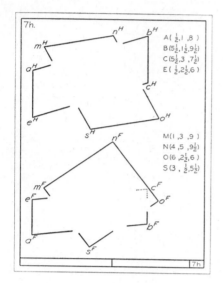

A(½,1 ,8)
B(5½,1½,9½)
C(5½,3 ,7½)
E(½,2½,6)

M(1 ,3 ,9)
N(4 ,5 ,9½)
O(6 ,2½,6)
S(3 , ½,5½)

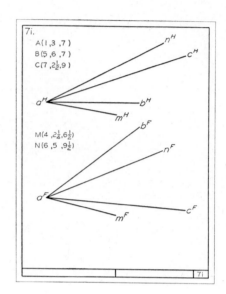

A(1 ,3 ,7)
B(5 ,6 ,7)
C(7 ,2½,9)

M(4 ,2¼,6½)
N(6 ,5 ,9½)

7h. Determine the intersection of the given planes and show the correct visibility.

7i. Determine a point common to the planes *ABC* and *AMN* and 2 in. from point *A*.

7j. Indicate whether the following statements are true or false. If assigned, provide written explanations or sketches to justify the answers.

(a) Two nonparallel planes intersect in a single straight line.

(b) Three nonparallel planes have a single point in common.

(c) If two parallel planes are intersected by a third plane, the lines of intersection are parallel.

(d) Two perpendicular planes intersect in a single point.

(e) A line of intersection of any two planes appears true length in either a top, front, or side view.

(f) The line of intersection of two planes is visible if no other planes are present.

ANGLE
BETWEEN
CHAPTER 8 | # PLANES

THE ANGLE FORMED by two intersecting planes is called a *dihedral* angle, Fig. 8–1(a). A view in which each of the given planes appears in edge view shows the true size of the dihedral angle, Fig. 8–1(b). Since a plane is seen edgewise in any view in which a line in the plane appears as a point,[1] a view showing a point view of the line of intersection of two planes produces an edge view of each of the planes.

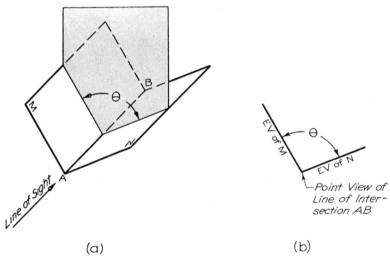

(a)   (b)

Fig. 8–1. Dihedral Angle

8.1 DIHEDRAL ANGLE—LINE OF INTERSECTION GIVEN

In Fig. 8–2, an application of the foregoing principles to an actual problem is illustrated. In order to manufacture or "fabricate" the *transition piece,* it is necessary to know the dihedral angles for the special bent-plate angles

---

[1] See Art. 5.3.

95

used at the corners. The construction shown illustrates the method of obtaining the angle for one of the bent-plate angles—the angle between surfaces *A* and *B* of the transition piece. A complete working drawing would, of course, include views showing all necessary angles.

In this problem, as is the case with many practical problems, the line of intersection *EG* between the two planes is known. To produce a point view of line *EG*, it is first necessary to construct view 1 which includes the true length of line *EG*. From view 1, view 2 is then projected, with a line of sight assumed parallel to e^1g^1. The resulting view 2 shows line *EG* as a point and consequently shows planes *A* and *B* in edge view. The desired dihedral angle may then be measured as indicated.

It will be noted in this example that the desired angle is greater than 90°. Theoretically, two intersecting planes form two dihedral angles which are supplementary (totaling 180°). In the absence of evidence to the contrary, it is customary to dimension the smaller or acute angle. In most practical examples, however, as in Fig. 8–2, it is evident which of the two angles is desired.

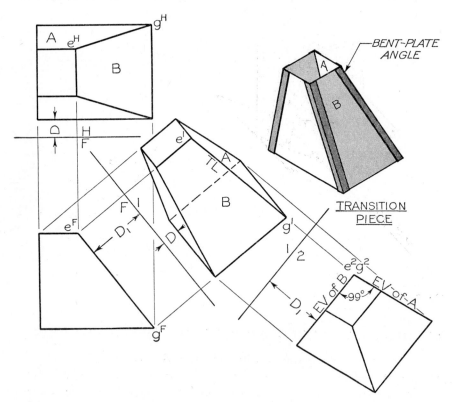

Fig. 8–2. Dihedral Angle—Line of Intersection Given

8.2 DIHEDRAL ANGLE—LINE OF INTERSECTION NOT GIVEN

Occasionally it is necessary to find the angle between two planes for which the line of intersection is not a part of the original drawing. In such cases, as in Fig. 8–3, the first construction is therefore the determination of the line of intersection.

In Fig. 8–3(b) the two-view, piercing-point method of Art. 7.2 is employed to obtain the line of intersection XY between given planes ABC and

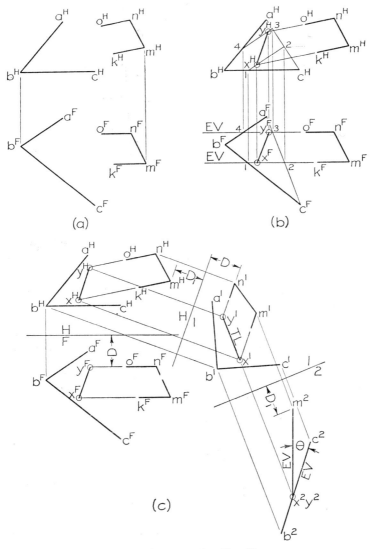

Fig. 8–3. Dihedral Angle—Line of Intersection Not Given

KMNO. Successive auxiliary views are then used to obtain the true length and point views of *XY* and the angle θ between the planes, Fig. 8–3(c).

Alternate Solution. Figure 8–4 illustrates an alternate method in which it

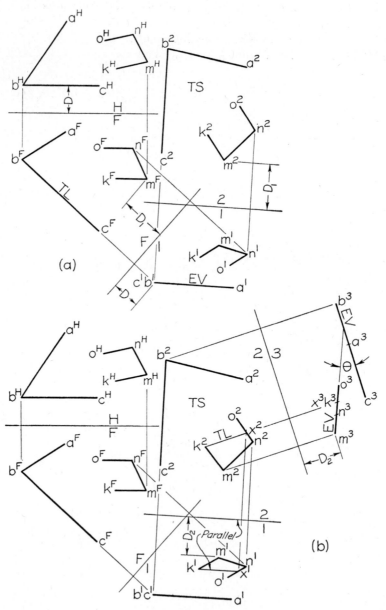

Fig. 8–4. Dihedral Angle—Line of Intersection Not Given (Alternate Method)

is not necessary to find the line of intersection to determine the dihedral angle.

Since line *BC* appears true length in the front view, auxiliary view 1 may be added as shown to obtain an edge view of plane *ABC*, Fig. 8–4(a). Auxiliary view 2 is then constructed, showing plane *ABC* in true size. Plane *KMNO* is also projected to these auxiliary views.

In Fig. 8–4(b), a line *KX* is added to plane *KMNO*, with k^1x^1 drawn parallel to folding line 1/2 so that k^2x^2 will be true length. A line of sight for auxiliary view 3 is assumed parallel to k^2x^2. The resulting view 3 shows both planes in edge view, and the dihedral angle may be measured as indicated.

This method may provide a solution when the line of intersection of the given planes is outside the working area of the drawing.

8.3 ANGLE BETWEEN OBLIQUE PLANE AND PRINCIPAL PLANE

A special application of the determination of the angle between two planes occurs when one of the planes is a horizontal, profile, or frontal plane. In Fig. 8–5 it is desired to find the angle between plane *ABC* and a frontal plane. Any frontal plane appears as a line horizontal on the paper in the top view. If such a plane is introduced, passing through a^H in Fig. 8–5, its line of intersection with plane *ABC* is frontal line *AF*. Since *AF* appears in true length in the front view, auxiliary view 1 shows the frontal plane and plane *ABC* in edge view, and the required angle is shown as indicated. Of course *any* frontal plane would appear in view 1 as a line parallel to folding line *F*/1. Hence the angle θ_F may be measured between $a^1b^1c^1$ and *F*/1 without the necessity of adding a specific frontal plane.

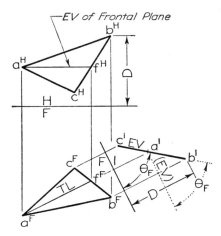

Fig. 8–5. Angle Between Plane and Frontal Plane

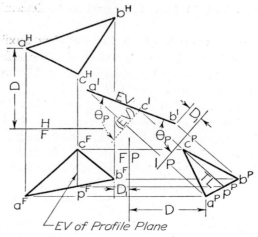

Fig. 8–6.   Angle Between Plane and Profile Plane

In Fig. 8–6 construction is shown for obtaining the angle θ_P between plane *ABC* and a profile plane. In this case it is necessary to add the side view to secure the true length of the profile line of intersection *CP*. Otherwise the construction corresponds to that of Fig. 8–5.

The angle between a plane and a horizontal plane can be found by adding a horizontal line to the oblique plane and proceeding in a similar fashion. In geology and mining engineering the angle between a sloping plane and a horizontal plane is called the *dip* of the sloping plane. See Art. 12.4.

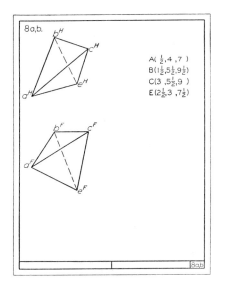

8a,b.

$A(\frac{1}{2},4,7)$
$B(1\frac{1}{2},5\frac{1}{2},9\frac{1}{2})$
$C(3,5\frac{1}{2},9)$
$E(2\frac{1}{2},3,7\frac{1}{2})$

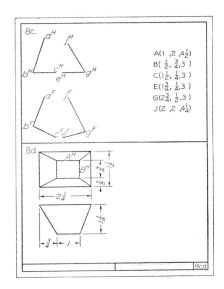

8c.

$A(1,2,4\frac{1}{2})$
$B(\frac{1}{2},\frac{3}{4},3)$
$C(1\frac{1}{2},\frac{1}{4},3)$
$E(1\frac{3}{4},\frac{1}{4},3)$
$G(2\frac{3}{4},\frac{1}{2},3)$
$J(2,2,4\frac{1}{4})$

8d.

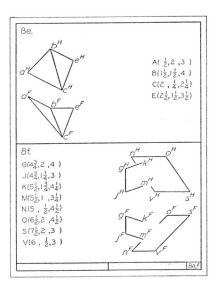

8e.

$A(\frac{1}{2},2,3)$
$B(1\frac{1}{2},1\frac{1}{2},4)$
$C(2,\frac{1}{4},2\frac{1}{4})$
$E(2\frac{1}{2},1\frac{1}{2},3\frac{1}{2})$

8f.

$G(4\frac{3}{4},2,4)$
$J(4\frac{3}{4},1\frac{1}{4},3)$
$K(5\frac{1}{2},1\frac{3}{4},4\frac{1}{4})$
$M(5\frac{1}{2},1,3\frac{1}{2})$
$N(5,\frac{1}{2},4\frac{1}{2})$
$O(6\frac{1}{2},2,4\frac{1}{2})$
$S(7\frac{1}{2},2,3)$
$V(6,\frac{1}{2},3)$

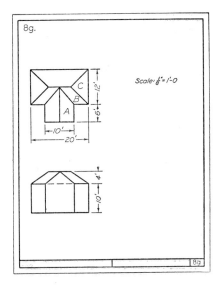

8g.

Scale: $\frac{1}{8}" = 1'-0$

8a. Find the true size of the dihedral angle formed by planes *ABC* and *BCE*.

8b. Find the true size of the dihedral angle formed by planes *ACE* and *CEB*.

8c. Find the line of intersection of, and the dihedral angle between, the two planes.

8d. Determine the true size of the angle formed by planes *A* and *B* so that a corner reinforcing plate can be correctly bent.

8e. Find the angle formed by the planes *ABC* and *BEC*.

8f. Find the line of intersection of, and the dihedral angle between, the given planes *GJKM* and *NOVS*.

8g. Determine the dihedral angles formed by roof planes *A* and *B* and the roof planes *B* and *C*.

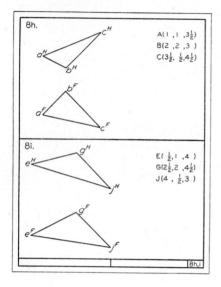

8h.

$A(1, 1, 3\frac{1}{2})$
$B(2, 2, 3)$
$C(3\frac{1}{2}, \frac{1}{2}, 4\frac{1}{2})$

8i.

$E(\frac{1}{2}, 1, 4)$
$G(2\frac{1}{2}, 2, 4\frac{1}{2})$
$J(4, \frac{1}{2}, 3)$

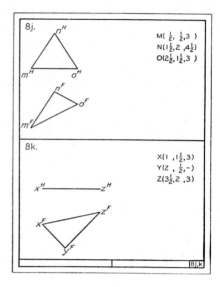

8j.

$M(\frac{1}{2}, \frac{1}{2}, 3)$
$N(1\frac{1}{2}, 2, 4\frac{1}{2})$
$O(2\frac{1}{2}, 1\frac{1}{2}, 3)$

8k.

$X(1, 1\frac{1}{2}, 3)$
$Y(2, \frac{1}{2}, -)$
$Z(3\frac{1}{2}, 2, 3)$

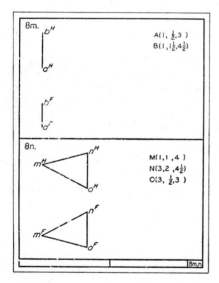

8m.

$A(1, \frac{1}{2}, 3)$
$B(1, 1\frac{1}{2}, 4\frac{1}{2})$

8n.

$M(1, 1, 4)$
$N(3, 2, 4\frac{1}{2})$
$O(3, \frac{1}{2}, 3)$

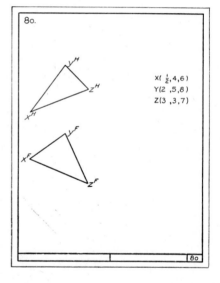

8o.

$X(\frac{1}{2}, 4, 6)$
$Y(2, 5, 8)$
$Z(3, 3, 7)$

8h. Determine the angle that plane *ABC* makes with a frontal plane.

8i. Determine the angle that plane *EGJ* makes with a horizontal plane.

8j. Determine the angle that plane *MNO* makes with a profile plane.

8k. Plane *XYZ* makes an angle of 30° with a frontal plane. Complete the top view of the plane.

8m. Line *AB* lies in a plane that makes an angle of 30° with a profile plane. Locate a point *S* on the plane that lies ½ in. above *B* and 1 in. to the right of *B*.

8n. Determine the angle that plane *MNO* makes with a horizontal plane. Locate a point *K* on the plane that lies ½ in. to the left of *N* and ¾ in. below *N*.

8o. Determine the angles that plane *XYZ* makes with the principal planes *H*, *F*, and *P*.

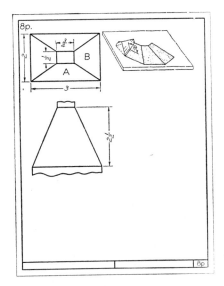

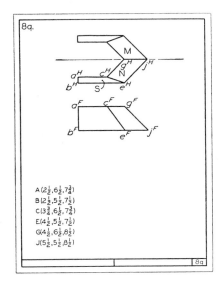

A $(2\frac{1}{2},6\frac{1}{2},7\frac{3}{4})$
B $(2\frac{1}{2},5\frac{1}{2},7\frac{1}{2})$
C $(3\frac{3}{4},6\frac{1}{2},7\frac{3}{4})$
E $(4\frac{1}{2},5\frac{1}{2},7\frac{1}{2})$
G $(4\frac{1}{2},6\frac{1}{2},8\frac{1}{2})$
J $(5\frac{1}{2},5\frac{1}{2},8\frac{1}{2})$

8p. The layout of a sheet-metal hopper is illustrated in its developed flat position and also with one face bent to its final angular position.

Find the true size of the bend angle θ formed by faces A and B.

8q. In order that support clips may be formed for the airplane windshield sections, determine the angles formed by planes M and N and by N and S.

8r. Indicate whether the following statements are true or false. If assigned, prepare written explanations or sketches to justify the answers.

(a) A view having a direction of sight parallel to a true-length view of the intersection of two planes shows the true size of the dihedral angle.

(b) The adjacent dihedral angles formed by two intersecting planes are complementary.

(c) Dihedral angles cannot be observed in principal views.

(d) Two intersecting oblique planes cannot both appear edgewise in the same view.

(e) The angles formed by an oblique plane with a horizontal and with a frontal plane are always complementary.

(f) If the line of intersection of two nonparallel planes is inaccessible in the given views, the dihedral angle cannot be found.

CHAPTER 9 | PARALLELISM

PARALLELISM OF LINES is a property that is preserved in orthographic projections. Thus lines parallel in space project as parallel lines in any view except in those views in which they coincide or appear as points—situations which do not alter the fact that the lines are parallel.

9.1 PARALLEL LINES

Oblique lines that appear parallel in two or more principal views are parallel in space. This principle is illustrated in Fig. 9–1(a), in which three principal views of two lines AB and CD are drawn. Since the views are respectively parallel, the lines themselves are parallel in space, Fig. 9–1(b).

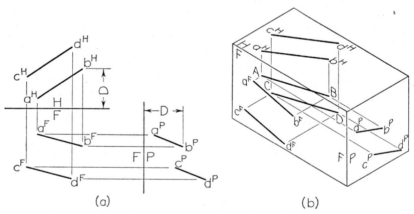

(a)   (b)

Fig. 9–1.   Parallel Oblique Lines

Two horizontal, two frontal, or two profile lines which appear to be parallel in two principal views may or may not be actually parallel in space. For example, in Fig. 9–2(a) the two horizontal lines MN and OS appear parallel in their front and side views. Without further study it might be concluded that the lines are parallel in space; but when the top view is added, Fig. 9–2(b), it is apparent that the two lines are not parallel. The true spatial relationship of the two lines is shown pictorially in Fig. 9–2(c). Non-intersecting, nonparallel lines are called *skew* lines.

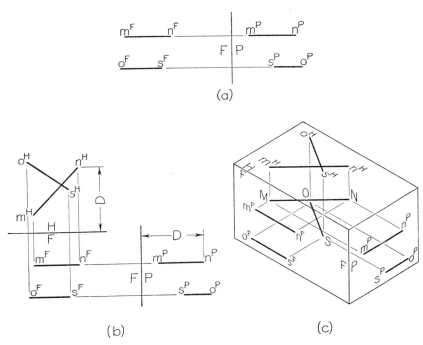

Fig. 9–2. Check of Parallelism of Principal Lines

As another example of the special requirements involved in parallel principal lines, let it be required to construct a line containing point C and parallel to profile line AB, Fig. 9–3(a). If the side view is added, Fig. 9–3(b), the true inclination of line AB becomes apparent, and the side view of the required line CE, of any appropriate length, may then be drawn parallel to $a^P b^P$, Fig. 9–3(c). The front and top views of point E are then established to complete the solution. It should be noted that a random location of point E only in the front and top views would not guarantee parallelism, since there would be no assurance that the inclination of such a line would be the same as that of AB.

The true distance between two parallel lines may be obtained either by constructing a view showing the lines as points, Fig. 9–3(c), or by obtaining a normal view of the plane of the two lines, Art. 5.4.

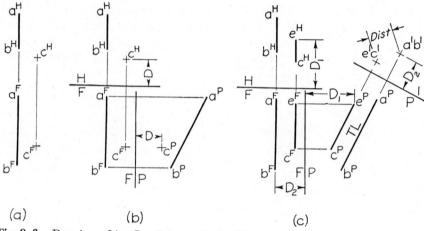

Fig. 9–3.   Drawing a Line Parallel to a Profile Line

Any two lines in a plane must either intersect or be parallel. In Fig.
9–4(a) it is evident that line *AB* cannot intersect line *ON* since their top
views are parallel. If it is known that line *AB* is in plane *MON*, lines *AB*
and *ON* must therefore be parallel in space. Consequently the front view of
AB may be established by projecting point *A* to the front view and by drawing $a^F b^F$ parallel to $o^F n^F$, Fig. 9–4(b).

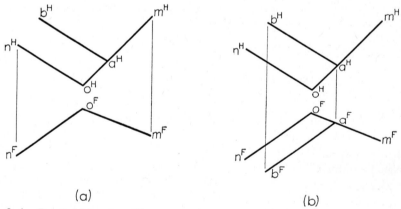

Fig. 9–4.   Parallel Lines in a Plane

9.2   PARALLEL PLANES

*If two planes are parallel, any line in one plane is parallel to the other
plane,* since it cannot intersect the other plane. If two intersecting lines in
one plane are parallel respectively to two intersecting lines in a second plane,
the planes are parallel in space, Fig. 9–5.

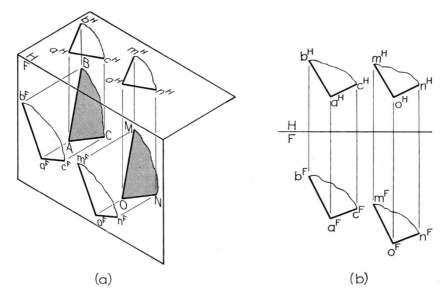

(a)   (b)

Fig. 9–5. Parallel Planes

If two planes are parallel, any view showing one of the planes in edge view must also show the other plane as a parallel edge view. This principle may be used to check or to establish parallelism of planes represented by nonparallel lines, Fig. 9–6. Parallelism of two such planes can also be checked by investigating the possibility of drawing a pair of intersecting lines in one plane parallel respectively to two lines in the other plane.

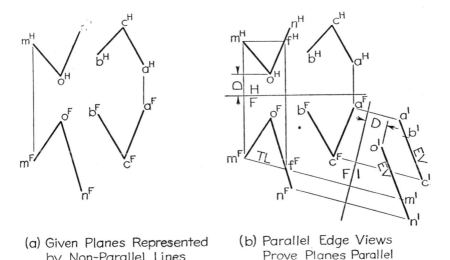

(a) Given Planes Represented   (b) Parallel Edge Views
    by Non-Parallel Lines   Prove Planes Parallel

Fig. 9–6. Checking Parallelism of Planes by Edge Views

9.3 LINES PARALLEL TO PLANES; PLANES PARALLEL TO LINES

If two lines are parallel, any plane containing one of the lines is parallel to the other line (or, as a special case, contains the other line). Hence a line may be drawn parallel to a given plane by making it parallel to any appro-

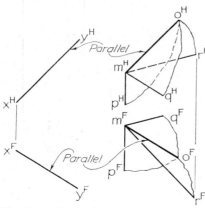

Fig. 9–7.   Planes Parallel to a Line

priate line in the plane. Two such lines, if intersecting, establish a plane parallel to the given plane, Fig. 9–5.

Conversely, a plane may be drawn parallel to a given line merely by having the plane contain a line parallel to the given line. In Fig. 9–7, each of the planes OMP, OMQ, and OMR is parallel to line XY, since line OM is parallel to XY. In fact, there is an infinite number of planes containing OM which are parallel to XY. On the other hand, there is only one plane containing, say, line MR and which is parallel to XY; namely, plane OMR.

This same principle is applied to another case in Fig. 9–8. Lines AB and CE as given are non-intersecting and thus do not lie in the same plane, but it is possible to establish planes parallel to both lines. If through the given point O, line OA_1 is established parallel to AB, and line OE_1 parallel to CE, the plane A_1OE_1 is parallel to both AB and CE.

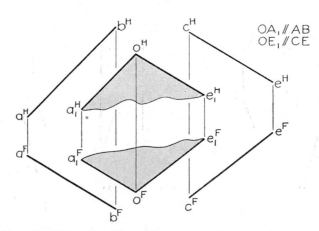

$OA_1 /\!\!/ AB$
$OE_1 /\!\!/ CE$

Fig. 9–8.   Plane Parallel to Two Skew Lines

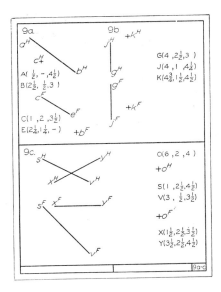

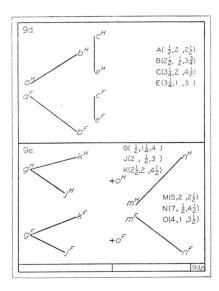

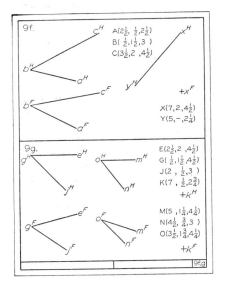

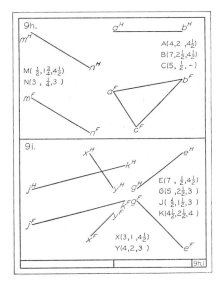

9a. Complete the views of the parallel lines AB and CE.

9b. Draw line KM 1 in. long and parallel to GJ.

9c. Pass a plane through O parallel to lines SV and XY.

9d. Draw a plane through AB parallel to CE.

9e. Show a line through O parallel to plane KGJ and intersecting line MN.

9f. Complete the front view of XY which is parallel to plane ABC.

9g. Pass a line through K parallel to the planes EGJ and MON.

9h. Plane ABC is parallel to line MN. Complete its top view.

9i. Pass a line parallel to EG and intersecting the skew lines JK and XY.

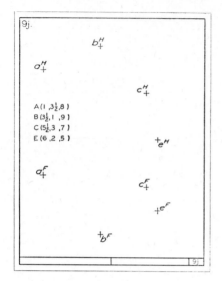

A(1 ,3½,8)
B(3½,1 ,9)
C(5½,3 ,7)
E(6 ,2 ,5)

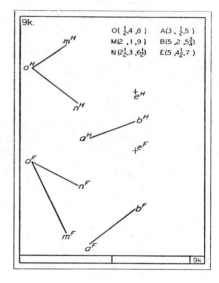

O(½,4 ,8)   A(3 , ½,5)
M(2 ,1 ,9)   B(5 ,2 ,5¾)
N(2½,3 ,6½)   E(5 ,4½,7)

9j. Through the four given points, represent four equidistant and parallel planes, each plane to contain only one of the points.

9k. Draw a line through E parallel to plane MON and intersecting line AB.

9m. Indicate whether the following statements are true or false. If assigned, prepare written explanations or sketches to justify the answers.

(a) Through a given point only one plane can be passed parallel to a specified plane.

(b) A plane can be passed through a point parallel to two non-intersecting lines.

(c) For a line to be parallel to a plane, the line must be parallel to a line in the plane.

(d) For a plane to be parallel to a horizontal line, it is essential that the plane be horizontal.

(e) Three parallel planes must also be equidistant.

(f) A line can be drawn through any point parallel to two nonparallel planes.

(g) A plane parallel to two nonparallel frontal lines is a frontal plane.

(h) A horizontal line can be drawn through any point parallel to an oblique plane.

(i) All horizontal lines are parallel.

CHAPTER 10 | PERPENDICULARITY

IN SOLID GEOMETRY an important theorem is stated thus: "If a line is perpendicular to a plane, it is perpendicular to every line in the plane *through the foot of the perpendicular*." In descriptive geometry it is useful to broaden this as follows: *If a line is perpendicular to a plane, it is perpendicular to every line in the plane.* In Fig. 10–1 lines *GJ* and *XY* are both considered to be perpendicular to line *EF*, since they lie in a plane perpendicular to *EF*. Thus, in descriptive geometry, perpendicular lines are *not necessarily* intersecting lines; that is, they do not necessarily lie in the same plane.

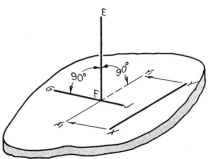

Fig. 10–1. Perpendicular Lines—Intersecting and Non-Intersecting

10.1 PERPENDICULAR LINES

A useful characteristic of perpendicular lines in orthographic projection is: *If two lines are perpendicular, they appear perpendicular in any view showing at least one of the lines in true length.*[1] Conversely, if two lines appear perpendicular in a view, they are actually perpendicular in space providing at least one of the lines is true length in the view.

---

[1] Exceptions occur when one line is shown as a point or when the plane of intersecting perpendicular lines appears in edge view. In these cases an adjacent view, given or constructed, shows the true right angle.

111

In Fig. 10–2 front and top views are shown of a 45° triangle in various positions. At (a) both legs of the 90° angle are true length and the true 90° angle appears in the front view. At (b) the true 90° angle still appears in the front view because one of the legs, $a^F b^F$, is true length. At (c), however, legs AB and BC of the 90° angle are both foreshortened, and the true 90° angle is not observed in either the top view or front view. It is suggested that the student view a triangle in various positions to verify these principles.

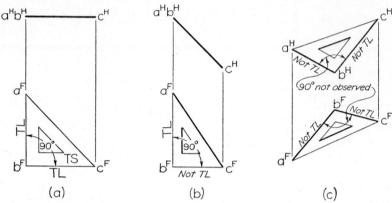

Fig. 10–2.   Views of Perpendicular Lines—A 45° Triangle

In Fig. 10–3 each of the lines CD, CD_1, CD_2, and CD_3 is perpendicular to line AB, since each front view is perpendicular to true-length view $a^F b^F$. The directions of the top views of the lines are immaterial.

The same principle may be used to test (or establish) perpendicularity of oblique lines. In Fig. 10–4 the true angular relationship of lines MN and OS

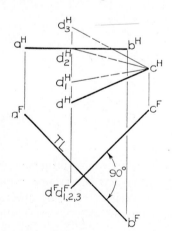

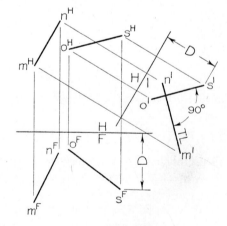

Fig. 10–3. Perpendicular Non-Intersecting Lines—One Shown True Length

Fig. 10–4.   Auxiliary-View Test for Perpendicularity

is not apparent in the front and top views; but when an auxiliary view is added showing one of the lines in true length, *MN* in this case, it becomes evident that the two lines are perpendicular in space.

10.2 PLANE PERPENDICULAR TO LINE

Two-View Method. A plane is perpendicular to a line if the plane contains two nonparallel lines each of which is perpendicular to the given line. Thus a plane may be drawn containing a given point and perpendicular to a given line as follows, Fig. 10–5: Let the given point be *X* and the given line *YZ*, Fig. 10–5(a). Horizontal line *XH* is drawn with its true-length view $x^H h^H$ perpendicular to $y^H z^H$, Fig. 10–5(b). Frontal line *XF* is drawn with its true-length view $x^F f^F$ perpendicular to $y^F z^F$, Fig. 10–5(c). Since lines *XH* and *XF* are thereby made perpendicular to line *YZ* in space, plane *HXF* is perpendicular to *YZ*. This is substantiated in the auxiliary "check" view, which shows plane *HXF* in edge view and line *YZ* in true length.

Auxiliary-View Method. As suggested by the check view in Fig. 10–5(c), a plane also may be established through a given point *E* perpendicular to a given line *GJ* by an auxiliary view showing line *GJ* in true length, Fig. 10–6(a), since in this true-length view the required plane appears in edge view and at a right angle to $g^1 j^1$. All lines in the required plane are perpendicular to line *GJ*. The front and top views may therefore be completed by projecting any random pair of points in the plane such as *K* and *M*, Fig. 10–6(b), back to the given views. With k^1 and m^1 assumed on the edge

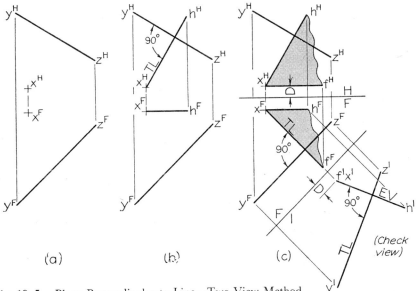

(a)   (b)   (c)   (Check view)

Fig. 10–5. Plane Perpendicular to Line—Two-View Method

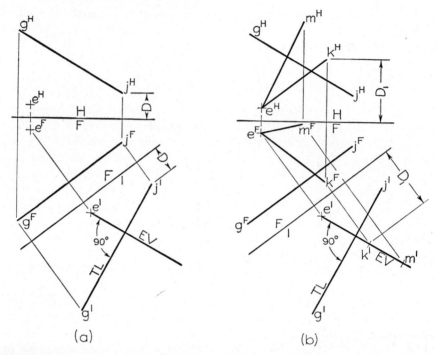

(a)   (b)

Fig. 10–6. Plane Perpendicular to Line—Auxiliary-View Method

view of the plane as shown, k^F and m^F may be placed anywhere along the projection lines from k^1 and m^1 to the front view. The points K and M are thus established at definite locations in space, and their top views are now located in the usual manner as indicated.

Example Problem Involving Plane Perpendicular to Line

PROBLEM, Fig. 10–7:

Draw the front and top views of a right square pyramid[2] having its axis along line XY, its vertex at point A, and one corner of its base at point B, Fig. 10–7(a).

ANALYSIS:

A view showing line XY in true length will show the plane of the base in edge view and perpendicular to the axis (because of the right pyramid specification). An additional view showing line XY as a point will thus show the base in true size and shape.

GRAPHIC SOLUTION:

Auxiliary view 1 is added showing line XY in true length, Fig. 10–7(a). The base of the pyramid must appear in edge view and contain point b^1 in this view. Auxiliary view 2 is then constructed showing line XY as a point and showing the true distance from B to XY.

---

[2] See Appendix III.1.

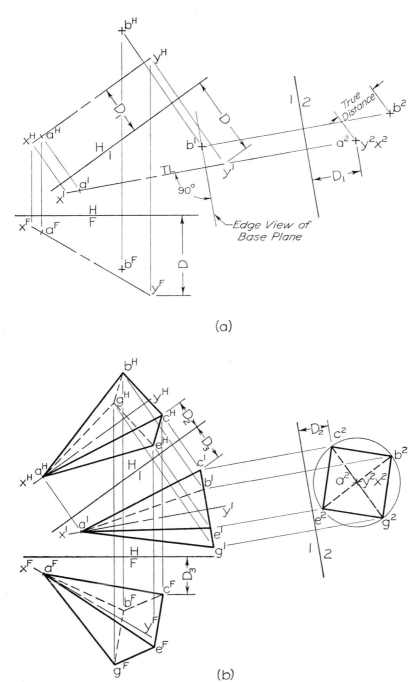

(a)

(b)

Fig. 10–7. Construction of Right Square Pyramid on Given Oblique Axis

Since the base of the pyramid must be centered at x^2y^2, line b^2e^2, Fig. 10-7(b), is a diagonal of the base and the square may be constructed as shown.[3] Points c^1, e^1, and g^1 are then established in the edge view of the base in view 1, from which the corresponding top and front views may be located in the usual manner. Drawing the lateral edges with proper visibility from the base corners to vertex A completes the solution.

10.3   LINE PERPENDICULAR TO PLANE

Two-View Method. As has been stated, a line perpendicular to a plane is perpendicular to all lines in the plane. Therefore, a line perpendicular to a plane appears perpendicular to a line in the plane in any view in which the line in the plane is true length. For example, let it be required to draw a line from point A perpendicular to plane MNO, Fig. 10-8(a). Since there are no true-length lines given in the plane, horizontal line MH is added, Fig. 10-8(b). The top view $a^H k^H$ of the required perpendicular AK may now be drawn perpendicular to $m^H h^H$ as shown. The length of AK is immaterial in this problem. It is important to realize that this construction establishes only the *top* view of the perpendicular. The front view must now be located by an additional construction.

A frontal line OF is added, Fig. 10-8(c). Front view $a^F k^F$ is then drawn perpendicular to true-length view $o^F f^F$, with k^F located on the projection line from k^H. The two views $a^H k^H$ and $a^F k^F$ thus drawn define a line AK perpendicular in space to plane MNO.[4]

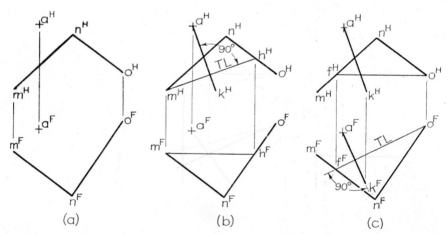

Fig. 10-8.   Line Perpendicular to Plane—Two-View Method

[3] See Appendix II.2.

[4] If it is required that a line must not only be perpendicular to a given plane but must terminate in that plane, the point in which the line pierces the plane must also be located by one of the methods of Chapter 6.

Auxiliary-View Method. If an auxiliary view is drawn showing the given plane in edge view, Fig. 10–9(a), the required line may be drawn perpendicular to the edge view. It may be noted that the true distance from point A to plane MNO is also apparent in this auxiliary view. If the measurement of this distance is a requirement of a particular problem, the auxiliary-view method is therefore more convenient than the two-view method.

Since view a^1k^1 is true length, top view a^Hk^H must be parallel to folding line $H/1$ (or perpendicular to the true-length view m^Hh^H), Fig. 10–9(b). The front view a^Fk^F is then established by projecting from k^H and transferring distance D_1.

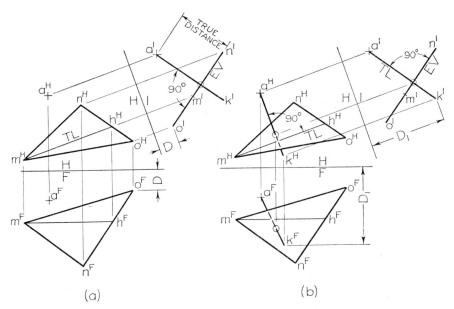

Fig. 10–9. Line Perpendicular to Plane—Auxiliary-View Method

10.4 COMMON PERPENDICULAR—POINT-VIEW METHOD

Connecting two skew (non-intersecting, nonparallel) lines is one and only one line which is perpendicular to both—the common perpendicular. Since the shortest distance from a point to a line is measured along the perpendicular from the point to the line, it follows that the shortest distance between two skew lines is measured along the line which is perpendicular to each of the skew lines.

In order to locate the common perpendicular between skew lines AB and CE, Fig. 10–10, use is made again of the principle that perpendicular lines appear perpendicular in any view showing one of them true length. Since neither of the given lines appears true length in the front and top views,

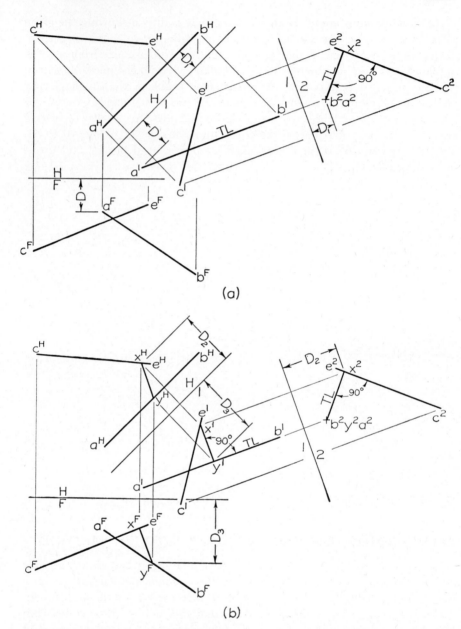

(a)

(b)

Fig. 10–10. Common Perpendicular—Point-View Method

auxiliary view 1 is added, Fig. 10–10(a), showing one of the lines true length, in this case AB. In view 1 any line perpendicular to AB must appear perpendicular to a^1b^1, but at this stage the points at which to draw the common perpendicular have not been established. Accordingly view 2 is added, showing line AB as a point. Although e^2c^2 is not true length, any line perpendicular to AB must appear true length. The common perpendicular may therefore be drawn in view 2 extending from a^2b^2 and at a right angle to e^2c^2, establishing x^2. The length of this perpendicular is the shortest distance between lines AB and CE.

To locate the other views of the common perpendicular, x^1 is established by projection from x^2, Fig. 10–10(b). The common perpendicular XY does not appear true length in view 1; but since a^1b^1 is true length, x^1y^1 is drawn perpendicular to a^1b^1, establishing point y^1. By projection from x^1 and y^1 to the top view and then to the front view, x^Hy^H and x^Fy^F are located. It is good practice to check the accuracy of location of the views by transfer distances such as D_2 and D_3.

10.5   COMMON PERPENDICULAR—PLANE METHOD

Another method of finding the common perpendicular between two skew lines is the *plane method,* which is particularly useful if only the shortest distance between the lines, and not the views of the perpendicular, is needed.

If a plane is passed through one of the two skew lines and parallel to the other (Art. 9.3), the distance between the plane and the second line is the shortest distance between the lines. Through point E of line CE in Fig. 10–11(a), line EH is drawn parallel to given line AB to establish a plane CEH parallel to AB. Auxiliary view 1 showing CEH in edge view is then drawn. Since a^1b^1 must appear parallel to edge view $c^1–e^1$, the shortest distance between AB and CE may be measured in view 1 as indicated.

If the views of the common perpendicular are desired, further construction is necessary since the location of the common perpendicular is not established in view 1. A true-size view of plane CEH will show as a point any line perpendicular to CEH. Consequently true-size view 2 is added, Fig. 10–11(b), and the common perpendicular XY appears as the point of intersection of a^2b^2 and c^2e^2. The remaining views of XY are then established by projection.

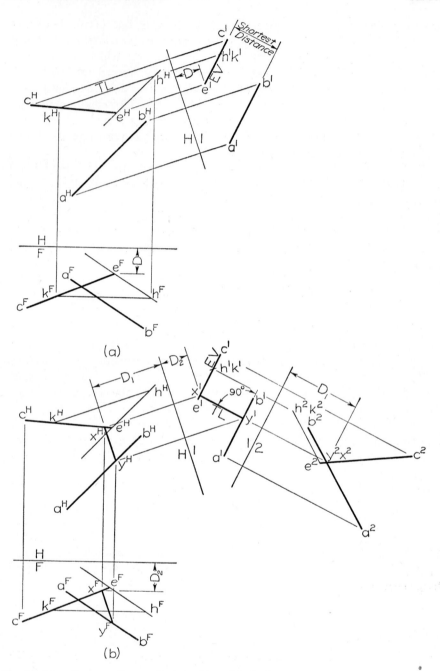

Fig. 10–11.   Common Perpendicular—Plane Method

10.6 SHORTEST HORIZONTAL LINE CONNECTING TWO SKEW LINES

Although it does not involve perpendicularity, the problem of finding the shortest horizontal line connecting two skew lines is included here because of the similarity of its solution to that of the plane method of Art. 10.5. The first step, Fig. 10–12(a), is again the passing of a plane CEA_1 through one of the lines and parallel to the other. View 1 is then added showing plane CEA_1 in edge view.

It should be carefully noted that the auxiliary view 1 is projected from the *top* view so that in the auxiliary view horizontal lines will appear parallel to the folding line $(H/1)$. The shortest horizontal distance between AB and CE may then be measured between a^1b^1 and c^1e^1 in a direction parallel to folding line $H/1$.

To locate the shortest horizontal line connecting the two given lines, view 2 is constructed for which the line of sight is taken parallel to folding line $H/1$ in order to show a point view of the shortest horizontal line. This point view appears as intersection point m^2n^2 of a^2b^2 and c^2e^2. The other views of line MN are then established by projection, Fig. 10–12(b).

A similar construction may be used to establish the shortest frontal line or shortest profile line connecting two skew lines.

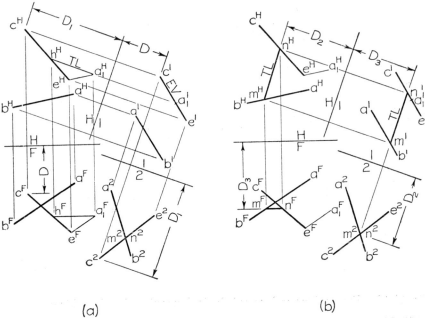

(a)   (b)

Fig. 10–12.   Shortest Horizontal Line Connecting Two Skew Lines

10.7 SHORTEST LINE AT SPECIFIED GRADE CONNECTING TWO SKEW LINES

The approach of the preceding article can be applied to the problem of Fig. 10–13, where it is required to find the shortest connecting line having a downward grade of 15 per cent from MN to OP. The first portion of the construction is the same as for view 1 of Fig. 10–12. It is essential that auxiliary view 1, Fig. 10–13(a), be projected from the top view, since per cent grade is measured with respect to horizontal (in space).[5] In auxiliary view 1 a line is drawn from any convenient point (such as m^1), parallel to folding line $H/1$, in order that the line will be horizontal in space. Along this line 100 units at any appropriate scale are set off and 15 units are then set off downward, or away from and perpendicular to folding line $H/1$. This establishes the direction and length of the line at the specified downward grade of 15 per cent, but it does not locate the line. With this established direction used for the line of sight, view 2 is then added, Fig. 10–13(b). The crossing point of m^2n^2 and o^2p^2 is a point view of the required connecting line XY. Projection back to the other views, as shown, completes the solution.

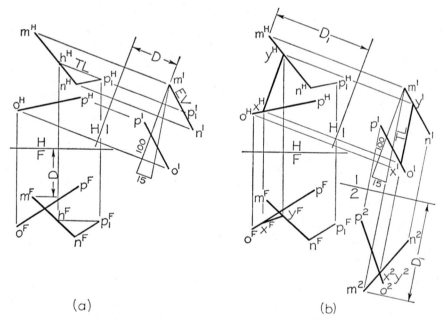

(a)   (b)

Fig. 10–13. Shortest Line at Specified Grade Connecting Two Skew Lines

---

[5] Art. 3.4.

10.8   PROJECTION OF A LINE ON A PLANE

The orthographic projection of a line on a plane is the line connecting the projections on the plane of the end points of the line. The projection of a point on a plane is the point in which a perpendicular from the point to the plane pierces the plane. See Fig. 10–14. With these definitions in mind, either of the following methods may be used to find the projection of a given line on a given oblique plane.

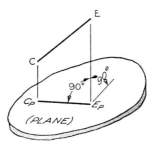

Fig. 10–14.   Projection of a Line on a Plane

Two-View Method. Lines are drawn from points A and B perpendicular to plane MNO, Fig. 10–15(a), by drawing their views respectively perpendicular to the true-length views of frontal line OF and profile line MP. (See Art. 10.3.) The piercing points A_P and B_P of these lines in plane MNO are then found by the two-view method, Fig. 10–15(b). Line $A_P B_P$ is the required projection of AB on plane MNO.

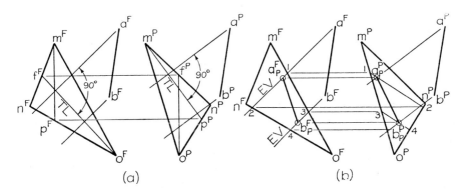

Fig. 10–15.   Projection of Line on Plane—Two-View Method

Auxiliary-View Method. View 1 is constructed showing plane *MNO* in edge view, Fig. 10–16. Lines are drawn perpendicular to this edge view from a^1 and b^1, establishing projections $a_p{}^1$ and $b_p{}^1$. Since the projection lines are true length in view 1, their side views must appear parallel to folding line $P/1$, as shown in view P.[6] Projection from $a_p{}^1$ and $b_p{}^1$ to view P then locates $a_p{}^P$ and $b_p{}^P$, from which $a_p{}^F$ and $b_p{}^F$ are established by projection and transfer of distances as indicated.

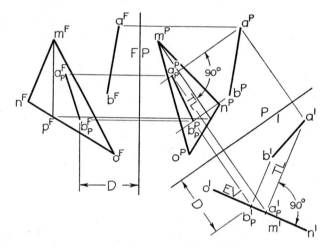

Fig. 10–16.   Projection of Line on Plane—Auxiliary-View Method

---

[6] Article 10.3, *Auxiliary-View Method.*

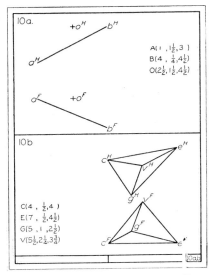

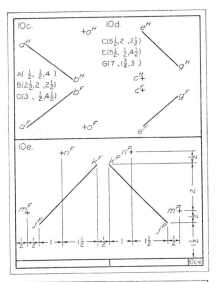

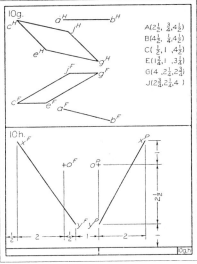

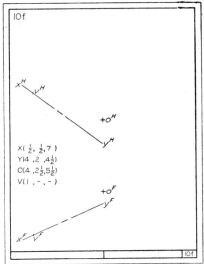

10a. Through O draw a line perpendicular to and intersecting AB. Find true length of the perpendicular. Use auxiliary-view method.

10b. Find the projections and true length of the altitude of the pyramid having its vertex at V. Use auxiliary-view method.

10c. Through O draw a 2-in. frontal line perpendicular to AB. Use the two-view method.

10d. Pass a plane through C perpendicular to EG. Use the two-view method.

10e. Locate the center of the circle passing through points M and N having its center on line JK. Use the two-view method.

10f. Draw the views of a right square pyramid that has its apex at V on the axis XY and a corner of the base at O.

10g. Use two methods to find the projection of AB on the plane.

10h. Use the two-view method to locate a line from O perpendicular to and intersecting XY.

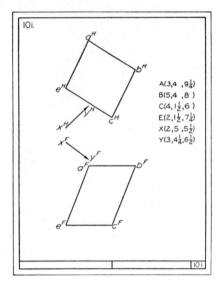

10i.

A(3,4 ,9¼)
B(5,4 ,8)
C(4,1½,6)
E(2,1½,7½)
X(2,5 ,5½)
Y(3,4¼,6½)

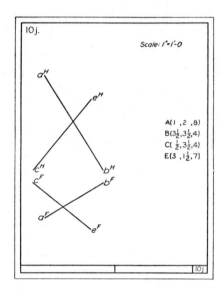

10j.

Scale: 1"=1'-0

A(1 ,2 ,8)
B(3½,3½,4)
C(½,3½,4)
E(3 ,1½,7)

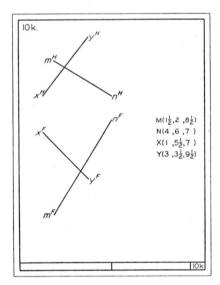

10k.

M(1½,2 ,8½)
N(4 ,6 ,7)
X(1 ,5½,7)
Y(3 ,3½,9½)

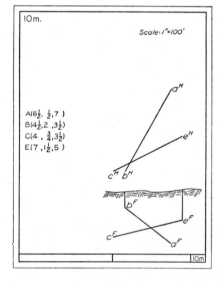

10m.

Scale:1"=100'

A(6½, ½,7)
B(4½,2 ,3½)
C(4 , ¾,3½)
E(7 ,1½,5)

10i. Using the two views only, locate the reflected ray having given the mirror surface *ABCE* and the light ray *XY*.

10j. Determine the clearance between the two control cables *AB* and *CE*.

10k. Locate the views of the shortest branch connecting pipes *MN* and *XY*.

10m. Find the following: (a) The true length and projections of the shortest shaft connecting the shafts *AB* and *CE*. (b) The true length of a vertical connecting shaft. (c) The true length and bearing of a horizontal connecting tunnel originating at point *E*.

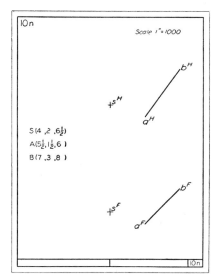

10n

Scale 1" = 1000

S(4,2,6½)
A(5½,1½,6)
B(7,3,8)

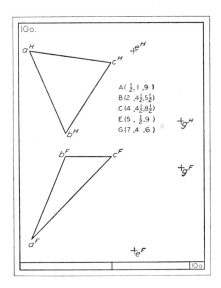

10o.

A(½,1,9)
B(2,4½,5½)
C(4,4½,8½)
E(5,½,9)
G(7,4,6)

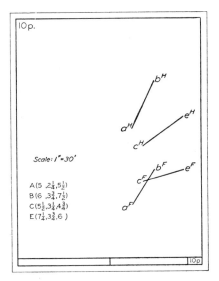

10p.

Scale: 1"=30'

A(5,2¼,5½)
B(6,3¾,7½)
C(5½,3¼,4¾)
E(7¼,3¾,6)

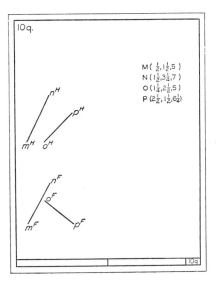

10q.

M(½,1½,5)
N(1½,3¼,7)
O(1¼,2½,5)
P(2½,1½,6¼)

10n. An airplane at S has a flight direction (corrected for drift) of N 60° and is gaining altitude at a rate of 200 ft in 1000 ft. Determine the minimum clearance between the flight path and an obstruction represented by line AB.

10o. Determine the locus of points equidistant from points E and G and lying in the limited plane ABC.

10p. Find the bearing and length and show the views of the shortest horizontal tunnel connecting AB and CE.

10q. Show the views of the shortest profile line connecting MN and OP.

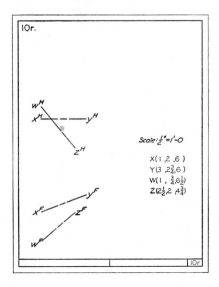

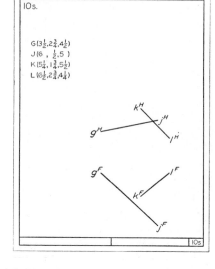

10r. Pipes XY and WZ are to be connected with a branch pipe having a downward grade of 20 per cent from XY to WZ. Find the length and show the views of the center line of the branch pipe.

10s. Find the views of a tube connecting tubes GJ and KL and having an upward slope of 30° from GJ to KL.

10t. Indicate whether the following statements are true or false. If assigned, prepare written explanations or sketches to justify the answers.

(a) Perpendicular lines do not necessarily intersect.

(b) The locus of points 2 in. from the ends of a 1-in. line is a circle.

(c) A sphere can be passed through any four points not in a straight line.

(d) The locus of points equidistant from three points not in a straight line is a line perpendicular to the plane of the three points and passing through the center of a circle circumscribing the points.

(e) The locus of all points equidistant from two given points is a perpendicular plane containing the two points.

(f) A line can be drawn perpendicular to each of two non-intersecting lines.

(g) Only one line can be drawn perpendicular to a given line through a specified point on the given line.

(h) Two lines perpendicular in space will appear perpendicular in any orthographic view.

ANGLE BETWEEN LINE AND OBLIQUE PLANE

CHAPTER 11

THE ANGLE BETWEEN a line and a plane lies in a plane that contains the given line and is perpendicular to the given plane.[1] This angle is also defined as the angle between the given line and its projection upon the given plane, Fig. 11–1.

11.1 ANGLE BETWEEN LINE AND PLANE—PLANE METHOD

In order to show in its true magnitude the angle between a line and a plane, it is necessary to show in the same view the line in *true length* and the plane in *edge view*.

For the general case of an oblique plane and line as in Fig. 11–2(a), it is necessary to construct three successive auxiliary views to achieve the desired

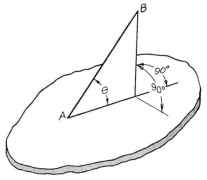

Fig. 11–1. Angle Between Line and Plane

view. In Fig. 11–2(b), the first auxiliary view shows the plane OMN in edge view. Since the line AB is not shown true length, the required angle does not appear true size. An additional view showing the true size of plane OMN is then drawn. Any auxiliary view projected from a true-size view of a plane produces an edge view of the plane. Therefore, if a line of sight 3 is introduced perpendicular to a^2b^2, the resulting view 3 shows line AB in true length and plane OMN in edge view. The required angle is then measured as indicated.

Unless there are reasons for obtaining data relative to the line and plane

---

[1] The three methods presented in this chapter are based on successive auxiliary views. For another variation see Art. 13.4. Problems involving the angle between a line and a principal plane are presented in Chapters 3 and 13.

other than the angle between the two, the construction necessary for the angle can be simplified in the second and third auxiliary views, Fig. 11–2(b). After obtaining an edge view of the plane, it is not necessary to project the plane into the successive views beyond the auxiliary view containing the edge view of the plane. Since in view 3 the edge view of the plane OMN must appear parallel to the folding line 2/3, the angle between the line and the plane may thus be measured between a^3b^3 and folding line 2/3. Hence for the purpose at hand it is not necessary to show plane OMN in views 2 and 3.

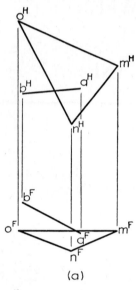

(a)

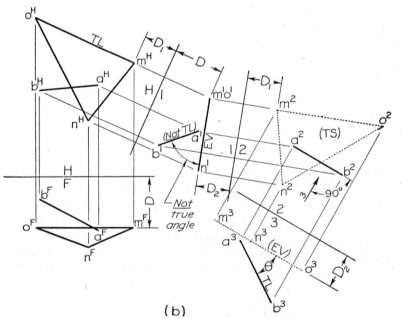

(b)

Fig. 11–2. Angle Between Line and Plane—Plane Method

11.2   ANGLE BETWEEN LINE AND PLANE—LINE METHOD

Another method of determining the true size of the angle between a line and a plane comprises a series of views first showing the given line in true length, then as a point, and finally in true length with the given plane in edge view.

In Fig. 11–3, the plane MNO and line AB are given. The first auxiliary view shows line AB in true length and the second auxiliary view shows it as a point, while plane MNO is projected to each view. Any view projected from view 2 will then show line AB in true length. A line NK is introduced in plane MNO in views 1 and 2 in such position as to appear true length in view 2. The third auxiliary view may then be drawn showing this line as a point and plane MNO as an edge view with line AB in true length. The true angle between this line and the plane is then measured as shown.

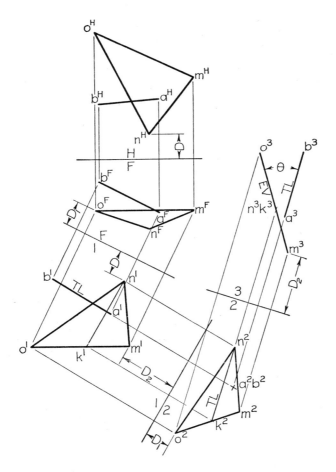

Fig. 11–3.   Angle Between Line and Plane—Line Method

This method is particularly advantageous in those problems in which the given line appears true length or as a point in one of the given views, situations which frequently occur in practice.

11.3   ANGLE BETWEEN LINE AND PLANE— COMPLEMENTARY-ANGLE METHOD

The angle between a line and a plane is also defined as the angle between the line and its projection on the plane, Fig. 11–4. Therefore, the true size of the plane determined by the given line and its projection would produce the required angle in true size. This procedure, however, involves considerable construction when applied to orthographic views. Further study of Fig. 11–4 reveals a simpler method. The triangle AOA_p is a right triangle and hence angle α is the complement of the required angle θ. The angle α may be formed by constructing a line from any point on the given line perpendicular to the given plane.

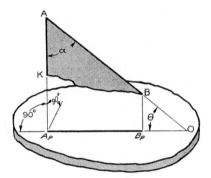

Fig. 11–4.   Complement of Angle Between Line and Plane

In Fig. 11–5(a) line BK is constructed perpendicular to plane MNO by the two-view method of Art. 10.3. Auxiliary views 1 and 2 are then added, Fig. 11–5(b), to show plane ABK and angle α in true size.[2] It must be remembered at this point that the angle at B, angle α, is *not* the required angle between line AB and plane MNO. The required angle is the complement of angle α. To obtain this complement, a right triangle is constructed as shown, with angle α as one of its acute angles. The other acute angle is then the required angle θ.

---

[2] See Art. 5.4.

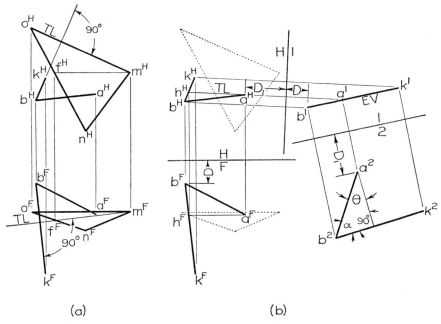

(a)   (b)

Fig. 11–5. Angle Between Line and Plane—Complementary-Angle Method

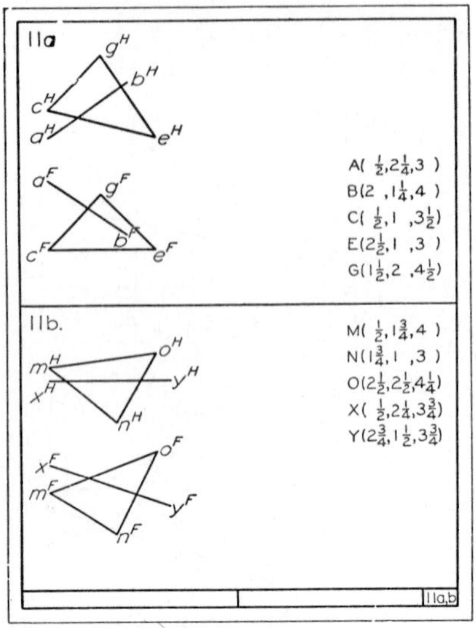
11a
A(½,2¼,3)
B(2 ,1¼,4)
C(½,1 ,3½)
E(2½,1 ,3)
G(1½,2 ,4½)
11b.
M(½,1¾,4)
N(1¾,1 ,3)
O(2½,2½,4¼)
X(½,2¼,3¾)
Y(2¾,1½,3¾)
11a,b

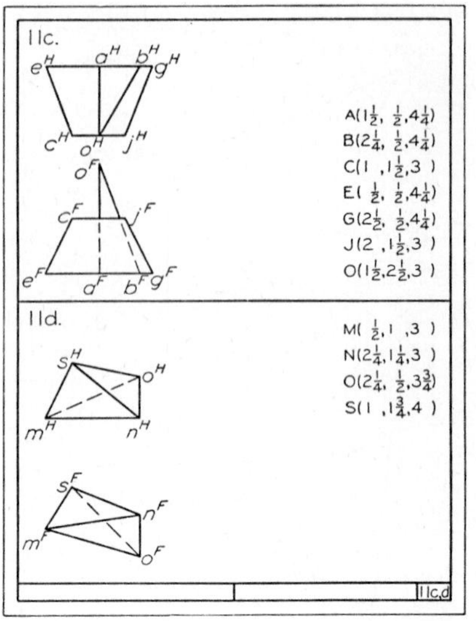
11c.
A(1½, ½,4¼)
B(2¼, ½,4¼)
C(1 ,1½,3)
E(½, ½,4¼)
G(2½, ½,4¼)
J(2 ,1½,3)
O(1½,2½,3)
11d.
M(½,1 ,3)
N(2¼,1¼,3)
O(2¼, ½,3¾)
S(1 ,1¾,4)
11c,d

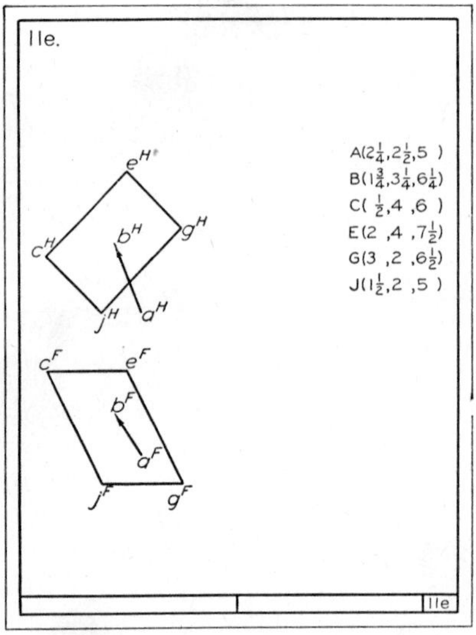
11e.
A(2¼,2½,5)
B(1¾,3¼,6¼)
C(½,4 ,6)
E(2 ,4 ,7½)
G(3 ,2 ,6½)
J(1½,2 ,5)
11e

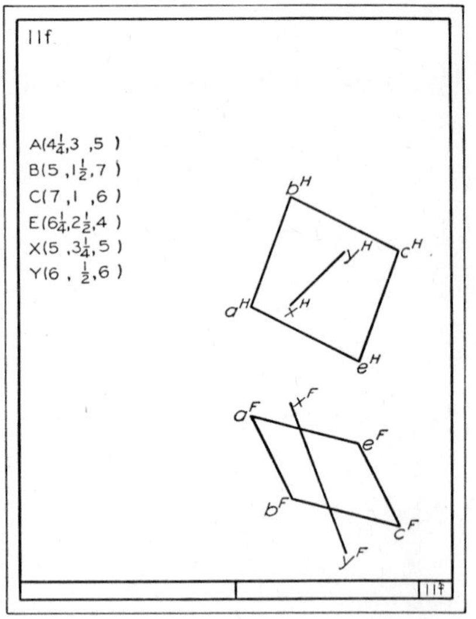
11f
A(4¼,3 ,5)
B(5 ,1½,7)
C(7 ,1 ,6)
E(6¼,2½,4)
X(5 ,3¼,5)
Y(6 , ½,6)
11f

11a. Find the true size of the angle between *AB* and plane *CEG*.

11b. Find the true size of the angle between *XY* and plane *MON*.

11c. Determine the angles formed by the guy wires *OA* and *OB* with the roof plane *CEGJ*.

11d. For the given tetrahedron find the angle between edge *SO* and base *MNO*.

11e. Find the angle of incidence and show the reflected ray of the light ray *AB* with the mirror surface *CEGJ*.

11f. Control cable *XY* passes through bulkhead *ABCE*. Determine the angle the cable makes with the bulkhead so that a bearing guide can be correctly designed.

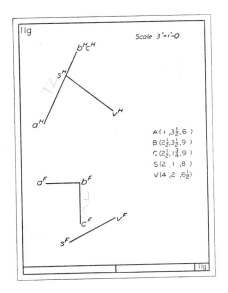

11g

Scale 3"=1'-0

A(1,$3\frac{1}{2}$,6)
B($2\frac{1}{2}$,$3\frac{1}{2}$,9)
C($2\frac{1}{2}$,$1\frac{3}{4}$,9)
S(2 ,1 ,8)
V(4 ,2 ,$6\frac{1}{2}$)

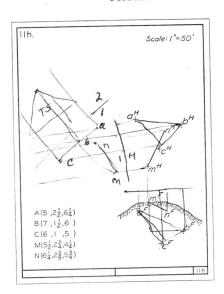

11h.

Scale: 1"=50'

A(5 ,$2\frac{1}{2}$,$6\frac{1}{4}$)
B(7 ,$1\frac{1}{2}$,6)
C(6 ,1 ,5)
M($5\frac{1}{2}$,$2\frac{3}{4}$,$4\frac{1}{4}$)
N($6\frac{1}{4}$,$2\frac{3}{8}$,$5\frac{3}{4}$)

✓**11g.** Line *VS* is an element of a right cone having its circular base in plane *ABC*. Find the true angle formed by *VS* and the base plane, and determine the diameter of the base circle.

✓**11h.** What distance must tunnel *MN* be extended to meet an ore vein determined by points *A*, *B*, and *C*? What angle is formed by *MN* and *ABC*?

11i. Indicate whether the following statements are true or false. If assigned, prepare written explanations or sketches to justify the answers.

(a) The corresponding angles formed by a line intersecting two parallel planes are equal.

(b) Supplementary adjacent angles are formed by a line intersecting a plane.

(c) The angle formed by a line and a given plane is contained in a plane through the line and perpendicular to the given plane.

(d) The true angle formed by a line and a plane is observed in any view in which the plane appears edgewise.

(e) The true angle formed by a frontal line and an oblique plane may be measured in a front view.

(f) Only a single plane can be passed through a line and perpendicular to a given plane.

11g. PROJECT "H" VIEW TO GET TS OF abc, THIS WOULD BE AN A' VIEW. THEN TAKE AN A² VIEW TO GET EDGE VIEW OF abc AND TL OF SV

11h. BASICALLY SAME AS 11g

CHAPTER 12

MINING AND CIVIL ENGINEERING PROBLEMS

ALTHOUGH GRAPHICAL METHODS may be used to advantage in all fields of engineering, the natures of many problems in mining and civil engineering particularly fit them for graphical representation and solution. The mining or civil engineer as well as the military strategist has frequent occasion to

Fig. 12–1. An exploration party surveying in the Cagayan Valley, on northern Luzon, Philippine Islands. (Courtesy Standard Oil Company of New Jersey.)

136

prepare or use *topographic maps,* which are graphical means of representing the irregularities of the earth's surface in single views. A topographic map is based on the principles of *horizontal projection.*

12.1　HORIZONTAL PROJECTION

Horizontal projection is a method of indicating the position of a point in space by means of its projection on a horizontal plane (top view) together with an accompanying symbol or number specifying the elevation of the point in relation to a horizontal datum plane. For topographic maps the most common datum plane is the mean level of the sea which is used as zero elevation.

Figure 12–2 shows in pictorial form the representation by horizontal projection of a point A in space. The height of point A above the datum plane is indicated by the subscript.

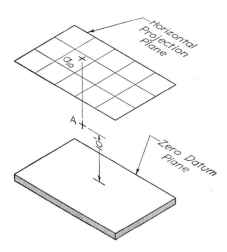

Fig. 12–2.　Horizontal Projection

12.2　TOPOGRAPHIC MAP

On a topographic map a series of points at a selected elevation may be connected with a line called a *contour line.* Thus a contour line approximately represents a continuous series of points of a designated elevation on a terrain. If a portion of the terrain were in the form of a cone, the contour lines would be a series of circles, Fig. 12–3. The cone is shown intersected by a series of horizontal cutting planes at 10-ft intervals in height, resulting in equally spaced, concentric contour cycles in the top view or map. The high point or vertex of the cone is indicated in the top view and is called a *topographic crest.*

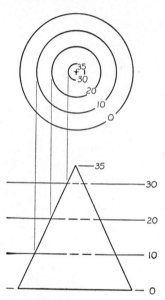

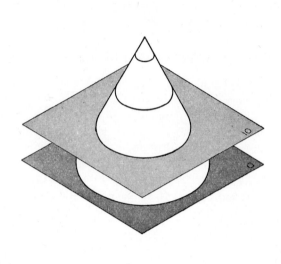

Fig. 12–3. Contour Lines on a Cone.

The surface of the earth, unlike a cone, is irregular, and therefore contour lines on the earth's surface are irregular. The plan view of Fig. 12–4 shows typical contour lines. If a large enough area is included, contour lines will be continuous and closed and will not cross each other unless an *overhang* is involved.

The elevation view of Fig. 12–4 is called a *profile* (section) of the terrain, resulting from the vertical cutting plane *A–A* shown in the plan view. A study of this profile together with the contour lines in the plan view reveals the fact that contour lines closely spaced indicate a relatively steep slope while the opposite condition suggests a gentle slope. It should be noted that the term profile in this usage does not refer to the profile (side) view. A profile in this context is the line of intersection of the earth's surface and any vertical cutting plane.

12.3   PREPARATION OF CONTOUR MAP USING GRID SURVEY

Before a topographic map can be prepared, a survey of the area must be made to determine the elevation of an adequate number of strategically selected points. The points chosen are dependent on the relative irregularity of the terrain involved and the proposed utilization of the map.

One frequently used method for locating points is the grid system shown in Fig. 12–5(a). After the field survey has established the elevation of each intersection on the grid, the map maker has the task of plotting the contour

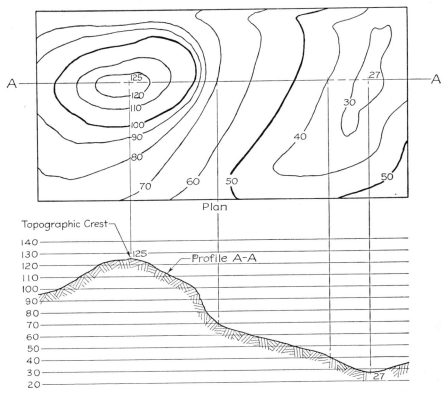

Fig. 12–4. Typical Contour Lines and Profile

lines. Assuming that the contour lines are to be plotted at 10-ft intervals, the following procedure would be used to locate the contour lines in grid *A*, which is shown enlarged in Fig. 12–5(b). The difference in elevation of points *B* and *C* is 12 ft. Based on the supposition that the slope between the corners *B* and *C* is constant, contour line 60 passes through a point four-twelfths or one-third of the distance from *C* to *B*. Contour line 50 passes through a point two-elevenths of the distance from *B* to *E*. These points may be approximated by eye or by a graphical method of proportion similar to Appendix II.1, depending on the accuracy necessary.

Points are obtained similarly for the sides of each grid. Contour lines are then drawn freehand through all points of the same elevation as shown.[1] If considered necessary, additional points on the contour lines may be secured by interpolation along one diagonal of each grid, preferably that diagonal which is more nearly perpendicular to the contour lines. This procedure is indicated in Fig. 12–5(c) which shows the altered contour lines 50 and 60 resulting from this additional interpolation.

----

[1] A specially designed contour pen is available for inking this type of line.

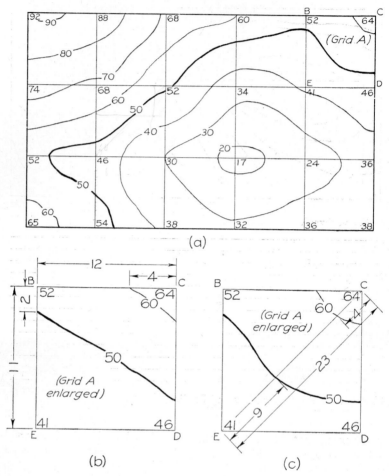

Fig. 12–5. Preparation of Contour Map Using Grid Survey

12.4   MINING AND GEOLOGY

The following definitions cover the pertinent technical terms among the many employed in mining and geology. They are illustrated in Fig. 12–6.

1. *Strike.* The bearing of a horizontal line in a plane, usually measured from north; for example, N 50° E.

2. *Dip.* The slope of a plane or angle between the plane and a horizontal plane [2] plus the *general* direction of downward slope of the plane; for example, 30° SE. The direction of the dip is always at a right angle to the strike line. The dip is indicated on the map (top view) as illustrated.

3. *Stratum.* A layer of rock. *Strata* usually lie below the earth's loose surface but

[2] Art. 8.3.

may be exposed by weathering. Since they were formed by sedimentation in ancient seas or rivers, their bounding surfaces may usually be considered as parallel planes within limited areas. The term *seam* is sometimes used in place of stratum, as in "a seam of coal."

4. *Bedding Plane.* A bounding surface of a stratum.

5. *Vein.* A deposit of mineral or ore formed in a fissure in rock frequently bounded by two bedding planes. A vein is sometimes called a *lode.*

6. *Fault.* A discontinuity or break in a stratum or vein involving a shifting of one portion with respect to the other. The term *fault plane* may be applied if the break and displacement take place along a plane.

7. *Outcrop.* An area of a stratum or vein exposed (or only lightly covered) at the earth's surface. The bounding edges of the area, which are the intersections of the bounding surfaces with the earth's surface, are called the *outcrop lines.*

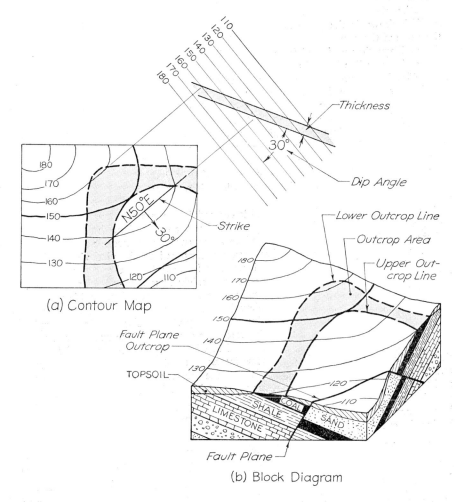

(a) Contour Map

(b) Block Diagram

Fig. 12–6. Mining and Geology Terms

12.5 STRIKE, DIP, THICKNESS, OUTCROP

A bedding plane is theoretically located by establishing three points on the plane. In practice, more than three points are usually located to allow for irregularities and measurement inaccuracies. These points may be on the outcrop line if it exists or may be determined by drilling.

PROBLEM, Fig. 12–7:

Points X, Y, and Z are given in the upper bedding plane of an ore vein and point W on the lower bedding plane. It is required to find the strike, dip, thickness, and outcrop of the vein.

GRAPHIC SOLUTION:

The elevations of the points are given in the top view Fig. 12–7(a), and from this information the front view is constructed according to the given scale. A horizontal line ZH is drawn in the plane XYZ, and its bearing is measured as N 65° W. This is the strike of the vein.

An auxiliary view projected from the top view with the line of sight parallel to the true-length strike line is used to obtain the dip angle of the vein. The size of the dip angle, 45°, is measured in the auxiliary view. The complete description of the dip includes in addition to the angle the general direction of downward slope of the vein. This direction is always at right angles to the strike line, and thus the possible directions are reduced to two if the strike is known. In Fig. 12–7(a) the strike is found to be N 65° W, so that immediately the general direction of the dip (which is all that need be given) must be either northeast or southwest. Study of the front view and/or the auxiliary view reveals that point Y is lower than the strike line ZH. Thus in the top view the arrow representing the direction of downward slope is drawn pointing from $z^H h^H$ in the general direction of y^H, which is northeast. Consequently the dip is recorded as "45° NE."

On the assumption that the upper and lower bedding planes of the vein are parallel, the edge view of the lower plane is drawn parallel to the upper plane through point w_1, and the thickness of the vein is measured on a perpendicular between the edge views.

In Fig. 12–7(b) a contour map has been superimposed on the plan view of plane XYZ. Points on the outcrop lines are located as follows: Since the contour lines lie in horizontal planes, they appear as a series of straight lines perpendicular to the line of sight in any elevation view. Accordingly these lines are spaced in auxiliary view 1 as shown using the given scale. [The elevations of the given points on the upper and lower bedding planes of the vein are given in the top view of Fig. 12–7(a).] A typical point $m^1 n^1$, at which the 40-ft contour intersects the edge view of the upper plane of the vein, represents the point view of a horizontal line in this upper plane at a 40-ft elevation. This line projected to the plan view intersects the 40-ft contour line at points 1 and 2. These are points on the upper plane of the vein and on the surface of the earth and thus are points on the upper outcrop line. Additional points are similarly located on other contour lines until all available points are secured on both the upper and lower outcrop lines. The curves are then drawn through these points as shown, establishing the outcrop area.

If a problem is encountered in which the outcrop lines are given and the strike, dip, and thickness are required, the above procedure is reversed as follows: Any two points in which an outcrop line intersects the same contour line, such as points 1 and 2, Fig. 12–7(b), determine a horizontal line and thus the strike of the vein. This in turn establishes the direction of sight to produce the edge views of the planes of the vein.

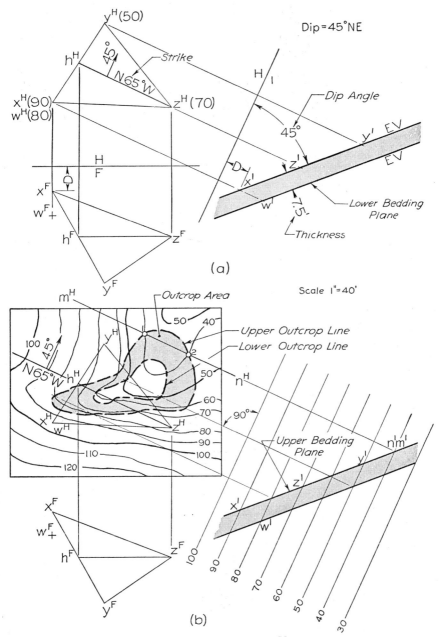

Fig. 12–7. Strike, Dip, Thickness, and Outcrop of a Vein

12.6   CUT AND FILL OR DUMP LINES

Although in a different field of engineering, the problem of locating the outlines of earth *fills* or *cuts* is similar to the preceding construction for outcrop lines. As an example, Fig. 12–8, the construction for the so-called *dump* lines (fill lines) is shown for an earth dam. As indicated, the dam is designed with a 1 on 3 slope on the upstream side and a 1 on 2½ slope on the downstream side. Since the front view is a vertical section of the dam, the given slopes establish edge views of the plane surfaces of the dam in the front view as shown. The intersection points of these edge views with the several horizontal planes are projected to the corresponding contour lines in the plan view to establish points on the dump lines just as in plotting outcrop lines. If it were desired to continue the dump lines across the stream area, it would of course be necessary to establish contour lines on the stream bed.

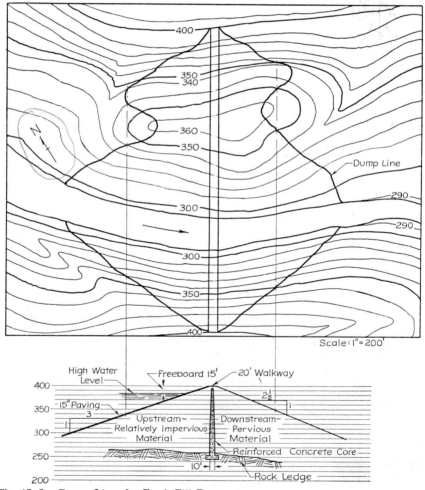

Fig. 12–8.   Dump Lines for Earth Fill Dam

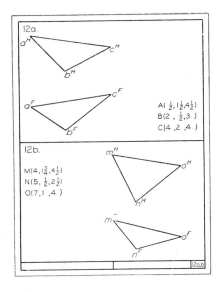

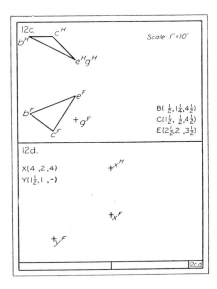

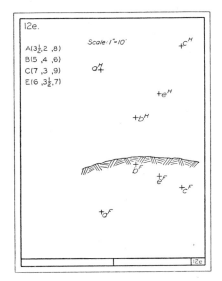

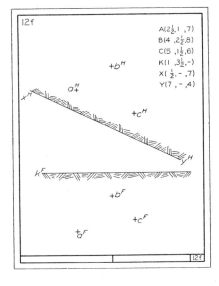

12a. Find and label the strike and dip of plane ABC.

12b. Find and label the strike and dip of plane MNO.

12c. Points B, C, and E are on the upper bedding plane of a vein. Point G on the lower bedding plane is 10 ft below E. Find the strike, dip, and thickness of the vein.

12d. A stratum containing points X and Y has a strike of N 75° W and a dip of 45° SW. Locate the top view of point Y.

12e. A, B, and C are points on the upper bedding plane of an ore vein. Point E is on the lower bedding plane. Find the strike, dip, and thickness of the vein.

12f. Find the strike and dip of a thin vein determined by points A, B, and C. Show the outcrop of this vein on the level ground surface at elevation K and on the vertical cliff passing through X and Y.

	A	B	C	D	E	F	G	H	J	K	
9	54	58	62	54	50	45	40	32	28	26	9
8	61	64	75	72	65	56	48	38	34	28	8
7	74	82	86	82	76	66	60	49	42	36	7
6	84	91	99	86	81	74	64	52	44	38	6
5	72	76	82	88	82	72	68	58	48	36	5
4	68	62	72	76	72	65	62	52	44	46	4
3	70	65	80	86	74	77	66	58	59	64	3
2	82	86	102	94	82	74	66	64	66	75	2
1	83	91	106	90	84	72	68	76	80	92	1
0	76	77	82	86	88	76	74	79	86	88	0
	A	B	C	D	E	F	G	H	J	K	

A GRID SURVEY

NOTE: In each of the following problems contour lines for either 5-ft or 10-ft intervals, as assigned, are to be drawn for the given grid survey. The grids are ½ in. apart. Scale: 1″ = 50′. For each problem the grid is to be placed in the upper left-hand corner ½ in. from the borders of the drawing paper which is to have the long side horizontal.

12g. Plot the profile along grid 6–6. On the profile, label the topographic crest and shade the *defiladed area* (space not visible from topographic crest). Label the *military crest* (that crest from which the previous defiladed area is visible).

12h. Show the outcrop of a thin vein that passes through point S at an elevation of 65 ft and has a strike of N 75° W and a dip of 15° NE.

12i. Show the dump lines for a 25-ft wide horizontal road extending from X to Y at a 70-ft elevation with the side slopes 1 to 1 for both the cut and fill.

12j. Plot the profiles along the grids assigned by the instructor.

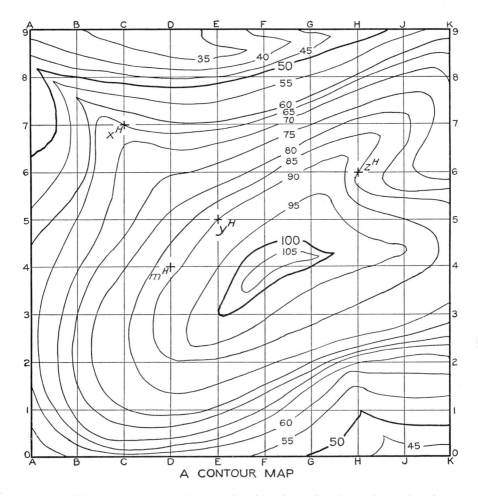

A CONTOUR MAP

NOTE: The contour map may be reproduced by the student by tracing or by using a cross-section grid paper. The grids shown are ½ in. apart. If the instructor so desires, the map may be simplified by using only the contour lines at 10-ft intervals. For each of the following problems the map should be placed in the upper left-hand corner ½ in. from the borders of the drawing paper which is to have the long side horizontal. Scale: 1″ = 50′.

12k. Show the outcrop line of a thin vein that passes through point *M* at an elevation of 70 ft and that has a strike of N 60° W and a dip of 20° NE.

12m. Points *X*, *Y,* and *Z* are on the surface of the terrain. Vertical test drills to the upper bedding plane of a vein are respectively 5, 10, and 40 ft deep. The drill at *X* is continued through the vein and breaks through the lower bedding plane at a total depth of 25 ft from the surface of the terrain. Find the strike, dip, and thickness of the vein and show the outcrop area.

12n. In the plan view plot the dump lines for a 20-ft horizontal roadway at an 80-ft elevation along grid 5–5. The cut and fill side slopes are 1 to 1.

12o. Plot the grid profiles as assigned by the instructor.

A	B	C	D	E	F	G	H	J	K
5 34	54	67	79	84	80	76	81	94	83 5
4 26	42	59	74	91	92	86	96	99	94 4
3 34	36	44	57	76	82	91	109	102	93 3
2 48	42	37	52	62	73	m H 84	97	94	88 2
1 58	49	52	54	49	60	69	76	86	80 1
0 62	56	61	49	39	47	58	n H 64	78	76 0

o H / 94

A   B   C   D   E   F   G   H   J   K

A GRID SURVEY

NOTE: For the given grid survey, plot contour lines at 5- or 10-ft intervals as assigned. The grids are ½ in. apart. Scale: 1″ = 40′. The grid is to be placed in the upper, right-hand corner ½ in. from the borders of the drawing paper which is to have the long side horizontal.

12p. Plot the profile along grid 3–3. On the profile, label the topographic crest and shade the *defiladed area* (the space in air or above earth's surface not visible from the topographic crest). Label the *military crest* (that crest from which the previous defiladed area is visible).

12q. Points *M, N,* and *O* are located on the outcrop of a thin vein. Determine the strike and dip of this vein and show its complete outcrop line.

12r. Plot additional profiles along the grids assigned by the instructor. Along each grid show the center line of a roadway with a uniform grade which does not exceed 10 per cent and which is such that the areas of cut and fill along the center line are approximately minimized and balanced.

12s. Indicate whether the following statements are true or false. If assigned, prepare written explanations or sketches to justify the answers.

(a) If the strike lines of two planes are parallel, the planes are parallel.

(b) The strike of a plane is the direction of a horizontal line on the plane and is always measured in a top view.

(c) A contour line represents points of approximately equal elevation on the surface of the earth.

(d) Contour lines cannot cross.

(e) The dip of a plane is observed in any view that shows the plane edgewise.

(f) The thickness of a vein is always measured in a front view.

(g) A dump line is a horizontal line.

(h) An outcrop of a vein is its intersection with a bedding plane.

(i) The relative space between contour lines on a map is an indication of the relative slope of the terrain.

CHAPTER 13 | REVOLUTION

DRAWING-BOARD PROBLEMS are usually solved by the addition of principal or auxiliary views. This procedure is called the *change-of-position* method because the successive views are obtained by successive changes in the position of the observer (or of the line of sight), with the object remaining stationary. It is also possible to consider the observer stationary and the object revolved to whatever position results in a new or altered view showing the desired information. As will be seen, this *revolution* method frequently requires less construction and less working space on the drawing. On the other hand, it often results in crowded or overlapping views with increased confusion. Consequently, in practice the revolution method is used only when it possesses a distinct advantage over the change-of-position method for a particular problem. Because of this latter possibility the engineer should be familiar with both methods.

13.1 REVOLUTION OF A POINT

For the purposes at hand, a point is considered as revolving only about a straight-line axis and only in a circular path lying in a plane perpendicular to the axis.[1] These are the conditions present in rotation of familiar objects such as wheels, pulleys, and hand-cranks, as illustrated in Fig. 13-1(a). The axis of revolution is the center line AB of the shaft, and points on the pulley, such as point C, rotate in circular paths lying in planes perpendicular to AB. Reduced to bare essentials and drawn in multiview arrangement, this rotation is demonstrated in Fig. 13-1(b), where point C is revolved through an angle of 120° in a clockwise direction. Two important characteristics of any revolution of this type may be observed in Fig. 13-1(b):

1. *In a view showing the axis of revolution as a point, the path of revolution of any point not on the axis appears as a circle* or as an arc of a circle

---

[1] Other types and positions of paths of revolution are, of course, theoretically possible but are of no utility in the solutions of problems illustrated in this chapter.

in case the revolution is less than 360°. The center of the circle is the point view of the axis, and the radius is the distance from the point view to the corresponding projection of the given point. This is illustrated in the front view of Fig. 13–1(b).

2. *In a view showing the axis of revolution in true length, the plane of the path of revolution of any point appears in edge view and perpendicular to the axis.* See the top view in Fig. 13–1(b). Experience shows that one of the most common errors in revolution constructions is the violation of this perpendicularity principle, particularly in rotation about an inclined or an oblique axis.

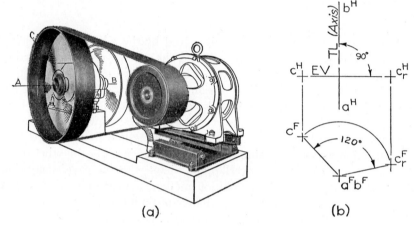

(a)   (b)

Fig. 13–1.   Revolution of a Point

13.2   REVOLUTION OF A LINE

As a line revolves about an axis, all points of the line revolve *through the same angle.* Otherwise the length of the line is altered and the end product becomes a different line instead of merely a new position for a given line.

As an example, Fig. 13–2(a), let it be required to revolve line CE about axis XY until CE lies in a horizontal plane above XY. The first step is the construction of view 1 showing axis XY as a point, since in that view arcs of revolution about XY show in their true circular shape. A line is then drawn from y^1x^1 perpendicular to c^1e^1, locating k^1. As c^1e^1 revolves, it remains tangent to the circular arc drawn through k^1.

In view 1 any horizontal plane appears as a line parallel to folding line $H/1$. Hence, in this case, point k^1 is revolved to k_r^1 in which position line CE in space becomes horizontal and above XY. Points c_r^1 and e_r^1 may be located as the intersections of their respective arcs of revolution with the horizontal plane through k_r^1 or, more accurately, by transferring lengths k^1c^1 and k^1e^1

to positions $k_r^1 c_r^1$ and $k_r^1 e_r^1$, respectively. The revolved line is drawn as a phantom line to make it readily distinguishable from the line in its original position.

Since axis XY appears true length in the top view, any arcs of revolution about XY must appear in the top view as straight lines perpendicular to the axis. Points c_r^H and e_r^H are therefore located by drawing construction lines from c^H and e^H perpendicular to $x^H y^H$ and projecting from c_r^1 and e_r^1, Fig. 13–2(b). The front view $c_r^F e_r^F$ is then established by projection from $c_r^H e_r^H$ and transfer of distance D_1.

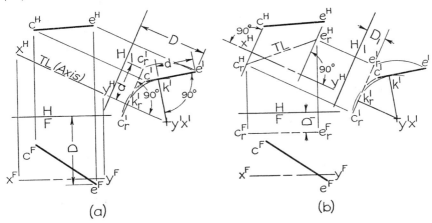

Fig. 13–2.   Revolution of a Line

13.3   TRUE LENGTH BY REVOLUTION

The true length of a line may be obtained by revolving the line about an axis which is parallel to a projection plane until the line itself is parallel to that projection plane. In Fig. 13–2(b) line CE was revolved into a horizontal plane. Its new top view $c_r^H e_r^H$ is therefore true length.

If, however, it is desired merely to obtain the true length of a line by any appropriate revolution, a more convenient axis may be chosen, resulting in considerably less construction. Since it is necessary to have both true-length and point views of the axis, the simplest arrangement is an axis which is parallel to one principal projection plane and perpendicular to an adjacent principal projection plane. Further simplification results from assuming an axis containing one end point of the given line, Fig. 13–3(a) and (b).

In this case the end point O on the arbitrarily chosen vertical axis remains stationary while all other points of the line, including point A, describe circular arcs, the whole effect being the generation of a right circular cone. For the position $o^H a_r^H$, line OA is frontal and view $o^F a_r^F$ is true length, Fig. 13–3(b). Since the entire cone is not used, the construction may be simplified to that of Fig. 13–3(c).

In its various positions the revolving line remains at a constant angle with the plane of the base of the cone. In Fig. 13–3 this plane is horizontal, so that in the true-length position $o^F a_r{}^F$, the true slope (θ^H) may be measured as indicated. It should be emphasized that the angle θ_H is obtained because the chosen axis is perpendicular to a horizontal plane. For purposes of comparison an auxiliary view is included in dotted form in Fig. 13–3(c) showing the true length and slope of line AB as obtained in Art. 3.3.

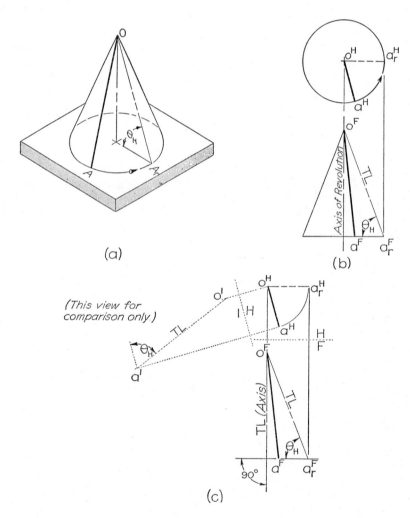

(a)

(b)

(This view for comparison only)

(c)

Fig. 13–3.   True Length and Slope of a Line by Revolution

If an axis perpendicular to a frontal plane is selected, Fig. 13–4(a), a given line may be revolved to a horizontal position as shown. The true length and the angle with the frontal plane (θ_F) are then measured in the top view.

If a given line is revolved about an axis perpendicular to a profile plane, Fig. 13–4(b), the true length and angle with the profile plane (θ_P) may be found as shown.

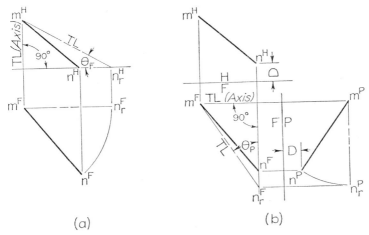

(a)   (b)

Fig. 13–4. True Length and Angles with Frontal and Profile Planes by Revolution

Examples of Converse Problems (Establishing Views with Slope Known):

Example 1

PROBLEM, Fig. 13–5:

Complete the front view of line *EG*, Fig. 13–5(a), if the line slopes upward from *E* at an angle of 30° with a horizontal plane.

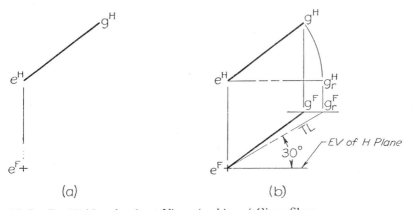

(a)   (b)

Fig. 13–5. Establishing the Front View of a Line of Given Slope

GRAPHIC SOLUTION:

The top view is revolved about a vertical axis to position $e^H g_r^H$, Fig. 13–5(b). The front view of the revolved line must then be true length and may be drawn at the true slope of 30° as shown. A vertical projection line from g_r^H establishes g_r^F. If line EG is then considered *counter-revolved* to its original position, point G moves horizontally in the front view from g_r^F to g^F, established by a vertical projection line from g^H. Line $e^F g^F$ is then the required front view of line EG.

Example 2

PROBLEM, Fig. 13–6:

Complete the front view of line AB, Fig. 13–6(a), if the line slopes upward from point A and makes an angle of 25° with a frontal plane.

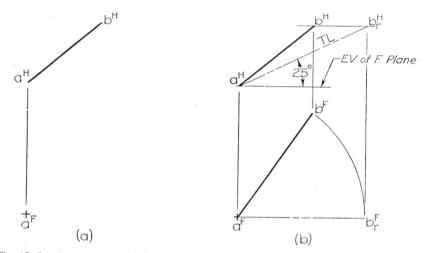

(a)   (b)

Fig. 13–6.   Establishing the Front View of a Line with Angle with Frontal Plane Given

GRAPHIC SOLUTION:

If the unknown front view is considered revolved to a horizontal position about an axis through point A, the revolved top view must then be true length and may be drawn at 25° with a frontal plane as shown, Fig. 13–6(b). The arc of revolution appears in the top view as a line parallel to the edge view of a frontal plane, establishing b_r^H, from which b_r^F is located by projection. Counter-revolution to the projection line from b^H establishes b^F.

13.4   ANGLE BETWEEN LINE AND OBLIQUE PLANE BY REVOLUTION [2]

In the preceding article the angles formed by a given line and the principal planes were found by revolution. As was emphasized therein, if it is

---

[2] For other methods see Chapter 11.

desired to find by revolution the angle between a line and any particular given plane, *the axis of revolution must be perpendicular to that plane.* Revolution about an axis not perpendicular to the given plane alters the angle being sought. Violation of this principle is a common error in applying the revolution method, and the student should take special pains to avoid this mistake.

To find the angle between line *GE* and plane *ABCD,* Fig. 13–7, auxiliary view 1 is first constructed showing the given plane in edge view. An axis of revolution perpendicular to the plane must appear true length in this view as indicated. View 2 is then added, showing the axis of revolution as a point. View e^2g^2 is revolved to position $e^2g_r{}^2$ and true-length view $e^1g_r{}^1$ is established. The angle θ between the line and plane may then be measured in view 1 as shown.

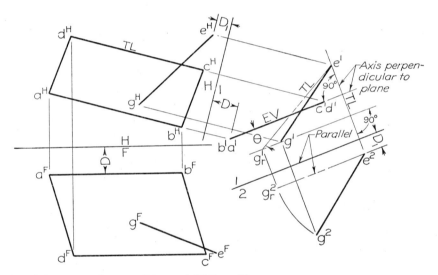

Fig. 13–7. Angle Between Line and Oblique Plane

13.5 NORMAL VIEW OF A PLANE BY REVOLUTION

The true size and shape of a plane surface may be found by revolving the plane as a unit until it is parallel to a principal plane. In Fig. 13–8(a) auxiliary view 1 is added, showing given plane *ABCE* in edge view. The plane is then revolved to position $b^1-c_r{}^1$, Fig. 13–8(b), where it becomes frontal. The resulting revolved front view $a_r{}^F b^F e_r{}^F c_r{}^F$ is therefore a normal or true-size view.

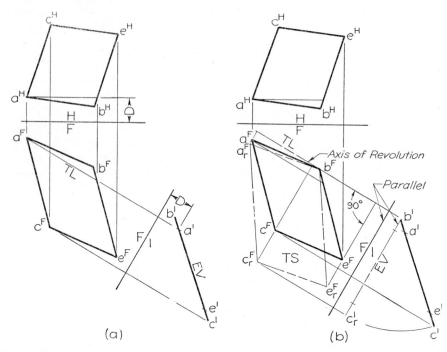

Fig. 13–8. Normal View of a Plane by Revolution

13.6 REVOLUTION OF A SOLID

A jig or fixture for holding a piece of work for machining must sometimes incorporate in its design provision for revolving the object to successive positions for each of several machining operations. Construction of the views of a revolved solid involves the principles discussed in the preceding material of this chapter. When a line, a plane, or any geometric form revolves, all points must revolve about the same axis and through the same angle. The following example illustrates a single revolution of a solid object.

PROBLEM, Fig. 13–9:

After plane *ABFG* of the jig block has been surface-milled, through what angle must the piece be revolved in order to bring surface *ABCE* into the same horizontal plane for milling? Draw the views of the revolved object.

GRAPHIC SOLUTION:

In Fig. 13–9(a) auxiliary view 1 is added to secure edge views of surfaces *ABCE* and *ABFG*. Figure 13–9(b) shows the revolution of the object through an angle of 60° to bring surface *ABCE* into the plane of the original position of surface *ABFG*, and the resulting new views of the object.

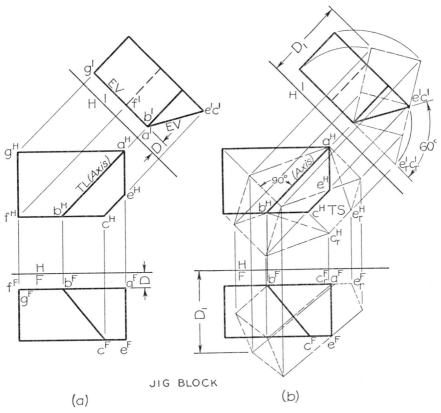

JIG BLOCK

(a)   (b)

Fig. 13–9. Revolution of a Solid

13.7 ESTABLISHING A LINE AT GIVEN ANGLES WITH TWO PRINCIPAL PLANES

Occasionally in practice it is necessary to establish a line forming a *compound angle* with the principal planes. In more familiar terms, the line must be located in such a position as to form given angles with each of two principal planes.

As an example of the solution of such a problem, let it be required, Fig. 13–10, to establish a ¾-in. line terminating at given point *O* and forming angles of 45° with a horizontal plane and 30° with a frontal plane. Since the elements of a right circular cone are at equal angles with the base plane, the intersection of two cones in appropriate positions and with proper base angles locates the required line, Fig. 13–10(a). One cone is established as shown in Fig. 13–10(b) with its vertex at given point *O* and ¾-in. elements at 45° with its horizontal base. This conical surface is the locus of all

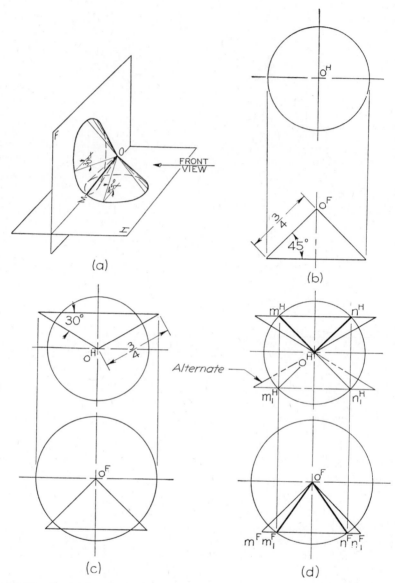

Fig. 13–10. Establishing a Line at Given Angles with Two Principal Planes

lines extending downward from point O which are of $\frac{3}{4}$ in. length and at 45° with horizontal.

The second cone is drawn, Fig. 13–10(c), with its vertex also at point O, but with its $\frac{3}{4}$-in. elements at 30° with a frontal plane. This surface is the locus of all $\frac{3}{4}$-in. lines extending backward from point O and forming 30°

angles with the frontal plane. Since the elements of the two cones are of the same length, the base circles intersect as shown in Fig. 13–10(d), and the two elements OM and ON are common to the two cones. Either of the two elements fulfills the requirements of the problem as stated.

It should be emphasized that the elements of the two cones *must* be drawn to the same length, otherwise the base *circles* will not intersect (although the base *planes* will). By reversing both or either of the cones in turn, it is possible to find eight different line segments (six in addition to OM and ON) which form the given angles. Four of these are aligned with the other four respectively, so that there are actually only four different lines of indefinite length which answer the requirements. In Fig. 13–10(d) the results of reversing the second cone (30°) are shown. In a practical application it is normally apparent which of the possible solutions is the one desired.

These same principles can be used to establish a line making given angles with *any* two intersecting planes (with certain exceptions as noted below). In practice a desired angle between the required line and a given plane may be larger than 90°; for example, 135°. The cone incorporating the angle would then be drawn with a base angle equal to the *supplement* of the given angle. In the example mentioned, the base angle of the cone would be 180° minus 135°, or 45°.

It should be noted that a line can be established at specified angles with two planes only within certain limits. For example, if the two planes are perpendicular, the sum of the two angles must fall in the range of 0° to 90° or 270° to 360°; otherwise the problem is incapable of solution. For a sum more than 90° but less than 270°, the two cones do not intersect. For the particular case of the sum being 90° or 270°, the two cones are tangent and the *element of tangency* is the required line. If this latter condition is applied to a situation similar to that in Fig. 13–10, the two possible elements of tangency are profile lines.

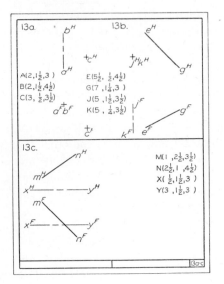

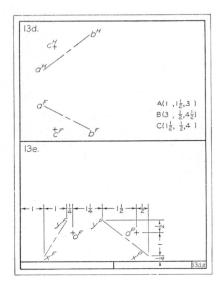

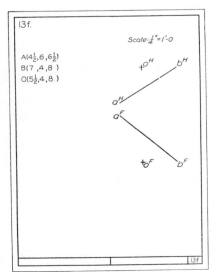

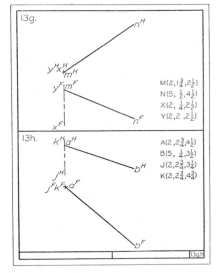

13a. Revolve point C 200° counter-clockwise about axis AB.

13b. Revolve line EG 90° clockwise about axis JK.

13c. Show the views of MN revolved about axis XY until MN appears true length in the front view.

13d. Revolve point C 90° counterclockwise about axis AB.

13e. Show the views of the path of point O revolved 360° about axis XY.

13f. Point O is the extreme tip of a lever revolving on shaft AB. Locate a frontal wall behind the lever that clears the lever by 3 ft.

13g. Revolve MN about axis XY until MN appears true length in the front view.

13h. Revolve AB about axis JK until AB appears true length in the top view.

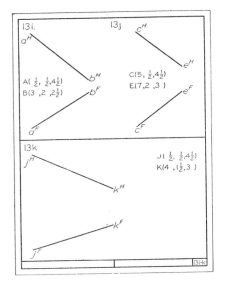

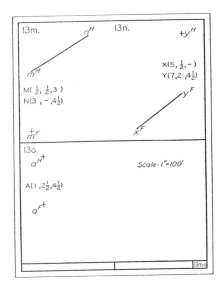

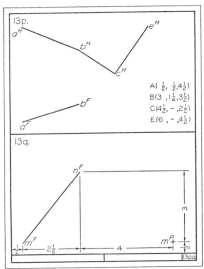

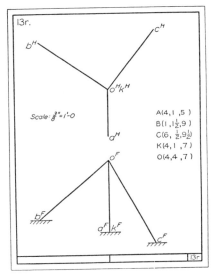

NOTE: Use revolution methods in the following problems:

13i. Find the true length and θ_H of AB.

13j. Find the true length and θ_F of CE.

13k. Find the true length and θ_P of JK.

13m. Complete the front view if MN is $3\frac{1}{4}$ in. long.

13n. Complete the top view of XY if θ_F is 30°.

13o. Show the views of a 600-ft pipeline AB that bears S 60° E on a 25 per cent down grade. What is the *head* produced at B?

13p. Find the grade of pipeline AB. Complete the views of segments BC and CE which have the same grade as AB.

13q. Complete the profile view of MN if θ_P is 30°.

13r. Determine the lengths of the guy wires OA, OB, and OC.

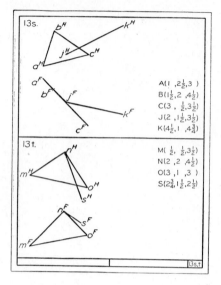

13s.

A(1 ,2½,3)
B(1½,2 ,4½)
C(3 , ½,3½)
J(2 ,1½,3½)
K(4½,1 ,4¾)

13t.

M(½, ½,3½)
N(2 ,2 ,4½)
O(3 ,1 ,3)
S(2¾,1½,2½)

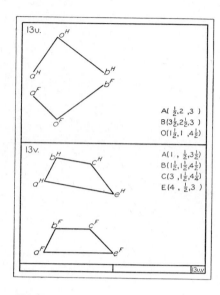

13u.

A(½,2 ,3)
B(3½,2½,3)
O(1½,1 ,4½)

13v.

A(1 , ½,3½)
B(1½,1½,4½)
C(3 ,1½,4¼)
E(4 , ½,3)

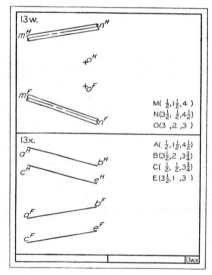

13w.

M(½,1½,4)
N(3½, ½,4½)
O(3 ,2 ,3)

13x.

A(½,1½,4½)
B(3½,2 ,3¾)
C(½, ½,3¾)
E(3½,1 ,3)

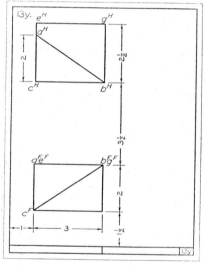

13y.

13s. Find the angle that *JK* makes with plane *ABC*.

13t. Find the angle that *NS* makes with plane *MNO*.

13u. Show the views of the bisector of angle *AOB*.

13v. Show the true size and compute the area of the trapezoid *ABCE*.

13w. Locate the center line of a branch pipe from *O* to the main line *MN* if the branch is connected to *MN* with a 45° Y-fitting.

13x. Determine the distance between the parallel lines *AB* and *CE*.

13y. Through what angle must the block be revolved about *AB* in order to bring surface *ABC* into a horizontal plane for surface milling? Using phantom lines show the revolved position of the block in all the views. Omit hidden lines.

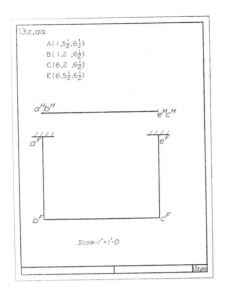

13z,aa.

A($1,5\frac{1}{2},6\frac{1}{2}$)
B($1,2,6\frac{1}{2}$)
C($6,2,6\frac{1}{2}$)
E($6,5\frac{1}{2},6\frac{1}{2}$)

Scale:$1''=1'-0$

13zaa

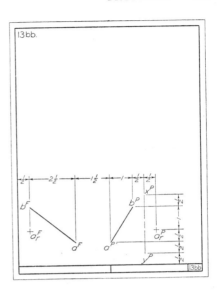

13bb.

13bb

13z. Trapeze *ABCE* is to be twisted so that cable *CE* will remain in its present position while cable *AB* will revolve until point *B* will be 1 ft 7 in. above its present position. Show the new positions for cable *AB* and bar *BC*.

13aa. Trapeze *ABCE* is to be twisted so that cable *AB* will remain in its present position while cable *CE* will revolve until its true angle with a horizontal plane will become 30°. Show the new positions for cable *CE* and bar *BC*.

13bb. Line *AB* is revolved about a frontal axis *XY* until point *A* takes the location A_r. Locate $x^F y^F$ and show the revolved position of line *AB*.

13cc. Indicate whether the following statements are true or false. If assigned, prepare written explanations or sketches to justify the answers.

(a) The path of rotation of a point lies in a plane perpendicular to the axis of rotation.

(b) The angle between a line and any given plane may be determined by revolving the line into a profile plane.

(c) The angle between a line and any given plane may be determined by revolving the line about an axis perpendicular to that plane.

(d) A line may be drawn that makes an angle of 30° with a horizontal plane and 30° with a frontal plane.

(e) Obtaining the true length of a line by the revolution method results in a somewhat larger value than the true length by other methods.

(f) If a point is revolved about an oblique axis, the path of rotation appears elliptical in a front view.

(g) If the axis of rotation is true length in a view, the path of rotation in that view appears edgewise and perpendicular to the axis.

CHAPTER 14	CONCURRENT VECTORS

GRAPHICAL METHODS ARE usually sufficiently accurate for engineering analyses of forces, velocities, accelerations, and other directional quantities in structural and machine design, mechanics, and other physical sciences. In addition graphical solutions are often more economical in time and are more easily understood than analytical methods.

14.1 DEFINITION OF TERMS

1. *Vectors.* Forces, velocities, and other directed magnitudes may be represented graphically by straight-line segments called *vectors.* These lines have definite lengths, relative positions, and directions in space. The true length of a vector, to an appropriate scale, represents its magnitude, and an arrowhead indicates the direction of action (*sense*) of the vector.

2. *Concurrent Vectors.* Vectors whose lines of action pass through a common point are known as concurrent vectors.

3. *Resultant.* The resultant of concurrent vectors is a vector that may be used to replace all the other vectors through a point.

4. *Equilibrant.* A vector that will balance all other vectors through a point is the equilibrant. It has the same magnitude as the resultant but acts in the opposite direction.

5. *Coplanar Vectors.* Vectors whose lines of action lie in one plane are known as coplanar vectors.

6. *Non-coplanar Vectors.* Vectors that lie in more than one plane are known as non-coplanar vectors.

7. *Vector Polygon.* If a system of concurrent coplanar vectors is in equilibrium, these vectors, when laid end to end in any sequence but in continuous direction, form a *closed* figure called a vector polygon.

14.2 RESULTANT OF CONCURRENT COPLANAR VECTORS

In Fig. 14–1(a) two forces, *B* and *C*, are shown acting through a given point. To find the direction and magnitude of a force that will replace these two concurrent forces, the *parallelogram method* is used, Fig. 14–1(b).

164

If two concurrent forces are represented by their vectors and both are acting either toward or away from their point of intersection, the diagonal of the completed parallelogram drawn through their intersection point represents the resultant of the two forces. A pushing or pulling force may be replaced by its opposite in order to satisfy the requirements for the parallelogram method. For example, if one of two given forces acts toward a point and the other force acts away from the point, the pushing force might be replaced by a pulling force of the same sense and magnitude. Then there would be two pulling forces and the parallelogram method could be applied.

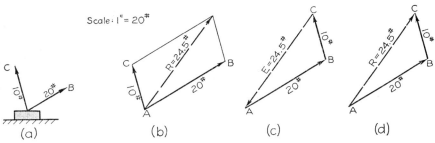

Fig. 14–1.   Resultant of Two Concurrent Forces Acting in Plane of Paper

Before the parallelogram is constructed, it is first necessary to establish the lengths of the vectors representing the given forces. Since the forces are acting in the plane of the paper, the vectors are shown in true length. The lengths of the vectors are determined directly from the given scale. The parallelogram is drawn, and the diagonal through the point of intersection of the forces represents the resultant R, which replaces the given forces. The magnitude of the resultant is established using the given scale, and the direction is indicated by the arrowhead.

By the vector-polygon method (Art. 14.1, definition 7), the vectors representing the forces are laid out end to end in continuous direction and parallel to the given positions of the forces, Fig. 14–1(c). The side or vector necessary to close the polygon represents the equilibrant force E, which maintains the given forces in equilibrium. The resultant R, which replaces the given forces, has the same magnitude as E but acts in the opposite direction, Fig. 14–1(d). The magnitude of this force is determined according to the given scale.

If several vectors are acting through a point, Fig. 14–2, the resultant vector can be more quickly determined by the vector-polygon method than by application of the parallelogram method to successive pairs of vectors. The vectors are laid end to end (tip to tail) in any sequence, Fig. 14–2(b). The vector necessary to close the polygon represents the equilibrant capable of balancing the given vectors 1, 2, 3, and 4. The resultant R, Fig. 14–2(c), acts in the opposite direction. In this illustration all the vectors are in the plane of the paper so that their magnitudes may be scaled directly.

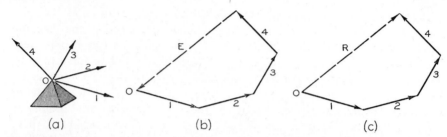

Fig. 14–2. Resultant of More than Two Concurrent Forces Acting in Plane of Paper

In many instances vectors acting through a point lie in an oblique or an inclined plane, and hence the true magnitudes of the vectors are not directly shown in principal views. For example, in Fig. 14–3(a) two concurrent vectors 1 and 2 acting in an oblique plane are represented by their front and top views. To find the resultant vector, a parallelogram is constructed in the two given views, Fig. 14–3(b).[1] The diagonal of the parallelogram through the intersection point of the vectors is the resultant. The true magnitude of

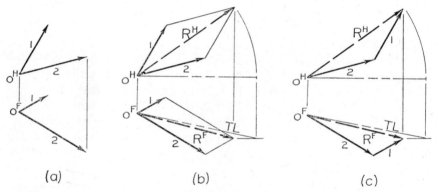

Fig. 14–3. Resultant of Two Concurrent Forces Acting in an Oblique Plane

the resultant may be determined by finding its true length by revolution as shown, or by the auxiliary-view method.

The vector-polygon method may also be used in this instance to find the resultant, as shown in Fig. 14–3(c). The true magnitude of the resultant is determined by scaling its true length as found by revolution.

14.3 RESOLUTION OF A VECTOR INTO CONCURRENT COPLANAR COMPONENTS

The resolution of a known vector into two concurrent coplanar vectors involves the reversal of the procedures used in securing the resultant.

---

[1] See Art. 9.1.

In Fig. 14–4(a) the directions and positions of the force R and components 1 and 2 are known. If the magnitude of R is given as 800 lbs, let it be required to resolve this force into components along 1 and 2. It is first necessary to revolve the resultant R into a true-length position and properly scale its length for the 800-lb force. To find a revolved true-length position of R, any convenient point such as X is selected and revolved as shown. The magnitude, 800 lbs, is then set off to scale, and the point K thus determined is counter-revolved to the original position of R. From points O and K, Fig. 14–4(b), the sides of the parallelogram are drawn parallel to the given views of vectors 1 and 2, respectively. The parallelogram thus formed determines the vector components along 1 and 2. The magnitudes of the forces in vectors 1 and 2 may now be found by revolution. For simplicity this true-length construction is not shown.

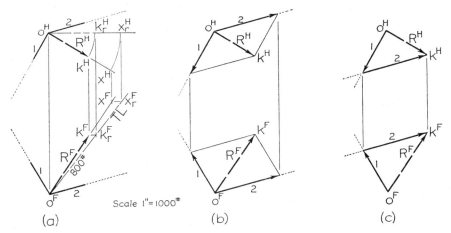

Fig. 14–4.   Resolution of a Force into Concurrent Coplanar Components

The vector-polygon method, Fig. 14–4(c), also furnishes a ready resolution of a force into two components. After laying out the force R as before, the polygon is closed by intersecting lines 1 and 2 drawn through points O and K parallel to the given views of Fig. 14–4(a). Again, the magnitudes of the components may be found by revolution.

14.4   RESULTANT OF CONCURRENT NON-COPLANAR VECTORS

The resultant of three vectors whose lines of action lie in more than one plane can be found by combining two of the vectors into a resultant and then combining this resultant with the third vector into a resultant for all three vectors. By continuing this procedure, any number of concurrent vectors may be finally combined into one resultant.

Plane Method. In Fig. 14–5(a) the three vectors 1, 2, and 3 acting through point O determine three planes with point O in common. Therefore, to find the resultant of any two of the vectors, the appropriate plane is selected and the parallelogram is constructed. In this case the vectors 2 and 3 were selected, and their resultant is shown by the diagonal r.

The next step is to combine the resultant r with the remaining vector 1. These two vectors determine still another plane. The parallelogram in this plane produces the resultant R of the three non-coplanar forces 1, 2, and 3. The true magnitude of the resultant R may be determined by revolution as shown.

Parallelepiped Method. A variation of the plane method utilizes the parallelepiped,[2] Fig. 14–5(b). Since the three vectors establish three planes that

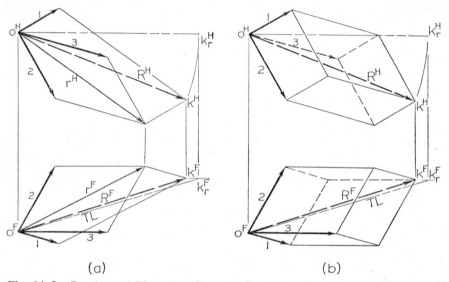

(a)   (b)

Fig. 14–5. Resultant of Three Non-Coplanar Concurrent Vectors, Plane Method and Parallelepiped Method

intersect at point O, the construction of a parallelogram in each plane produces three sides of a parallelepiped. The opposite sides (parallelograms) are drawn parallel respectively to the three parallelograms established by the views of the vectors. The diagonal of the parallelepiped through the point of intersection of the vectors is the resultant of the three vectors. The true magnitude of the resultant R is obtained by revolution.

14.5 RESOLUTION OF A FORCE INTO CONCURRENT, NON-COPLANAR COMPONENTS

It is often necessary in engineering practice and design work to resolve a known force into concurrent, non-coplanar components.

---

[2] See Appendix III.1.

For example, in Fig. 14–6(a) it is required to resolve the 1500-lb vertical force into components in the three legs of the supporting structure or tripod. The vector AB representing the 1500-lb force, Fig. 14–6(b), is the diagonal of a parallelepiped of which three of the edges coincide with the legs of the tripod. To begin the construction of the parallelepiped, a plane is passed through the end point B of the vector AB and parallel to a plane determined by any two of the tripod legs. In this case the plane E_1BD_1 is passed parallel to the plane of legs AD and AE, Fig. 14–6(b), thereby establishing a plane of an opposite face of the parallelepiped. In order to determine the length of the edges between the two parallel faces, the piercing point Z of leg AC in plane E_1BD_1 is then found. This procedure establishes the length of one component vector AZ. The parallelepiped can now be drawn and the remaining components thus established, Fig. 14–6(c).

The foregoing procedure is shown in multiview form in Fig. 14–6(d).

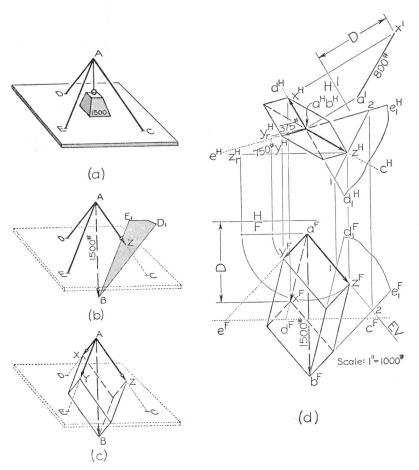

Fig. 14–6. Resolution of a Force into Concurrent Non-Coplanar Components

The piercing point Z of AC in plane E_1BD_1 is found by the two-view method of Art. 6.2. The parallelepiped is completed with parallel lines in the two given views, and the magnitudes of the components are determined by revolution as shown for AZ and AY, or by auxiliary views as shown for AX.

14.6 OTHER VECTOR PROBLEMS

Thus far the vector examples have been forces. A great variety of graphical solutions has been devised for other force problems involving nonconcurrent forces, both parallel and nonparallel, moments, couples, and so on. Other vectors arising in connection with velocities and accelerations are also amenable to graphical treatment. These problems are encountered by the engineering student in his later courses and so will not be treated here except for the following discussion of velocity vectors.

14.7 VELOCITY VECTORS

Concurrent velocity vectors may be combined in exactly the same manner as forces. As an example, let it be required to find the true ground speed of an airplane in level flight at point A if the indicated air speed is 400 knots on a compass course of N 120° and there is a 100-knot wind blowing due north, Fig. 14–7(a). One knot is a velocity of one nautical mile per hour or 6080 ft per hour.

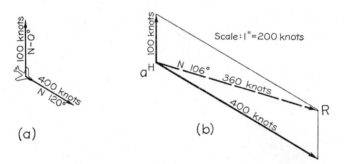

Fig. 14–7. Sum of Velocity Vectors

The pilot's compass indicates the direction in which the plane is headed. The air-speed indicator tells him his velocity with respect to the air in which the plane is flying. If, however, the air is also moving with respect to the earth's surface (which is considered stationary for reference purposes), the absolute movement of the plane with respect to ground is represented by the vector sum of the two velocities. Thus in Fig. 14–7(b) the plane and wind vectors are laid out in the prescribed directions and to the given scale. Only the top view is needed here because the plane is in level or horizontal flight. The vector sum indicates that the plane is moving with respect to the earth's surface at a velocity of 360 knots on a course of N 106°.

14.8 RELATIVE MOTION

Another example involving velocity vectors is illustrated in Fig. 14–8. Here two ships represented by points X and Y are on their indicated courses of N 45° at 12 knots and N 330° at 15 knots, respectively. The problem is to find how close the ships will pass.

The given velocity vectors are specified with respect to the earth. The real concern here, however, is the motion of one of the ships relative to the other, which is the vector difference of the two motions. This involves reversing one vector before adding it to the other, which is equivalent to considering one ship stationary while the other moves in the composite direction represented by the vector difference. Hence in Fig. 14–8(a) ship Y is temporarily considered stationary while the motion of ship X becomes that indicated by vector R. It is then evident that ship X will pass ship Y with a clearance of 600 ft.

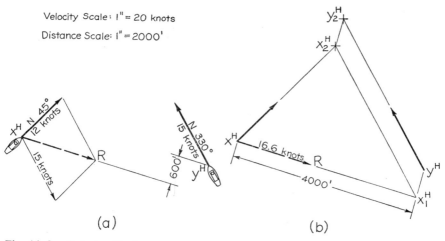

Fig. 14–8. Relative Motion

It must be remembered that the distance and velocity scales are independent. Thus, if the elapsed time to closest approach is to be calculated, the relative distance of travel of X is measured at the given distance scale, which gives 4000 ft, Fig. 14–8(b). The relative velocity of X is the length of vector R, 16.6 knots, at the vector scale. Thus the elapsed time becomes:

Time to closest approach = distance ÷ velocity

$$= (4000 \text{ ft}) \div \frac{(16.6 \text{ naut. mph}) (6080 \text{ ft/naut. mile})}{(60 \text{ min/hr})}$$

$$= \frac{(4000 \text{ ft}) (\text{hr}) (\text{naut. mile}) (60 \text{ min})}{(16.6 \text{ naut. mile}) (6080 \text{ ft}) (\text{hr})}$$

$$= 2.38 \text{ min, or } 2 \text{ min } 23 \text{ sec}$$

If it is desired to show the location on the water at which this closest approach occurs, the clearance distance $y^H x_1{}^H$ is simply moved along the direction of vector Y until $x_1{}^H$ falls on the path of vector X at $x_2{}^H$, Fig. 14–8(b). The actual positions of the ships at this moment would then be at $x_2{}^H$ and $y_2{}^H$.

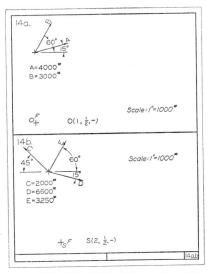

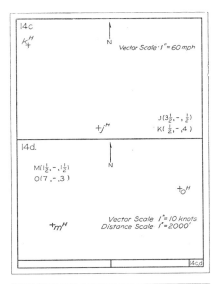

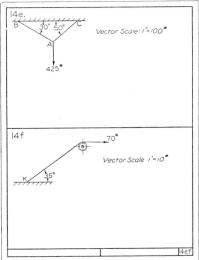

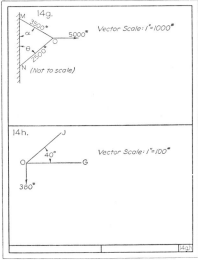

14a. Starting the vector polygon at O, find the resultant of vectors A and B.

14b. Starting the vector polygon at S, find the resultant of the vectors C, D, and E acting in a frontal plane.

14c. An airplane at J is flying at an air speed of 250 mph on a compass course of N 45°. Find the true flight direction and resulting ground speed if there is a 75-mph wind blowing due south. With the same air speed and wind force, in what direction should the plane fly to pass over K? What is the resulting ground speed?

14d. A ship at M is traveling at 20 knots and N 30°. A ship at O is traveling at 10 knots and N 330°. How close will the ships pass? Find time needed to reach this position.

14e. Find the tensions in the members AB and AC acted upon by the given force.

14f. Determine the horizontal and vertical components of the force on the cable anchorage at K.

14g. Find the angles α and θ, if the 5000-lb force at O produces the given stresses in cables OM and ON.

14h. Find the stresses in OJ and OG.

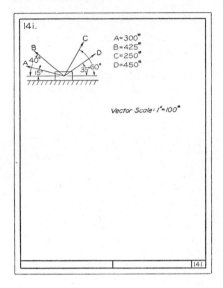

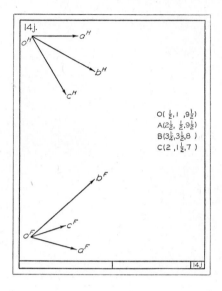

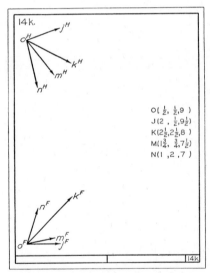

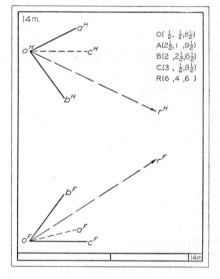

14i. Determine the resultant of the forces A, B, C, and D and the horizontal and vertical components of the resultant.

14j. Find the views and the true magnitude of the resultant of the three forces A, B, and C. Complete the parallelepiped.

14k. Find the views and the true magnitude of the resultant of the forces J, K, M, and N.

14m. Resolve the vector R into components along the members A, B, and C.

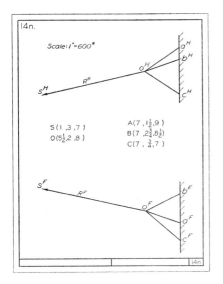

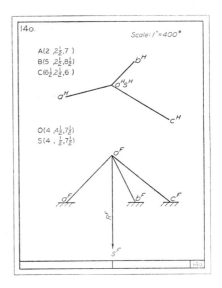

14n. For the applied force R find the tension in each of the frame members OA, OB, and OC.

14o. For the vertical force R determine the compression in each member of the tripod frame.

14p. Indicate whether the following statements are true or false. If assigned, prepare written explanations or sketches to justify the answers.

(a) The magnitude of the resultant of any two given vectors is always greater than either of the given vectors.

(b) Two concurrent vectors are always coplanar.

(c) Two parallel vectors are non-coplanar.

(d) The equilibrant has the same magnitude as the resultant but acts in the opposite direction.

(e) An inclined force is greater than either its vertical or horizontal component.

(f) A vector-polygon always has an even number of sides.

(g) In problems involving relative motion of two objects, a vector may be introduced to put one of the objects at rest.

CHAPTER 15

PLANE
TANGENCIES

A PLANE TANGENT to a ruled surface [1] such as a cylinder or a cone contains one and only one straight-line element of that surface. A plane tangent to a double-curved surface such as a sphere contains one and only one point in that surface. Since all lines tangent to a curved surface at a particular point or at points along the same straight-line element lie in the plane tangent at that point or element, a tangent plane may be conveniently represented in one of the following manners, depending on the situation:

1. By two straight lines, one an element (the element of tangency) and the other a line tangent to the surface at a point on the element.

2. By two straight lines, both tangent to the curved surface at the same point.

15.1 LINES TANGENT TO CURVED SURFACES

A line may be drawn tangent to a curved surface by drawing it tangent to a curve lying in that surface. This is a general statement which is most often applied in practice to surfaces in which the curve in the surface is a circle. Examples in this chapter will be confined to objects of that nature, such as a circular cylinder, a circular cone, a sphere, or a torus.

Although the student is probably familiar with the mechanics of drawing a line tangent to a circle, he should realize that such constructions encountered previously have been *plane geometry* constructions. If the construction is understood to be confined to a plane, it is sufficient to define a line tangent to a circle as being a line which contains one and only one point of the circle. But if a circle or other plane curve is regarded as existing *in space* rather than on paper, it should be borne in mind that: A line tangent to a circle *must lie in the plane of the circle*. This is necessary because, mathematically speaking, a line tangent to a curve has the same *slope* as the curve at the

---

[1] See Appendix III.2.

point of tangency. In other words the tangent line must coincide with the curve for a very short (actually infinitely short) distance.

Thus, in Fig. 15–1, while both lines AB and XY are *apparently* tangent to the circle in the auxiliary view 1, only line AB is *actually* tangent to the circle, since line XY does not lie in the plane of the circle. The truth of this statement becomes evident when the resulting top view is examined, since $x^H y^H$ crosses the ellipse, while $a^H b^H$ is tangent to the ellipse. The student should keep this principle constantly in mind as he studies the following constructions.

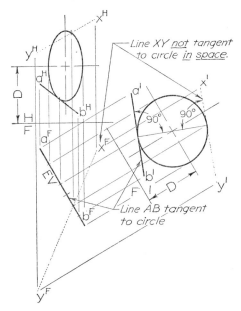

Fig. 15–1.   Line Tangent to a Circle

15.2   PLANES TANGENT TO CONES

Example 1:   Tangent Plane Containing a Given Point on the Surface of the Cone

Let the top view of the point and the front and top views of the cone be given, Fig. 15–2(a). The element VT through A is drawn, Fig. 15–2(b), by drawing $v^H t^H$ through a^H and projecting to t^F in the front view. The front view of point A is located by projecting from a^H to $v^F t^F$. Element VT is then the element lying in the required tangent plane. Line HT is drawn tangent to the circular base of the cone by constructing $h^H t^H$ tangent in the top view and drawing $h^F t^F$ in coincidence with the front view of the base. Intersecting lines HT and VT both lie in the desired tangent plane and therefore represent that plane.

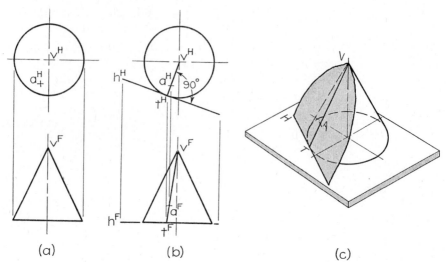

Fig. 15–2.   Plane Tangent to Cone and Containing Given Point on the Surface of the Cone

Example 2:   Tangent Plane Containing a Given Point Outside the Surface of a Cone

Let the given cone and point be as in Fig. 15–3(a). Since all elements of a cone pass through the vertex, line BV joining the given point and vertex must lie in the required tangent plane, Fig. 15–3(b). In this case a line tangent to the base must coincide with the top view of the base. In order to lie in a plane with line BV, the tangent line must intersect BV, which could occur only at point P, the point at which line BV extended pierces the plane of the base. Line PT is then drawn tangent to the base, completing the representation of the tangent plane. If desired, the element of tangency VT may be added as indicated. There are actually two solutions to the problem, the alternate tangent plane being plane VPT_1. In a practical application it is normally apparent which tangent plane is needed.

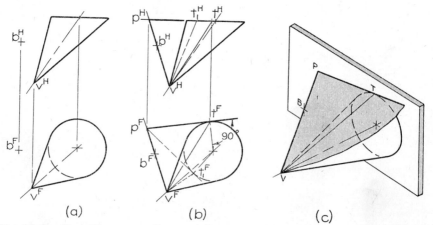

Fig. 15–3.   Plane Tangent to Cone and Containing Given Point Outside the Cone

Example 3:   Tangent Plane Parallel to Given Line

Let the given cone and line be as shown in Fig. 15–4(a).

A plane is parallel to a given line if it contains a line parallel to the given line.[2] Thus, if a line VP is drawn through the vertex V of the cone and parallel to the line CE, Fig. 15–4(b), a tangent plane containing VP fulfills the problem requirements. Line VP pierces the base plane of the cone at P, from which tangent line PT may be drawn as shown. An alternate solution may be secured by drawing line PT tangent on the opposite side of the base. This is not shown.

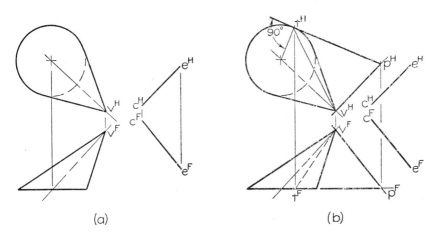

(a)	(b)

Fig. 15–4. Plane Tangent to Cone and Parallel to Given Line

15.3 PLANES TANGENT TO CYLINDERS

Example 1:   Tangent Plane Containing a Given Point on the Surface of a Cylinder

Let the cylinder and the front view of the point be given, Fig. 15–5(a).

Element AT is drawn in the front view and then in the top view, Fig. 15–5(b). A line tangent to either base at the corresponding end of the element completes the representation of the tangent plane.

Example 2:   Tangent Plane Containing a Point Outside the Cylinder

Let the cylinder and point B be given, Fig. 15–6(a).

Since all elements of a cylinder are parallel, a line BP drawn parallel to the axis of the cylinder is parallel to the element of tangency and is thus in the same plane as the element of tangency. Point P is the piercing point of line BP in the plane of the lower base, and thus line PT may be drawn tangent to this base as shown. The element of tangency through T may be added if desired. There is an alternate solution, since line PT may be drawn on the opposite side of the base.

[2] Art. 9.3.

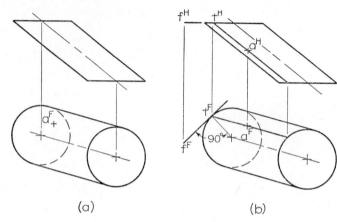

(a)   (b)

Fig. 15–5. Plane Tangent to Cylinder and Containing Given Point on Surface of Cylinder

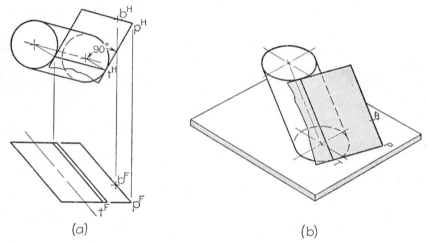

(a)   (b)

Fig. 15–6. Plane Tangent to Cylinder and Containing Given Point Outside the Cylinder

Example 3: Tangent Plane Parallel to Line Outside the Cylinder

Let the cylinder and line EC be given as in Fig. 15–7(a).[3]

Since at the beginning a point on the cylinder at which to start the construction is not known, this problem is solved indirectly. A plane containing the given line and which is parallel to the axis of the cylinder is parallel to the required tangent plane. This is true because a plane (in this case the tangent plane) which is parallel to another plane is parallel to all lines in the second plane. Consequently the first step, Fig. 15–7(b), is to construct plane ECH parallel to the axis of the cylinder by drawing line CH parallel to the axis. Since the bases of the cylinder in this case are horizontal, any

---

[3] If the given line is parallel to the given cylinder, the solution is similar to Example 2.

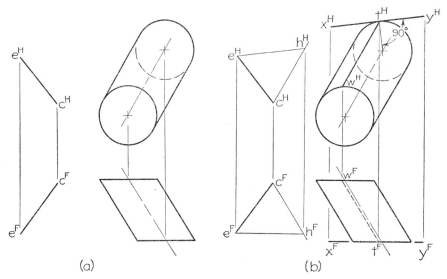

Fig. 15–7. Plane Tangent to Cylinder and Parallel to Given Line

line tangent to one of the bases is of necessity a horizontal line. Therefore a horizontal line *EH* is drawn in plane *ECH*. This establishes in the top view the direction of all horizontal lines in plane *ECH* and in all planes parallel to *ECH*. Line *XY* is then drawn tangent to one base and parallel to line *EH*. This line *XY* plus the element of tangency *TW* completes the representation of a tangent plane which is parallel to plane *ECH* and thus to given line *CE*. Again there is an alternate solution which is omitted for simplicity.

15.4 PLANES TANGENT TO SPHERES

Example 1: Tangent Plane Through a Point on the Surface of the Sphere

Let a sphere and the front view of a point *A* on its surface be given, Fig. 15–8(a).

The top view of point *A* may be found by passing a horizontal plane through point *A*. This plane cuts from the sphere a horizontal circle which contains point *A*. This circle is then drawn in the top view and a^H is located on it as shown in Fig. 15–8(a). A line *AH* tangent to this circle must be a horizontal line and is also tangent to the sphere. A frontal circle through point *A* and lying on the surface of the sphere is then added as in Fig. 15–8(b). Frontal line *AF* drawn tangent to this circle at *A* is also tangent to the sphere. The two lines *AH* and *AF* thus represent a plane tangent to the sphere at point *A*.

The same result may be obtained by utilizing the principle that a plane tangent to a sphere is perpendicular to the radius drawn to the point of tangency. This construction may be performed as demonstrated in Art. 10.2, obtaining exactly the same lines, *AH* and *AF*.

A third line tangent at point A may be used in place of AF or AH, Fig. 15–8(c). If the *meridian* [4] through A is revolved to a frontal position, it will coincide with the circle representing the front view of the sphere. A line drawn tangent to the revolved meridian will locate M on the extended vertical axis. If the meridian is counter-revolved, point M will remain stationary and line AM will be the tangent to the meridian. The required tangent plane will be thus represented as MAH.

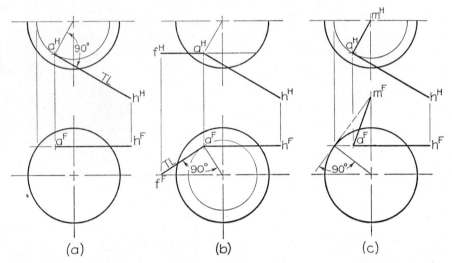

(a)   (b)   (c)

Fig. 15–8.   Plane Tangent to Sphere at a Given Point on the Surface of the Sphere

Example 2:   Tangent Plane Containing Given Line—Line Not Intersecting Sphere

In this construction, Fig. 15–9, an auxiliary view is added to show given line AB as a point. In this view any plane containing AB must appear in edge view, and thus the

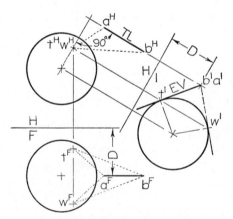

Fig. 15–9.   Plane Tangent to Sphere and Containing Given Line

---

[4] See the introduction to Chapter 22.

required tangent plane may be drawn in edge view as a line tangent to the auxiliary view of the sphere either at t^1 or w^1. Projection of any suitable points of the planes to the top and front views completes the representation. In this illustration it was chosen to project the actual points of tangency T and W, so that the alternate solutions would be plane ABT and plane ABW.

15.5 PLANE TANGENT TO A TORUS AT A GIVEN POINT ON ITS SURFACE

Assuming that the front view a^F of the point is given, Fig. 15–10(a), a horizontal plane may be passed through A, cutting two circles which appear in their true circular form in the top view. Thus the top view of A may be at a^H, $a_1{}^H$, or $a_2{}^H$ or $a_3{}^H$. The tangent plane construction is shown in Fig. 15–10(b) for a^H only and is similar to Fig. 15–8(c). A line AH is drawn

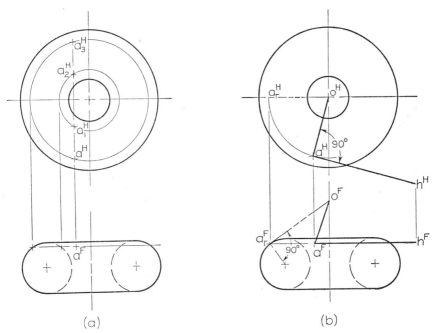

(a)   (b)

Fig. 15–10. Plane Tangent to a Torus at a Given Point on the Surface of the Torus

tangent to the horizontal circle through A. The vertical right section of the torus through A is a circle lying in a vertical plane. When this circle is revolved to a frontal position along with point A, line A_rO may be drawn tangent to the circle as shown, locating point O on the vertical axis of the torus. In counter-revolving to the original position of A, point O remains stationary. Hence the tangent plane is represented by OAH.

15.6 APPLICATION OF TANGENT PLANE—REPRESENTATION OF PLANE CONTAINING GIVEN LINE AND MAKING SPECIFIED ANGLE WITH GIVEN PLANE

All elements of a right circular cone form the same angle with the base plane of the cone. Therefore all planes tangent to a given right circular cone form this same angle with the base plane. This principle may be used as the basis for the representation of a plane making a specified dihedral angle with a given plane when the line of intersection of the given and required planes is not known.

Example 1

PROBLEM, Fig. 15–11:

Represent a plane containing line EG and making an angle of $60°$ with a horizontal plane, Fig. 15–11(a).

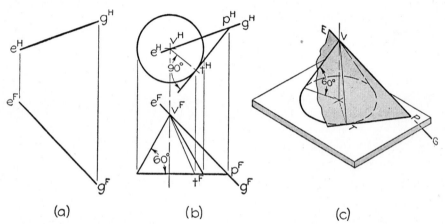

(a)   (b)   (c)

Fig. 15–11.   Plane Containing Oblique Line and Forming a Specified Angle With a Horizontal Plane

ANALYSIS:

If a right circular cone has its base in a horizontal plane and if its elements make a $60°$ "base angle" with the horizontal plane, any plane tangent to the cone forms a $60°$ dihedral angle with horizontal. In order to make it possible for the required plane both to contain line EG and be tangent to the cone, the vertex of the cone must be placed at some point such as V on line EG.

GRAPHIC SOLUTION:

The cone may be of any height consistent with accuracy and available space. The tangency construction becomes similar to Fig. 15–3(b). The piercing point P of line EG and the base plane is located in the front view at p^F and is projected to the top view establishing p^H. From this point, $p^H t^H$ is drawn tangent to the base of the cone. Location of the corresponding front view of the tangent line completes the representation of the required plane. There is an alternate solution, but in a practical application additional data permit selection of one of the two possible planes. Such an application may also require the addition of other lines to complete the views of an actual object as demonstrated in Example 3.

Example 2

PROBLEM, Fig. 15–12:

Given the front and side views of line XY, Fig. 15–12(a), complete the representation of a plane XYZ if the plane is known to be at $60°$ with a profile plane.

ANALYSIS:

The introduced right circular cone must have its vertex on the oblique line XY and its base in a profile plane.

GRAPHIC SOLUTION:

For simplicity of construction the $60°$ cone is placed with its vertex at point X and its base in the profile plane through point Y, Fig. 15–12(b). In the right-side view a line may then be drawn from y^P tangent to the circular base of the cone. Selection of any suitable point Z on the tangent line completes the representation. There would, of course, be an alternate solution in which the tangent line is drawn on the opposite side of the base.

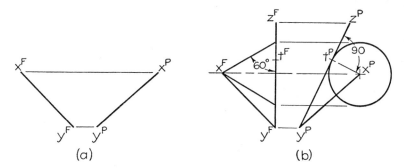

(a)   (b)

Fig. 15–12. Plane Containing Oblique Line and Forming a Specified Angle With a Profile Plane

Example 3

PROBLEM, Fig. 15–13:

Given the side view and the incomplete front view of a *guide block,* Fig. 15–13(a), and given that the dihedral angle between surfaces ABX and BCX is $65°$, complete the front view.

ANALYSIS:

Since line AB is completely given and since the position of plane BCX is established by virtue of the fact that it appears in edge view in the side view, the solution involves the following requirement: "Represent a plane containing line AB and making an angle of $65°$ with plane BCX." This rewording makes it apparent that the problem is merely another variation of the preceding Example 1.

GRAPHIC SOLUTION:

A right circular cone having a base angle of $65°$ is introduced, Fig. 15–13(b), with its vertex on line AB at point A and with its base in plane BCX. An auxiliary view showing plane BCX in true size and shape is then added. In this view the base of the cone appears as a circle, and since point B is the point at which line AB pierces the plane of the base, b^1t^1 may be drawn tangent to the circle as shown.[5] A plane making the required angle of 65° with plane BCX is then represented by ABT. Since line BT is common to planes ABT and BCX, it is the line of intersection of these planes and is therefore a segment of edge BX. A projection line from x^P thus establishes x^1 on b^1t^1 extended, Fig. 15–13(c). Transfer distance D_1 then locates x^F, and the remaining edges are drawn to complete the front view as shown.

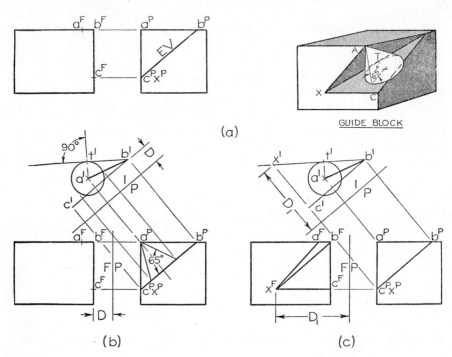

(a)

GUIDE BLOCK

(b)

(c)

Fig. 15–13. Application of Tangent Plane

[5] A question for the student: Why not draw line BT tangent on the opposite side of the base?

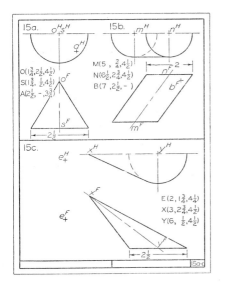

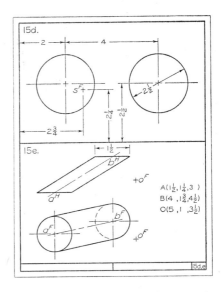

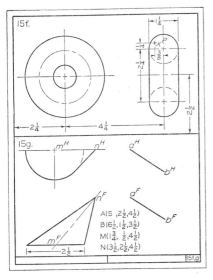

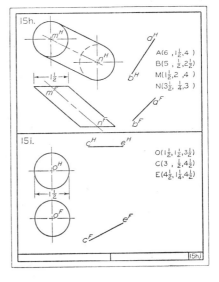

15a. Pass a plane tangent to the cone and containing point A on the surface of the cone.

15b. Pass a plane tangent to the cylinder and containing B on the surface of the cylinder.

15c. Pass a plane tangent to the cone and containing point E.

15d. Pass a plane tangent to the sphere and containing point S on its surface.

15e. Pass a plane tangent to the cylinder and containing point O.

15f. Pass a plane tangent to the torus and containing X on its surface.

15g. Pass a plane tangent to the cone and parallel to line AB.

15h. Pass a plane tangent to the cylinder and parallel to line AB.

15i. Pass a plane tangent to the sphere and containing line CE.

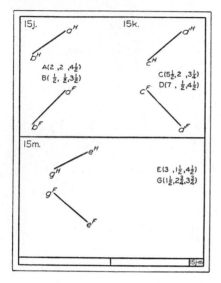

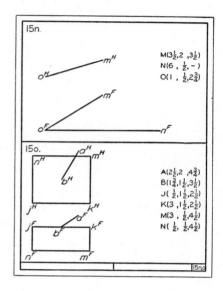

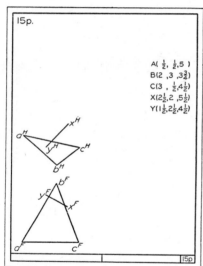

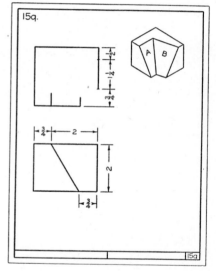

15j. Pass a plane containing line AB and making an angle of 45° with a frontal plane.

15k. Pass a plane containing line CD and having a dip of 60° NW.

15m. Pass a plane containing line EG and making an angle of 60° with a profile plane.

15n. Plane MON makes a 50° angle with a horizontal plane. Locate the top view of N.

15o. Pass a plane containing line AB and making an angle of 60° with plane $JKMN$.

15p. Pass a plane containing line XY and making an angle of 60° with plane ABC.

15q. The dihedral angle formed by planes A and B is 120°. Complete the top view.

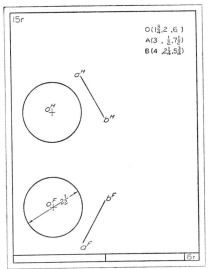

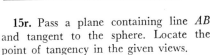

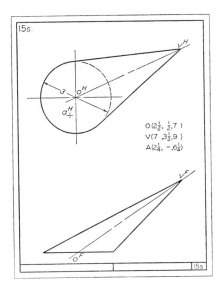

15r. Pass a plane containing line *AB* and tangent to the sphere. Locate the point of tangency in the given views.

15s. Through point *A* on the lateral surface of the oblique elliptical cone, draw a 2-in. line perpendicular to the conical surface. Suggestion: First pass a plane tangent to the cone at *A*.

15t. Indicate whether the following statements are true or false. If assigned, prepare written explanations or sketches to justify the answers.

(a) A plane tangent to the lateral surface of a cone contains the vertex of the cone.

(b) A line tangent to a circle lies in the plane of the circle.

(c) A plane tangent to a cylinder contains a single element of the cylinder.

(d) Only one plane can be passed through an outside point and tangent to a cone.

(e) A plane can be passed through an outside line and tangent to a sphere.

(f) A plane containing the vertex of a cone is tangent to the lateral surface of the cone.

(g) A plane that contains an outside line and is tangent to a cylinder contains an element of the cylinder which is parallel to the outside line.

(h) A single plane may be passed tangent to any two oblique cones.

(i) A plane tangent to a sphere can be passed through a line that intersects the sphere.

INTERSECTIONS OF PLANES WITH SOLIDS

CHAPTER 16

PROBLEMS INVOLVING THE intersections of two surfaces may in general be solved by one of two methods:

1. Lines in one surface are selected and their piercing points with the other surface are found. For practical reasons, the selected lines should be of a type convenient to handle, such as straight lines or circles.

2. Additional cutting surfaces are introduced, cutting pairs of lines from the given surfaces. The point of intersection of the two lines of one pair is a point common to the given surfaces and is therefore on their line of intersection. The additional cutting surfaces are usually planes but may be spheres for certain problems.[1]

These methods have already been applied in finding the line of intersection of two planes, the first method in Arts. 7.1 and 7.2, and the second in Art. 7.3. The methods will now be employed in finding the intersections of planes with the surfaces of solids and will appear again in Chapter 18, Intersections of Surfaces.

16.1 INTERSECTION OF PLANE AND PYRAMID

Figure 16–1 illustrates the use of the two-view method to secure the intersection of plane $ABCD$ and the pyramid $OEGJ$. An edgewise cutting plane is passed through $a^H b^H$. This cutting plane intersects the plane OGJ in the line 1,2 and intersects the plane OEG in the line 1,3. The intersections of the front views of these two lines with $a^F b^F$ produce the front views of the piercing points P_1 and P_2 of AB with surfaces OGJ and OEG. The top views of these two points are then obtained by projection to $a^H b^H$. The piercing points P_3 and P_4 of line CD with the pyramid are obtained similarly by the use of a

---

[1] See Art. 18.7.

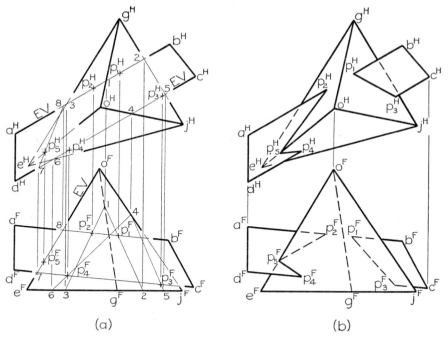

(a)   (b)

Fig. 16–1. Intersection of Plane and Pyramid

cutting plane passed through $c^H d^H$ that intersects the pyramid in the lines 4,5 and 4,6.

Plane $ABCD$ intersects plane OGJ in the line P_1P_3, Fig. 16–1(b), as both these piercing points lie on the same surface of the pyramid. Since P_2 and P_4 lie on different surfaces of the pyramid, it is evident that a single line connecting these two piercing points does not represent a line of intersection of the plane and solid. In such a situation the lines of the intersection cannot be completed until an intermediate piercing point of a line of the solid with the given plane is obtained. To secure this missing point, an edgewise cutting plane is passed through $o^F e^F$, Fig. 16–1(a). This cutting plane intersects plane $ABCD$ in the line 7,8. The intersection of line 7,8 with $o^H e^H$ in the top view locates the required point P_5. Since P_2 and P_5 are points common to the planes $ABCD$ and OEG, the line connecting these two points represents the line of intersection of these two planes, Fig. 16–1(b). Similarly the line connecting P_4 and P_5 represents the intersection of planes $ABCD$ and EOJ. The solution is completed by indicating the correct visibility of the plane and pyramid as shown. Since, in practice, combinations of intersecting forms are usually portions of a single (one piece) object, the hidden line segments of the plane which fall inside the pyramid are omitted.

16.2 INTERSECTION OF PLANE AND OBLIQUE CONE

In the problem of Fig. 16–2 the given plane is shown edgewise in the front view. Thus the front view of the intersection of the plane and oblique cone coincides with this edge view of the plane. Since this intersection must necessarily lie on the surface of the cone, its top view may be secured by projecting points on elements of the cone in the front view to the corresponding views of these elements in the top view. Piercing points P_4 and P_{10} on elements 4 and 10 illustrate this procedure. A sufficient number of points to assure an accurate line of intersection should be obtained. This does not always mean that equally spaced elements must be used nor that equally spaced points on the intersection are necessarily desirable. Rather one should plan to secure points more closely spaced on the line of intersection where the rate of change of curvature is greatest. Tangent points P_3 and P_8 are other points that are needed to produce an accurate intersection, which in this case is an ellipse.

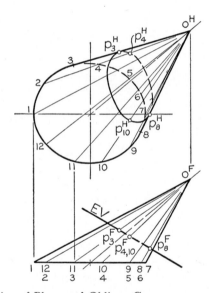

Fig. 16–2. Intersection of Plane and Oblique Cone

If the base of the cone in Fig. 16–2 had been circular rather than elliptical, this intersection could also have been found by the method of Art. 16.3.

If the intersecting plane as given does not appear in edge view, an auxiliary view is added, showing this plane in edge view. Then the solution is obtained as before. In this situation both the given views show the intersection as ellipses, although it is possible under particular circumstances for the intersection to appear circular. The construction would be similar to that of Fig. 16–5.

16.3 INTERSECTION OF PLANE AND RIGHT-CIRCULAR CONE

In Fig. 16–3 the intersection of the plane and right-circular cone could be obtained as in the preceding example by using elements of the cone. However, in the case of a right cone some of the elements would appear too nearly vertical to assure accurate direct projection of points on these elements from one view to the other.

To avoid the inaccuracy that might occur by the use of elements of the cone, horizontal cutting planes are used in this illustration to produce concentric circles in the top view. Points such as P_1 and P_4 are then obtained on the line of intersection by projecting from the front view to the corresponding circle in the top view. The resulting curve in the top view is a portion of an ellipse, one of the *conic sections* that will be discussed in more detail in Chapter 21.

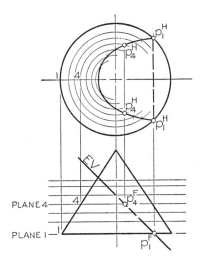

Fig. 16–3.   Intersection of Plane and Right Circular Cone

16.4 INTERSECTION OF PLANE AND PRISM

Figure 16–4(a) shows the addition of an auxiliary view which includes an edge view of the given plane *MON*. In this view the piercing points 1, 2, and 3 of the edges of the prism with the plane *MON* are obtained. Figure 16–4(b) shows the projection of these points to the side and front views.

The correct indication of the visibility of the lines connecting these points completes the solution. This problem might also be solved using only the given views, by the two-view piercing-point method of Chapter 6. The auxiliary-view method shown, however, affords a direct check of accuracy by means of transfer distances such as D_1 in Fig. 16–4(b).

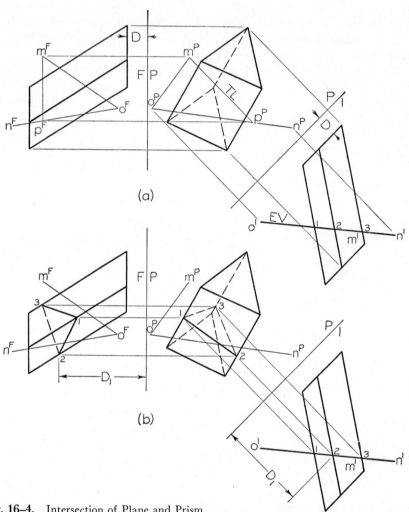

Fig. 16–4.   Intersection of Plane and Prism

16.5 INTERSECTION OF PLANE AND CYLINDER

The more convenient solution of this problem is obtained by the auxiliary-view method, as in the preceding example. An auxiliary view projected from the top view, Fig. 16–5, is convenient because the bases of the cylinder in this case are horizontal and appear in edge view in any auxiliary elevation. Since there are no "edges" of the cylinder as there were on the prism, it is necessary to add corresponding elements in each view of the cylinder. Piercing points of these elements with plane MON appear in the auxiliary view which shows the plane in edge view. These points, of which P_1 and P_4 are examples, are then projected back to the given views. The transfer distance D may be used as a check on the accuracy of the location of $p_1{}^F$ and $p_4{}^F$. Drawing the resulting ellipses in correct visibility in the given top and front views completes the problem.

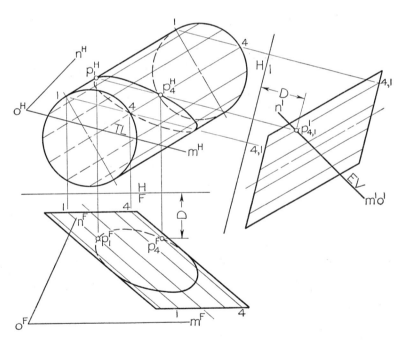

Fig. 16–5. Intersection of Plane and Cylinder

16.6   INTERSECTION OF PLANE AND TORUS

Figure 16–6 shows the use of horizontal cutting planes to obtain the intersection of the plane ABC and the half-torus. These planes cut straight lines in the plane ABC and form semicircles on the surface of the torus. The construction for plane 3 is labeled in detail to illustrate the method. Plane 3 cuts line 3 in plane ABC and circles 3 on the torus. The intersections of line 3 and the corresponding circles in the top view produce points p_3^H on the required line of intersection. The front views of these points are obtained by projection back to cutting plane 3. After an adequate number of points is secured by repetition of this procedure, the line of intersection is completed as shown.

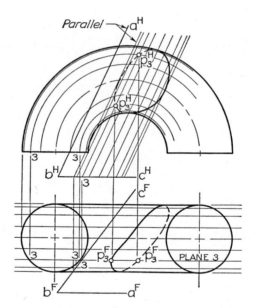

Fig. 16–6.   Intersection of Plane and Torus

16.7   REPRESENTATION OF FAIR SURFACES

Double-curved surfaces such as a ship hull, an airplane fuselage, or the various portions of an automobile body, which do not fall under standard geometrical classifications such as sphere, torus, and ellipsoid, are called *fair* surfaces. They are represented on a drawing by curves of intersection of various planes with the surfaces. For instance the surface of the hull of a boat is described as illustrated in Fig. 16–7. The *frame lines* are the intersections with the hull of vertical planes perpendicular to the longitudinal axis of the boat. The *buttock lines* are the intersections of vertical planes parallel to the boat's axis. The *water lines* are the intersections of horizontal planes with the hull. These various lines serve as elements of the curved surfaces in intersection problems such as those following, Art. 16.8.

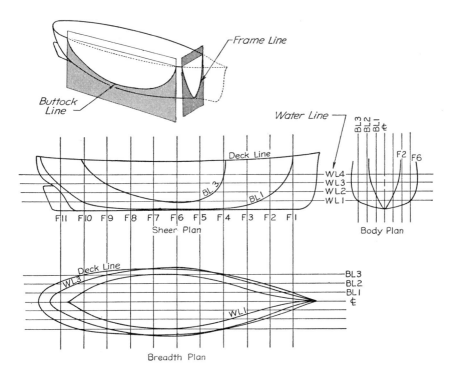

Fig. 16–7.   Fair Surface—Lines of a Boat

16.8   INTERSECTION OF WINDSHIELD AND AIRPLANE FUSELAGE

In Fig. 16–8 it is required to find the line of intersection of the plane of the windshield with the fuselage, having given the buttock lines and the straight sides of the windshield. Since the buttock lines appear as straight lines in the plan view, vertical cutting planes containing the buttock lines appear in edge view coinciding with the buttock lines in the plan view. The parallel lines of intersection of these planes with the plane of the windshield are then located by projecting points 1, 2, 3, and 4 to the side view [2] as shown, and their intersections in turn with buttock lines 10, 20, 30, and 40 are points on the required curve. The plan views of the points on the curve are then located by projection and the curves are drawn as shown.

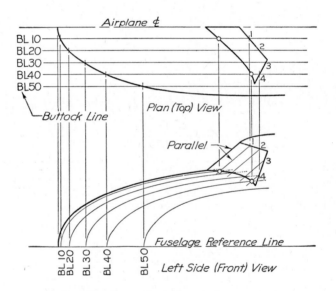

Fig. 16–8.   Intersection of Windshield and Fuselage of Airplane

---

[2] The term *side view* as applied in the aeronautical industry refers to the view showing the left side of the airplane, which conventionally is used as the principal view.

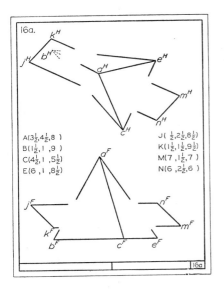

16a.

A(3½,4½,8)
B(1½,1 ,9)
C(4½,1 ,5½)
E(6 ,1 ,8½)

J(½,2½,8½)
K(1½,1½,9½)
M(7 ,1½,7)
N(6 ,2½,6)

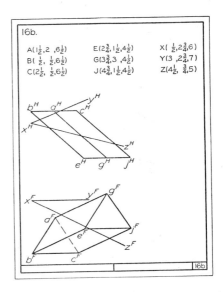

16b.

A(1½,2 ,6½)   E(2¾,1½,4½)   X(½,2¾,6)
B(½, ½,6½)   G(3¾,3 ,4½)   Y(3 ,2¾,7)
C(2½, ½,6½)   J(4¾,1½,4½)   Z(4½, ¾,5)

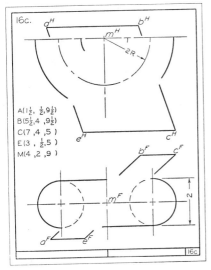

16c.

A(1½, ½,9½)
B(5½,4 ,9½)
C(7 ,4 ,5)
E(3 , ½,5)
M(4 ,2 ,9)

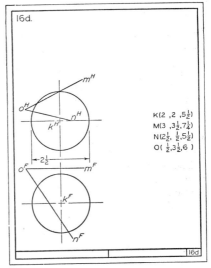

16d.

K(2 ,2 ,5½)
M(3 ,3½,7¼)
N(2½, ½,5½)
O(½,3½,6)

16a. Find the intersection of the plane *JKMN* and the pyramid. Show complete visibility.

16b. Using the auxiliary-view method, find the section cut from the prism by the unlimited plane *XYZ*.

16c. Find the intersection of the plane *ABCE* and the torus. Show complete visibility.

16d. Show the views and the true size of the section cut from the sphere by the unlimited plane *MON*.

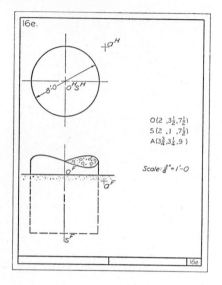

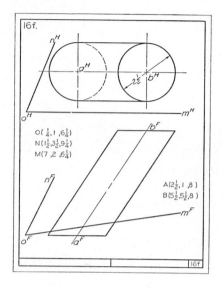

16e. A cylindrical support column is anchored into a rock ledge, the upper surface of which is a plane that passes through point A and has a strike of N 60° W and a dip of 30° SW. Determine the volume in cubic yards of rock removed, and plot in the front view the intersection of the column and the ledge surface.

16f. Using only the given views, obtain the intersection of the unlimited transparent plane NOM and the cylinder.

16g. Indicate whether the following statements are true or false. If assigned, prepare written explanations or sketches to justify the answers.

(a) The intersection of an unlimited plane and a solid consists of a continuous closed path.

(b) A plane can cut the lateral surface of a cylinder in two straight lines.

(c) A plane intersecting a sphere always produces a circle.

(d) A plane intersecting a triangular prism produces lines of intersection which always take the form of a triangle.

(e) On a curved line of intersection it is desirable to obtain points more closely spaced where the radius of curvature is greatest.

(f) A plane can cut a conical solid such that the lines of intersection form a triangle.

| CHAPTER 17 | # DEVELOPMENTS |

THE DEVELOPMENT OF a surface is the unfolding or unrolling of the surface of a form into a plane as in Fig. 17–1. The resulting plane figure gives the true size of each area of the form, so connected that when it is folded or *fabricated* the desired form is obtained. Containers and other products made of flat stock or sheet materials are first laid out on the flat sheets before the folding or bending operations bring them into the desired form. In case of quantity production, this process is used for the original layout necessary for setting up the blanking, stamping, or pressing operations. A commercial product largely fabricated from sheet-metal layouts is shown in Fig. 17–2.

In the aircraft industry and in light-gage metal work such as is used in heating and ventilating, it is common practice to make the layout so that the fold lines are on the outside of the form when completed. In heavy-gage and plate shops, it is the practice to make the layout such that it will be on the inside when the form is completed.[1] For sake of uniformity, in this text all developments are inside up.

The edges that must be joined are usually connected by seaming, riveting, welding, or soldering, and the allowance made for joining depends on the

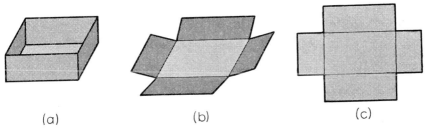

(a) (b) (c)

Fig. 17–1. A Simple Development

---

[1] Actually the dividing line between "inside up" and "outside up" developments is not critically dependent upon the material. It is determined largely by the nature of the shop equipment used to fabricate the product. In cases of doubt, therefore, a development should be clearly labeled "inside" or "outside" as the case may be.

201

Fig. 17–2. Cyclone DusKolector (Courtesy Hammond Machinery Builders, Inc., Kalamazoo, Mich.)

type of joint used. Usually the length of joint is kept to a minimum for reasons of economy and ease of handling.

On sheet metal heavier than 24 gage (0.0250 in.) a *bend allowance* must be taken into account according to the practice of the particular trade because of the fact that the thicker sheets cannot be readily formed into absolutely sharp corners. However, for purposes of simplicity, this aspect is omitted from the developments in this text.

In general, the procedure in development is to select lines on a given surface which are easy to handle and then to find the true, or approximate, surface relationships of these lines. Reproduction of the relationships on a plane surface produces the development. For a pyramid or a cone the convenient lines are usually those passing through the vertex. For a prism or a cylinder the lines parallel to the axis are convenient.

Three general groups of developments, classified according to the type of surface involved or the method employed to construct the development, are as follows: (1) radial-line developments, the method used for pyramids and cones; (2) parallel-line developments, used for prisms and cylinders; (3) triangulation, used to break a given surface into a series of triangular

areas, resulting in an exact development for a plane surface and an approximate development for other surfaces.

Warped surfaces and double-curved surfaces are theoretically not developable, but they may be approximated by division into units which are
developable by one of these three methods.

17.1 RADIAL-LINE DEVELOPMENTS

The lateral surfaces of a pyramid are triangular areas, and the development consists of these triangles so arranged as to give the desired form when
folded. The surface of a cone may be divided into narrow segments ap-
proaching the triangular form, and these "triangles" in proper sequence
approximate the desired form when rolled to form the cone.

The true size of any triangle can be found by determining the true lengths
of the three sides and assembling these true lengths to form the triangle.
See Art. 24.4.

17.2 RADIAL-LINE DEVELOPMENT—PYRAMID

To develop the surface of the pyramid given in Fig. 17–3(a), it is necessary to find the true lengths of each of the edges bounding the four triangular surfaces. In this instance edges OE and OA are revolved into a

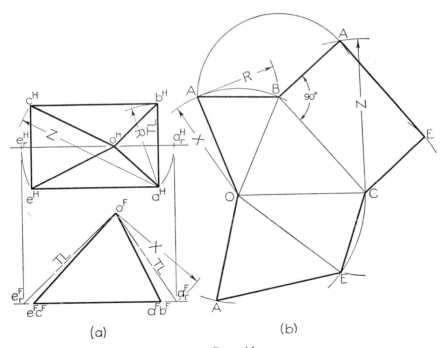

(a)   (b)

Fig. 17–3. Radial Line Development—Pyramid

frontal plane, and their true lengths appear in the front view as $o^F e_r^F$ and $o^F a_r^F$, respectively. Since this pyramid is symmetrical about a frontal plane through the vertex O, the true lengths of OC and OB are identical to OE and OA, respectively. The base plane, being horizontal, shows in true size in the given top view, and consequently its four sides AE, EC, CB, and BA are shown true length in the top view. With the true lengths of all the edges known, the development now becomes a matter of assembly, Fig. 17–3(b).

Notice that the development starts with AO, which is one of the shorter edges. (OB could have been selected for a starting edge.) Point O is arbitrarily set and an arc with radius X equal to the true length of OA and OB is drawn. The true length of AB is then added by radius R. This now completes the surface OAB with the inside up. Surfaces OBC, OCE, and OEA are added in turn in similar manner. The base plane $ABCE$ is added to the development at a longer base edge such as BC. In this case it is easy to construct the rectangular base by utilizing its 90° angles. As a check, or where the base angles are other than 90°, a diagonal such as Z may be used to construct the base as two triangles in a fashion similar to Fig. 17–12.

17.3   RADIAL-LINE DEVELOPMENT—TRUNCATED PYRAMID

The development of a truncated pyramid with vertex accessible as given in Fig. 17–4(a) is best constructed by first developing the whole pyramid and then eliminating the portion containing the vertex.

The true lengths of the lateral edges of the pyramid are found by revolution and are shown in the front view as $o^F c_r^F$ and $o^F e_r^F$. Since the pyramid is symmetrical about a frontal plane through the vertex O, the true lengths of OB and OA are identical to those of OC and OE respectively. Since CE and BA of the base are frontal lines, their true length is obtained from their front view. The base edges CB and EA are horizontal lines and consequently are true length in the top view. The true lengths of all these edges now enable the engineer to construct the layout of the pyramid as shown in Fig. 17–4(b).

The use of the true length of OB and OC (radius X) together with the true length of BC (radius Y) makes possible the construction of the panel OBC in true size and with the inside up in the layout. In similar fashion panels OCE, OEA, and OAB are added in turn. Next, points j_r^F and k_r^F are located as shown on the true-length views of edges OB and OC. These points are then transferred to the lateral edges in the layout as indicated by the radius Z. Similarly points M and G are established, and the layout for the truncated pyramid is completed as shown.

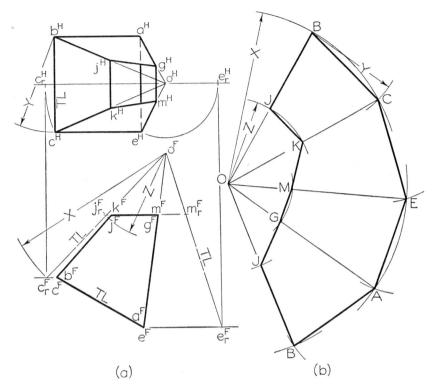

Fig. 17–4.   Radial-Line Development—Truncated Pyramid

17.4   RADIAL-LINE DEVELOPMENT—RIGHT-CIRCULAR CONE

To develop the surface of a truncated right-circular cone as given in Fig. 17–5(a), the conical surface may be broken into a series of small segments approximating triangles. These surfaces are then laid out in true size and assembled in proper sequence to approximate the surface of the original cone, Fig. 17–5(b). It should be observed that arc $O–1$ on the cone is not exactly equal in length to arc $O–1$ on the development. This discrepancy will accumulate with the use of each succeeding segment so that the resulting developed cone will be somewhat smaller than the original. If greater accuracy is necessary, the dimensions of the development may be calculated as follows: The right-circular cone development is a sector of a circle with a radius of the *slant-height S,* since all the elements are of the same length. The distance around the sector, $2\pi S\theta/360°$, must be the same as the circumference of the base of the cone, $2\pi R$. When these two terms are equated and simplified,

$$\theta = \frac{R}{S}\,(360°)$$

Since in this case only a half-cone is shown, the angle used is one-half that required for a full development.

To complete the layout of the truncated cone, the intersection points of the elements and the upper base are projected horizontally to the true-length extreme elements. The true distance of each intersection point from the vertex is now available and is transferred to the appropriate element in the layout. If the angle method is used to develop the cone, the intermediate elements are located by dividing the sector into the same number of equal parts as the base of the cone. A smooth curve is next faired through the points, and the resulting layout is a *half-development* of the cone divided along $V6$, the line of symmetry. Half-developments are used frequently in practice to save time. Obviously a half-development may be used only when the development is symmetrical, and moreover, the division *must* be made along an axis of symmetry. In such cases, the caption "half-development" should be added as shown in Fig. 17–5(b).

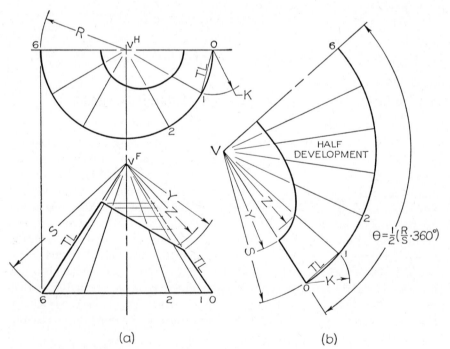

$$\theta = \tfrac{1}{2}\!\left(\tfrac{R}{S}\cdot 360°\right)$$

(a)   (b)

Fig. 17–5. Radial-Line Development—Right Circular Cone

17.5   RADIAL-LINE DEVELOPMENT—OBLIQUE CONE

To develop the surface of the truncated cone given in Fig. 17–6, the cone is first divided along a line of symmetry and equally spaced elements are established. These elements are then revolved into a frontal plane to establish their true lengths. The distance between them at the base, radius Z in the top view, is used for the development as shown, much as if the cone were a multisided pyramid. Since chordal distances are employed rather than arc lengths, the development is somewhat inaccurate. The error is, however, usually minor and can be compensated for in practice in the seam allowance together with slight deformation of the material to secure a satisfactory fit.

The points of intersection of the elements and the upper base are projected to positions on their respective true-length elements in the TL dia-

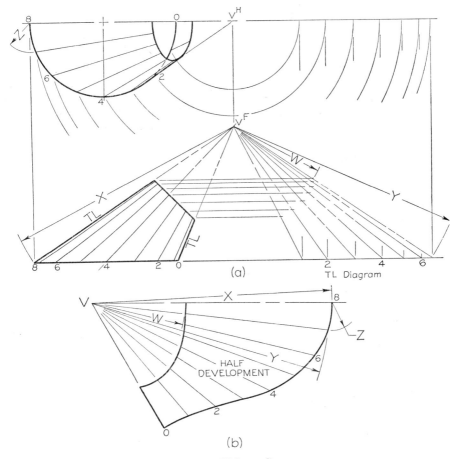

Fig. 17–6. Radial-Line Development—Oblique Cone

gram. These points are in turn located in the layout, the resulting fair curve through the points completing the half-development.

17.6 PARALLEL-LINE DEVELOPMENTS

The forms involving parallel lateral edges or elements are the prism and cylinder. In contrast to the radiating lateral edges or elements in the developments of the pyramid or cone, the lateral edges or elements of the prism or cylinder are parallel in the developments of these surfaces.

17.7 PARALLEL-LINE DEVELOPMENT—TRUNCATED RIGHT PRISM

To develop the surface of a prism, three conditions must be known:

1. The true lengths of the lateral edges.
2. The relative positions of the parallel lateral edges with respect to a *right section* (a plane figure formed by the intersection of a cutting plane perpendicular to the axis of a form).
3. The perimeter of the right section of the prism or perpendicular distances between the lateral edges.

The two given views of the prism of Fig. 17–7 conveniently give the true lengths of the lateral edges and the perimeter or distances between the edges.

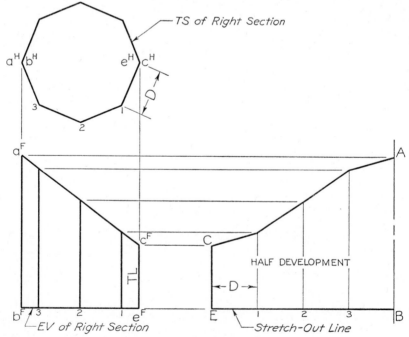

Fig. 17–7.   Parallel-Line Development—Right Prism

Since a development must show lateral surfaces in true size, angles as well as distances are retained in the development. In the given example the lower base plane is perpendicular to the lateral edges, and hence its perimeter unrolls into a straight line perpendicular to the parallel lateral edges in the development. This line is called the *stretch-out line*. The half-development shown is thus constructed by transfer of distances D between the lateral edges and by transfer of the true lengths of the lateral edges. Note that the development is started on a line of symmetry and that for economy the seam is established at the shortest lateral edge CE.

17.8 PARALLEL-LINE DEVELOPMENT—OBLIQUE PRISM

In engineering practice the information necessary for the development of a surface is not always so conveniently given as in the preceding case. In order to find the true length of the lateral edges of the prism in Fig. 17–8,

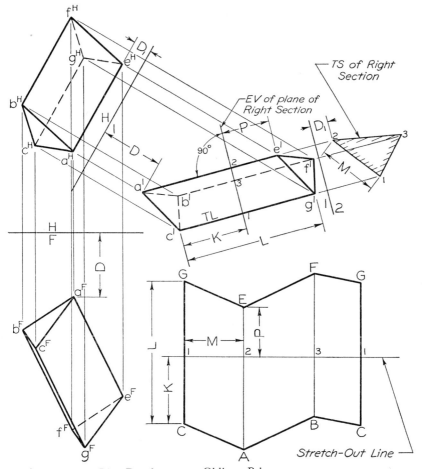

Fig. 17–8. Parallel-Line Development—Oblique Prism

the auxiliary elevation 1 is drawn. In this view the edge view of a right section such as 1–2–3 is added at any convenient location. Section 1–2–3, being perpendicular to the lateral edges, must unroll into a straight line (the stretch-out line). Auxiliary view 2 is now constructed to secure the true size of section 1–2–3, which gives the perimeter of the prism or the length of the stretch-out line.

Since in this example all lateral edges of the prism are the same length, the development may be started at any desired edge such as CG. The stretch-out line is drawn at any convenient location, and CG is drawn perpendicular to it at one end. The length of CG is established in the development by transfer dimensions K and L.

The true distance between edges CG and AE, distance 1–2, is transferred from view 2 to the stretch-out line as indicated by dimension M, AE being selected as the second lateral edge in order to produce an inside-up development. The remaining dimensions of the right section are transferred in similar manner and in the proper order. The lengths of the lateral edges are then transferred to complete the development.

17.9   PARALLEL-LINE DEVELOPMENT—RIGHT-CIRCULAR CYLINDER

If the curved surface of a cylinder is divided into segments by the addition of an appropriate number of elements, usually equally spaced for convenience, the surface may be developed in a manner similar to that used for a prism.

In Fig. 17–9 the length of the development may be approximated by lay-

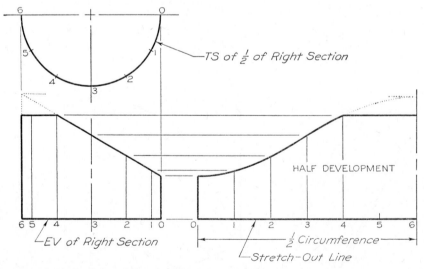

Fig. 17–9. Parallel-Line Development—Right-Circular Cylinder

ing out the chordal distances 0–1, 1–2, 2–3, etc., along the stretch-out line. For a more accurate development this length is made equal to the calculated semicircumference of the base circle as indicated. This distance is then subdivided into the same number of parts as those selected for the given views, and the elements are drawn perpendicular to the stretch-out line at these division points. The true length of each element is transferred from the front view. A smooth curve is faired through the end points of elements 0, 1, 2, 3, 4 as shown. The remaining outlines of the developed cylindrical surface are added to complete the half-development.

17.10 PARALLEL-LINE DEVELOPMENT—OBLIQUE CYLINDER

To construct the development of an oblique cylinder such as that given in Fig. 17–10, an auxiliary view showing the axis of the cylinder in true length is drawn, and subsequently a secondary auxiliary view showing the true size of a right section of the cylinder is constructed. In this view the circum-

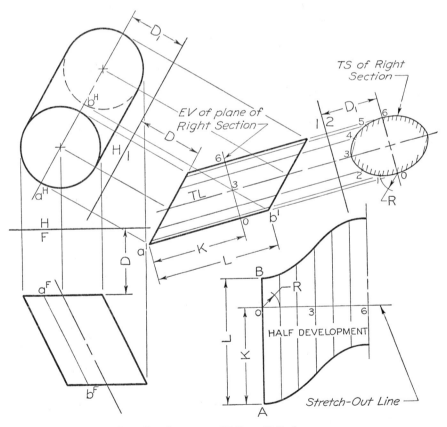

Fig. 17–10. Parallel-Line Development—Oblique Cylinder

ference is divided into segments by points at equal chordal distances,[2] thus establishing the elements of the cylinder which are used in the development. The elements are then projected to the first auxiliary view. The development of the cylinder is now constructed by transferring the lengths of the elements to the layout as shown and by spacing the elements along the stretch-out line as indicated by the radius R. A smooth curve is faired through the end points of the elements to complete the half-development.

17.11   SPECIAL APPLICATION OF CYLINDER DEVELOPMENT

Figure 17–11 exemplifies a practical application in which it is necessary to construct a development before the given views can be completed. The views as first given show the cylindrical screw-conveyor tube, the conical hopper, and their line of intersection MKN. For details of construction of the intersection see Art. 18.7. The problem is to add a reinforcing collar 6 in. wide about the intersection.

The first step is to construct the pattern (development) for the opening in the cylinder. Since the elements of the cylinder appear in true length in the front view, the pattern may be most simply constructed by transferring these lengths vertically downward to the available space below. The true right section of the cylinder appears in the profile view, from which the distances between the elements, such as D and D_1, are transferred to the layout as shown. A smooth curve faired through the points on elements 1, 2 $\cdots$ 6 completes the development of the opening in the cylinder.

Since the opening corresponds to the inner edge of the required 6-in. reinforcing collar (neglecting thickness), the collar is now added to the layout by drawing a series of arcs of 6-in. radius centered at successive points on the layout of the opening and by fairing the curve of the outer edge tangent to these arcs.

The points of intersection of the elements 1, 2 $\cdots$ 6 with the outer curve are now transferred to these elements in the front view. Additional elements 7 $\cdots$ 10 are introduced in the development to establish additional points, and these are located first in the profile view and then in the front view. The curve representing the outer edge of the collar is now drawn in the front view to complete the solution.

---

[2] Any desired method may be used to construct the ellipse (Appendix II), but for convenience in development, the elements should be equally spaced. The formula for the circumference of an ellipse, while it would theoretically give a more accurate length for the development, is rather unwieldy and is therefore rarely used in practice. The circumference may be approximated by the expression $2\pi \sqrt{\dfrac{a^2 + b^2}{2}}$, where a is one-half the major axis and b is one-half the minor axis of the ellipse.

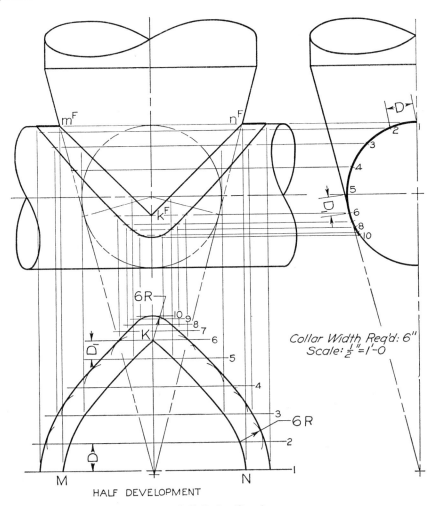

Fig. 17–11. Special Application of Cylinder Development

17.12   TRIANGULATION

It is often necessary to construct patterns for surfaces that cannot be developed by the radial-line or parallel-line methods. Many such surfaces may be developed or approximately developed by *triangulation*.

Example 1:   Object Composed of Plane Surfaces

The hopper shown in Fig. 17–12 (which is *not* pyramidal) is developed by breaking each of the four plane surfaces into two triangular surfaces. In this case the true lengths of the sides of the triangles are found by a method frequently used in the sheet-metal industry. The construction is drawn to one side to avoid confusion. To exemplify the method, line $e^H m^H$ in the top view is assumed to be the edge view of a vertical plane. Edge EM of the hopper is then the hypotenuse of a right triangle lying in this vertical plane. The base of the triangle is equal in length to the top view $e^H m^H$, distance W. The altitude of the triangle is the vertical distance from E to M, distance H, measured in the front view. These two lengths, W and H, are transferred to the True-Length Diagram as shown, and the true length of line EM is thus established.[3] As a further aid to clarity, the solid and dashed true lengths are drawn on opposite sides of the diagram.

These lengths are then combined successively, starting with the shortest edge AG, to form the development as shown.

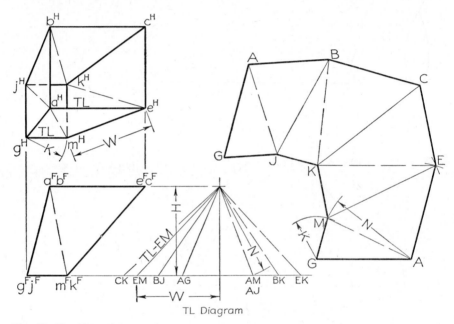

Fig. 17–12.   Triangulation—Development of a Hopper

Example 2:   A Transition Piece

A piece that connects two differently shaped and/or sized conductors is known as a *transition piece*. This type of connector is used quite frequently in the heating and ventilating fields as well as in other industries.

As can be seen in Fig. 17–13 the given transition piece could be employed to connect a vertical cylindrical conductor to an inclined rectangular duct. Further examination of the transition piece reveals that it is composed of four plane triangular surfaces, as $C3E$, and four portions of oblique cones, such as $O3C$.

---

[3] Actually, a comparison with Art. 13.3 shows this to be equivalent to finding the true length by revolution.

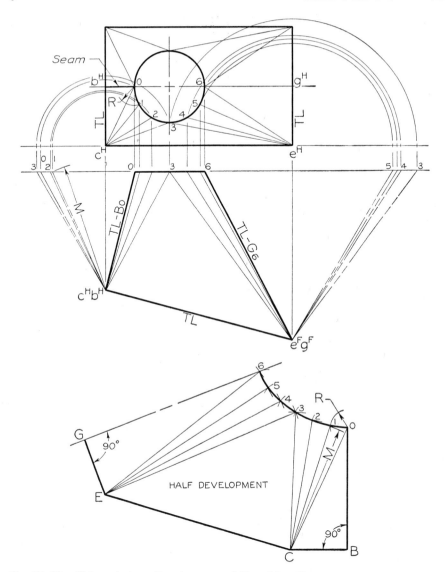

Fig. 17–13. Triangulation—Development of Transition Piece

To produce the development, the true lengths of the sides of the plane surfaces are required plus the true lengths of the sides of the small approximate triangles created by breaking down the conical surfaces into several plane surfaces.

These true lengths are then assembled in proper relationship to reconstruct each triangular area, with the areas arranged in sequence to give the symmetrical development as shown. The seam is placed at the center of one of the flat surfaces for convenience in fabrication.

17.13   WARPED AND DOUBLE-CURVED SURFACES [4]— APPROXIMATE DEVELOPMENT

Occasionally surfaces that are theoretically nondevelopable occur in engineering practice. In such a case the surface is approximated with a series of small developable surfaces.

Example 1:   Warped Transition Piece

In Fig. 17–14 the surface of the transition piece is broken into a series of small triangles that approximate the original form. Note that the same number of equally spaced divisions is used on both the upper and lower openings. To avoid later confusion, the sides of the triangles are drawn alternately solid and dashed. The true lengths of the lines that make up each triangle are found in the manner discussed in Example 1 of Art. 17.12 and are assembled to give the true size of each triangle in turn.

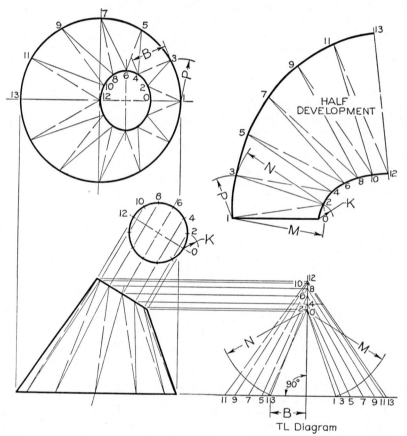

Fig. 17–14.   Approximate Development—Warped Transition Piece

[4] See Appendix III.3.

Example 2:   Sphere—Gore Method

Double-curved surfaces may be approximated by the use of small portions of cylinders or cones. The spherical surface in Fig. 17–15(a) may be cut into a series of small *gores* by a number of cutting planes passed through the same diameter. Each gore is then approximated as a portion of a cylinder. The length of the gore around the half-cylinder is equal to the distance πR. This length is divided into segments corresponding to elements such as AB on the cylindrical surface. The length of AB is transferred to its respective elements 4 and 8 in the development. The remaining points are similarly determined, with the resulting gore being one of twelve needed to approximate the development of the spherical surface. This method is also called the *polycylindric* method.

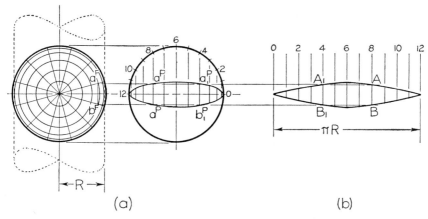

Fig. 17–15.   Approximate Development of a Sphere—Gore Method

Example 3:   Sphere—Zone Method

The surface of a sphere may also be approximately developed by the division of the surface into a series of zones which may be approximated by cone frusta—the zone or *polyconic* method. Each zone, Fig. 17–16, is a frustum of a right-circular cone. If the cones are circumscribed about the sphere, the resulting development will be slightly oversized. If the cones are inscribed in the sphere, the development will be slightly undersized. In practice either of these approximations is usually satisfactory.

If, however, it is necessary to secure a closer approximation of the surface of the sphere, the cones are so constructed that part of the sphere is outside and part is inside. This may be accomplished by dividing each arc, such as EC in Fig. 17–16, into four parts and passing the extreme element of the cone through points 1 and 3, with R_2 as the slant height of the complete cone of which the zone from E to C is considered a portion.

The remaining zones are treated similarly, resulting in the distances R, R_1, R_2, and R_3 for laying out the required cones. The size of the segment of the circle required for each frustum is determined by transferring the circumference of the base of each cone by chordal distances or by calculation as in Art. 17.4. The widths of the conical surfaces needed for each frustum are obtained as indicated in the enlarged detail.

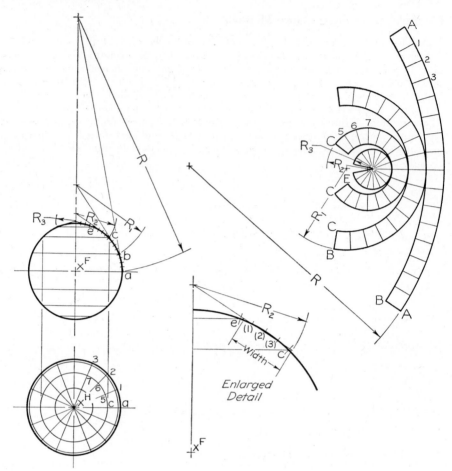

Fig. 17–16. Approximate Development of Sphere—Zone Method

Example 4: Right Helicoid

A right helicoid is a helicoid [5] in which the elements are perpendicular to the axis. In practice, as exemplified by the screw conveyor of Fig. 17–17, the elements usually intersect the axis when extended and are all of the same length. For simplicity the views in Fig. 17–17(a) show only one complete turn or *flight* of the helicoid.

As is true of all warped surfaces, the helicoid is theoretically not developable. Its surface may, however, be closely approximated by division into small segments as indicated in Fig. 17–17(a). Since in this example the elements e of the helicoid are all of the same length, the approximate development, Fig. 17–17(c), is a sector of a circle with a circular central portion omitted to allow for the solid core of the conveyor.

The inner circular arc should have the same length (h) as the inner helix (on the cylindrical core) of the helicoid. This length is expressed by

$$h = \sqrt{(\pi d)^2 + (\text{lead})^2}$$

---

[5] See Appendix III.3.

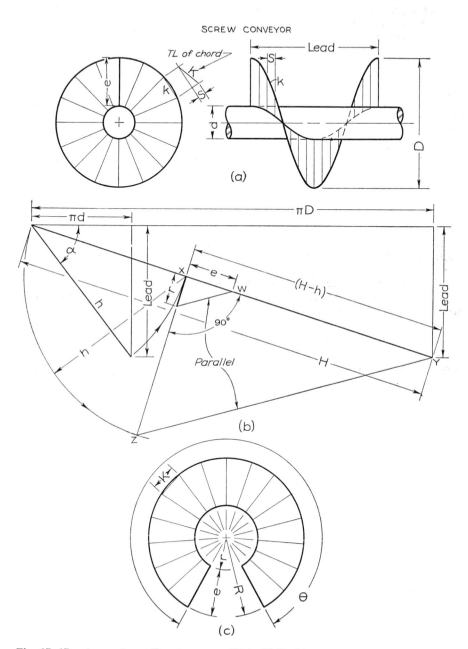

Fig. 17–17. Approximate Development—Right Helicoid

which may be calculated or obtained mathematically and graphically as shown at the left of Fig. 17–17(b). In similar fashion the length of the outer helix, distance H, may be calculated or obtained graphically as shown.

In the approximate development the inner and outer circular arcs extend through the same total angle θ. This condition makes it possible to derive mathematically a formula for radius r of the development, the result being

$$r = \frac{h}{H - h} \ (e)$$

where e is the element length obtained from the circular view of Fig. 17–17(a). Again the formula may be evaluated by calculation, or it may be solved graphically as follows, Fig. 17–17(b):

Distance h is set off from one end of H to establish graphically the quantity $(H - h)$. Distance h is then established at right angles to $(H - h)$ and triangle XYZ is completed. Distance e is set off from point X along side XY to locate point W, and a line is drawn from W parallel to hypotenuse YZ. The remaining leg of this smaller triangle is then equal to radius r, since by similar triangles,

$$\frac{r}{e} = \frac{h}{H - h} \quad \text{or} \quad r = \frac{h}{H - h} \ (e)$$

Using this radius and the radius $R = r + e$, the approximate development is now constructed. The distance around the circumference of the outer circle may be closely approximated by finding the true length K of a chord of one section, as shown in Fig. 17–17(a), and by setting off this chord successively around the outer circle of the development. The distance around the circle may also be established by calculating the angle θ from one of the following:

$$\theta = \frac{h}{2\pi r} \ (360°) \quad \text{or} \quad \theta = \frac{d}{2r \cos \alpha} \ (360°)$$

where α is the helix angle of the inner helix, Fig. 17–17(b).

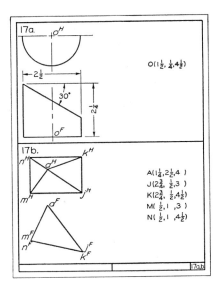

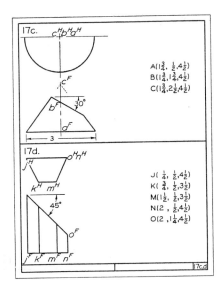

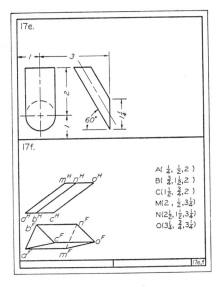

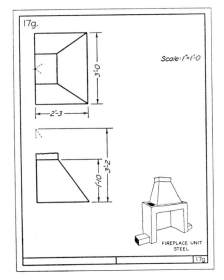

17a. Lay out one-half the development of the cylinder.

17b. Lay out the development of the five surfaces of the pyramid.

17c. Lay out one-half the development of the right cone.

17d. Lay out the development of the right prism.

17e. Lay out the development of the elliptical duct.

17f. Lay out the development of the prism.

17g. Develop the given pyramidal portion of the steel fireplace unit.

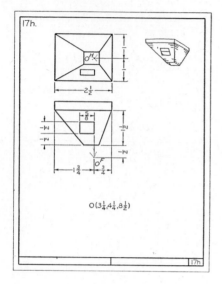

17h.

O^H

$2\frac{1}{2}$

$\frac{5}{8}$

$-\frac{1}{2}$

$-\frac{1}{2}$

$-\frac{1}{2}$

$-\frac{1}{2}$

O^F

$1\frac{3}{4}$ $\frac{3}{4}$

$O(3\frac{1}{4},4\frac{1}{4},8\frac{1}{2})$

17h

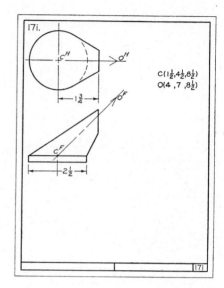

17i.

$+C^H$ O^H

$1\frac{3}{4}$

O^F

C^F

$2\frac{1}{2}$

$C(1\frac{1}{2},4\frac{1}{2},8\frac{1}{2})$
$O(4,7,8\frac{1}{2})$

17i

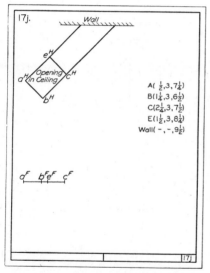

17j.

Wall

e^H

d^H Opening c^H
    in Ceiling

b^H

$A(\frac{1}{2},3,7\frac{1}{4})$
$B(1\frac{1}{4},3,6\frac{1}{2})$
$C(2\frac{1}{4},3,7\frac{1}{2})$
$E(1\frac{1}{2},3,8\frac{1}{4})$
Wall$(-,-,9\frac{1}{2})$

a^F $b^F e^F$ c^F

17j

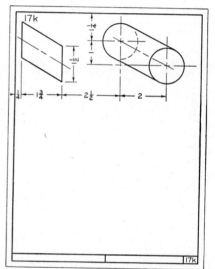

17k

$-\frac{1}{4}$

$-\frac{1}{2}$

$\frac{1}{4}$ $1\frac{3}{4}$ $2\frac{1}{2}$ 2

17k

17h. Develop the pyramidal portion of the sheet-metal hopper.

17i. Lay out one-half the development of the oblique conical elbow section.

17j. The sheet-metal package chute makes an angle of 30° with horizontal. Show the true size of a right section and complete the front view. Lay out the development.

17k. Show the true cross section of the cylindrical duct. Lay out the development.

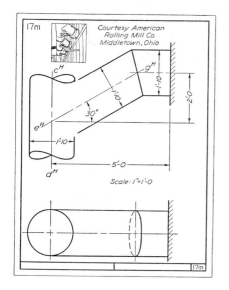

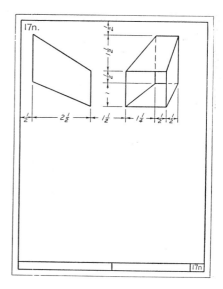

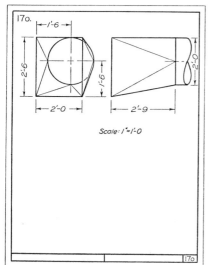

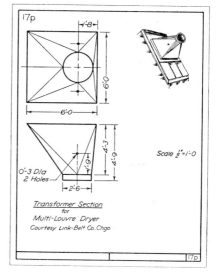

17m. Show the intersection of the circular ducts *CD* and *EG* (see Art. 18.7). Lay out one-half of the development of the duct *EG*.

17n. Lay out the development of the transition piece.

17o. Lay out the development of the transition piece.

17p. Develop the front half of the *transformer section*. Show the 3-in. hole on the development.

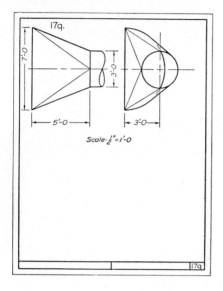

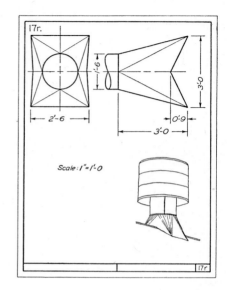

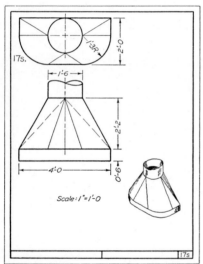

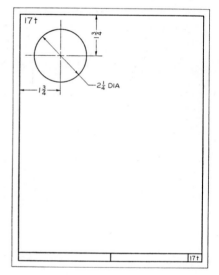

17q. Lay out one-half the development for the *dryer transition unit.*

17r. Lay out one-half the development of the *ventilator transition unit.*

17s. Lay out one-half of the development of the chemistry laboratory *hood.*

17t. Develop one-half the given sphere by the gore or zone method as assigned.

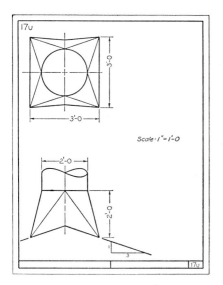

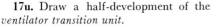

Scale: 1" = 1'-0

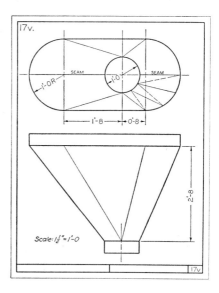

17u. Draw a half-development of the *ventilator transition unit*.

17v. On a separate sheet prepare a half-development of the transition piece which was designed for the processing of pharmaceutical products.

17w. Indicate whether the following statements are true or false. If assigned, prepare written explanations or sketches to justify the answers.

(a) The development of the lateral surface of a right cylinder is a rectangle.

(b) The development of a right cone is a triangle.

(c) Triangulation is the recommended method used in the development of a prism.

(d) The elements of an elliptical cone are equal in length.

(e) A right section implies that a right-side view shows the true perimeter of a prism or cylinder.

(f) A stretch-out line has an elastic quality such that it can be lengthened to provide extra material for a welded seam.

INTERSECTIONS
OF SURFACES

CHAPTER 18

A MACHINE PART or structure of any kind may be assumed to consist of a number of geometric shapes arranged to produce the desired form. Geometric shapes may sometimes be combined or interlocked in a pattern that is easily represented; but frequently the adjoining surfaces of these basic shapes meet in lines of intersection which require considerable effort to produce in multiview projection. When a form is constructed of sheet metal, other fabricated parts, or bonded material, an accurate representation of the intersecting surfaces becomes important, since the component parts must fit accurately and smoothly for optimum function and appearance. Figure 18–1 shows a typical intersection pattern formed by the adjoining cones, cylinders, and prisms of the "P-D Recirculator Dust Collector."

Fig. 18–1. P-D Recirculator Dust Collector. Courtesy American Air Filter Co., Louisville, Ky.

The principles of intersections of planes and surfaces were discussed in Chapter 16. Here these principles will be applied to the more intricate problems resulting from the intersections of prisms, pyramids, cones, and cylinders. Selection of the particular procedure to be employed in a given problem is largely a matter of judgment.

18.1   INTERSECTION OF PRISMS—EDGE VIEWS GIVEN

The intersection of two prisms involves the determination of the lines of intersection of the limited surfaces of the solids. These lines of intersection are obtained by finding the existing piercing points of the edges of one prism with the surfaces of the second prism, and then the existing piercing points of the edges of the second prism with the surfaces of the first.

In Fig. 18–2 the problem is somewhat simplified, since the top view shows edge views of the lateral surfaces of the triangular prism, and the side view shows edge views of the lateral surfaces of the rectangular prism. Thus the piercing points 1 and 2 of line AB with two of the surfaces of the triangular prism are apparent in the top view and are projected to the front view as indicated. Points 3, 4, 5, and 6 are obtained similarly. The piercing points 7 and 8 of line CE with two of the surfaces of the rectangular prism are observed first in the side view, which shows these surfaces in edge view, and are then projected to the front view. In completing the intersection of the

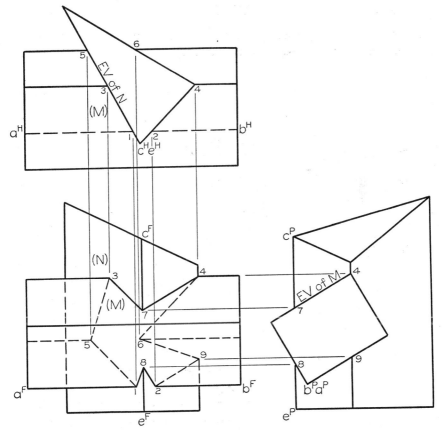

Fig. 18–2.   Intersection of Prisms—Edge Views Given

prisms, care must be exercised to add only those lines which represent lines of intersection of the adjacent surfaces of the two prisms. For instance, a line of intersection between points 3 and 7 is drawn, since these two points are common to both planes M and N. Line 3,7 thus represents the line of intersection of these two surfaces. On the other hand a line connecting points 1 and 3 would be incorrect, since it would lie *inside* the rectangular prism and thus could not be common to the *surfaces* of the prisms. The completed solution includes the correct visibility as shown.

Note that the edges of each prism are terminated at the points of intersection with the surfaces of the other prism. In other words the completed problem is treated as if the intersecting forms consisted of a one-piece casting. In most practical applications such a form would either be solid or would be fabricated from sheet or plate, in which latter case it would need to be hollow for the passage of liquids, gases, or finely divided materials.

18.2 INTERSECTION OF PRISM AND PYRAMID— AUXILIARY-VIEW METHOD

In contrast to the preceding problem the lateral surfaces of the prism of Fig. 18–3 are not shown edgewise in either of the principal views. In this

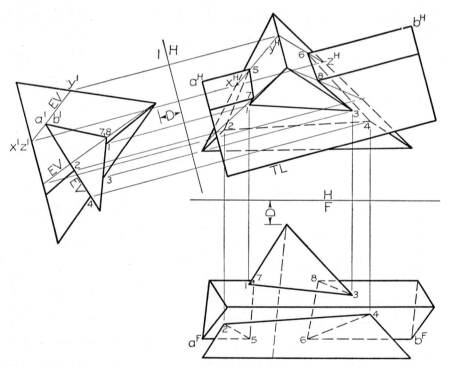

Fig. 18–3. Intersection of Prism and Pyramid—Auxiliary-View Method

illustration an auxiliary view is drawn which does include the edge views of these planes. Next, piercing points 1, 2, 3, and 4 of two edges of the pyramid with two surfaces of the prism are located in this auxiliary view and are then projected to the top and front views. Piercing points 5, 6, 7, and 8 are obtained by the two-view piercing-point method, since the addition of the auxiliary views needed to show each surface of the pyramid in edge view would be cumbersome. An edgewise cutting plane, containing edge AB of the prism and intersecting the surfaces of the pyramid in lines YX and YZ, is introduced in the auxiliary view to locate piercing points 5 and 6. A similar construction is employed to secure points 7 and 8. The solution is completed by connecting the various piercing points as shown.

18.3 INTERSECTION OF TWO PRISMS—TWO-VIEW METHOD

By the use of the two-view piercing-point method, the construction for the intersections of prisms and pyramids may be confined to any two views.

For clarity the construction needed for the location of only three of the several piercing points is shown in Fig. 18–4. An edge-view cutting plane passed through line AB in the front view intersects one surface of the triangular prism in line 1,2 which, when projected to the top view, locates piercing point M of line AB in this surface. This point is then projected back to the front view. Piercing point N is obtained by the use of a cutting plane through line CE, intersecting a surface of the quadrangular prism in the line 5, 6. A similar construction is shown to locate point S. Although some cutting planes may be tried which do not produce piercing points within the areas of the limited surfaces of the solids, this trial approach can be reduced to some extent by a careful preliminary study of the problem to locate edges which obviously do not pierce the other solid. All the existing piercing points are secured when the lines of intersection form one or more closed paths.

18.4 INTERSECTION OF PRISM AND CONE

The intersection of the prism and cone of Fig. 18–5 represents a problem occurring frequently in practice. For this solution profile cutting planes 1, 2, 3, and 4 are used. Since these cuts are parallel to the circular base of the right cone, they intersect the cone in four circles. The intersection of circle 2 in the side view with the front edge-view surface of the prism results in the two piercing points X and Y, which are then projected to the front view. The remaining points on the curved line of intersection [1] are found by the same procedure. Note that only those cutting planes are used that produce circles on the surface of the cone which will intersect the lateral surfaces of the

---

[1] This curve is a portion of a hyperbola, Art. 21.3.

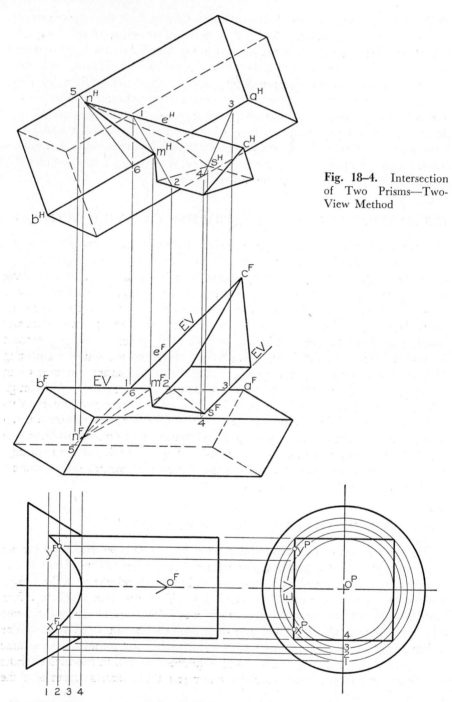

Fig. 18–4. Intersection of Two Prisms—Two-View Method

Fig. 18–5. Intersection of Prism and Cone

prism. With this fact in mind, the observing student would probably first add the concentric circles in the side view and then project to the front view to secure the corresponding cutting plane lines.

18.5 INTERSECTION OF RIGHT-CIRCULAR CYLINDERS

In sheet-metal duct work, in piping, and in steel-plate tank work, the representation of the intersection of cylinders is a frequently occurring problem. In Fig. 18–6 frontal cutting planes are used, since these cuts intersect both cylinders in elements as is illustrated in the pictorial. In the top view the intersection of cutting plane 2 with the circular view of the vertical cylinder locates elements 2 of this cylinder, which are then projected to the front view. Since the front view of the corresponding element 2 of the horizontal cylinder cannot be projected directly from the top to the front view, use is made of the partial side view. The element is first projected to the side view and then transferred to the front view by means of transfer distance D_1. The intersections of the correspondingly numbered elements in the front view locate points X and Y on the required line of intersection. Other cutting planes are added, spaced as shown, to locate points on the intersection where they are most needed to produce an accurate curve.

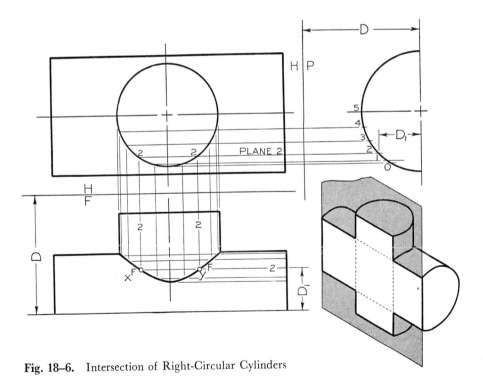

Fig. 18–6. Intersection of Right-Circular Cylinders

If intersecting cylinders, such as those illustrated in Fig. 18–7(a), have a greater relative difference in their diameters, the line of intersection more nearly approaches the form of a circular arc. Thus for many practical problems of this type, where representation alone and *not* development is necessary, a circular arc may be a satisfactory substitute for the actual curve. The radius of the larger cylinder is used, since the resulting arc when properly centered on the axis of the smaller cylinder passes through the critical points *A* and *B* of the true curve.

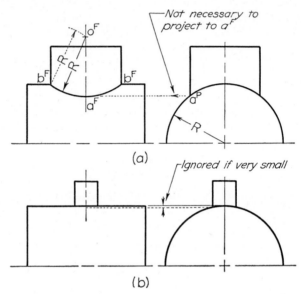

Fig. 18–7. Conventional Intersections—Used Where Intersection Is Not Prominent and Accuracy is Unimportant

When the relative diameters differ even more, as illustrated in Fig. 18–7(b), the conventional practice is to ignore entirely the slight curvature of the intersection unless a development is needed.

18.6 INTERSECTION—RIGHT CYLINDER AND CONE

For the intersection problem of Fig. 18–8 horizontal cutting planes are used, since they cut circles on the cone and elements on the cylinder. The pictorial shows the cone and cylinder intersected by a single horizontal plane. Cutting plane number 4, as an example, cuts the cone in circle 4, the top view of which is obtained by direct projection. This same cutting plane cuts the cylinder in element 4, which is located in the top view by the use of the transfer distance D_1 secured in the partial side view. The intersection point of circle 4 and element 4 in the top view is x^H, a point on the required line of intersection. Point x^F is obtained by projection to the front view. Additional cutting planes are added until a sufficient number of points are located to produce an accurate curve.

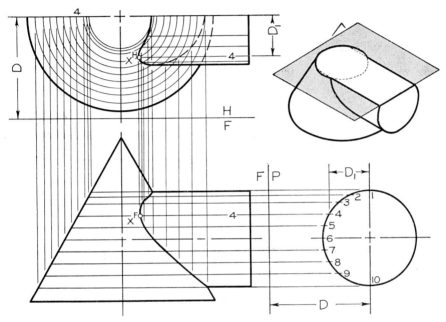

Fig. 18–8.   Intersection of Right Cylinder and Cone

Alternate Method. Under similar circumstances the intersection of a right cone and cylinder may also be plotted by assuming a series of cutting planes containing the vertex of the cone and which appear in edge view in the side view, Fig. 18–9. In this case appropriately spaced elements of the cone are introduced in the side view, including the important elements 1 and 11 tangent to the cylinder. These elements are then located in the top view, as suggested by transfer distance D_1 for element 3, and are projected to the front view. Edge-view cutting planes containing the cone elements are then introduced in the side view. These planes also cut elements from the cylinder which, when projected to the front and top views, locate points of the intersection such as A_1 and A_2 on element 3.

Still another method for plotting the intersection of a right-circular cone and cylinder is discussed in Art. 18.7, following.

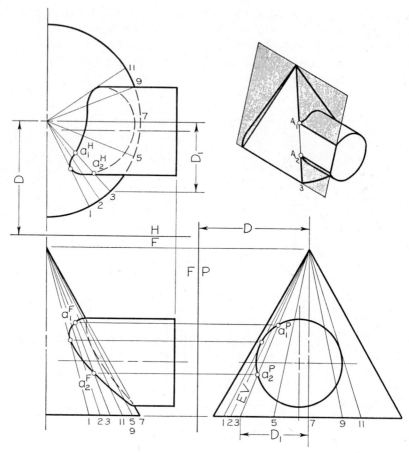

Fig. 18–9. Intersection of Right Cylinder and Cone (Alternate Method)

18.7 INTERSECTION OF SURFACES—SPHERE METHOD

A unique one-view method may be used for finding the intersection of two curved surfaces when the following conditions exist: (1) *the surfaces have circular right sections*, (2) *the axes intersect*, (3) *the axes appear true length in the same view*. This solution is based on the fact that a sphere centered on the axis of a surface, such as the circular cylindrical surface of Fig. 18–10(a), intersects the surface in circles which appear edgewise in a view that shows the true length of the axis of the cylinder.

Figure 18–10(b) shows a similar intersection for a sphere and a conical surface.

When the cylindrical and conical surfaces intersect as in Fig. 18–10(c), an imaginary sphere centered at the intersection of their axes cuts edgewise circles from both these surfaces. These four circles intersect to determine

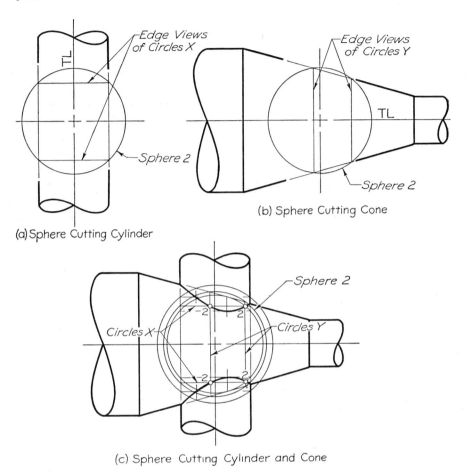

(a) Sphere Cutting Cylinder

(b) Sphere Cutting Cone

(c) Sphere Cutting Cylinder and Cone

Fig. 18–10.   Intersection of Surfaces of Revolution—Sphere Method

points common to both surfaces, since the circles lie on the same imaginary spherical surface. As an example, sphere 2 cuts edgewise circles X on the cylinder and circles Y on the cone. The crossing points 2 of X and Y are points on the required intersection. Other concentric cutting spheres are used as shown to complete the solution.

A special case of this spherical cutting plane method materializes when a sphere centered on the intersecting axes of circular cones or cylinders is tangent to both surfaces, Fig. 18–11. For these conditions the resulting curves of intersection are ellipses appearing edgewise in any view showing both axes true length.

The sphere enveloped by the two cylinders of Fig. 18–11(a) is tangent to the surfaces of both cylinders only when they have equal diameters. For this situation the resulting intersection appears as straight lines as shown.

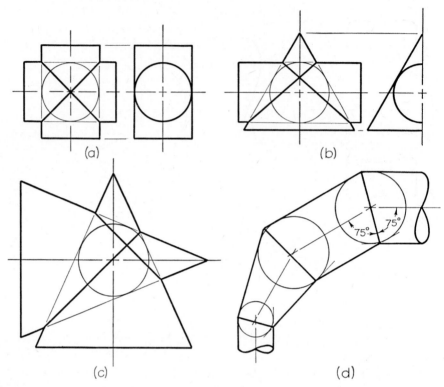

Fig. 18–11. Intersection of Surfaces of Revolution—Special Cases

Figure 18–11(b) shows the resulting straight-line intersection for a cone and cylinder which tangentially envelop the same sphere. In Fig. 18–11(c) is shown the intersection for two cones fulfilling the same conditions. For simplicity of design and fabrication, sheet-metal elbows in circular ducts are usually designed in this manner, Fig. 18–11(d).

18.8   PLANES CUTTING ELEMENTS FROM OBLIQUE CONES AND CYLINDERS

In previous illustrations of intersecting cylinders and cones, the given forms have been in normal positions—horizontal or vertical in space. In these cases planes which cut elements from the surfaces appear in edge view in one or more of the given views, and their representation is relatively simple. When the given forms are oblique, however, planes containing elements are also oblique, and their representation is correspondingly more involved. This article is concerned with the requirements which must be met by planes which cut elements from oblique cones and cylinders and with the

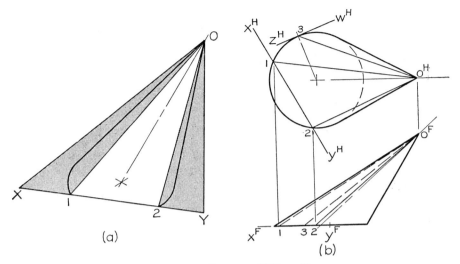

Fig. 18–12. Planes Cutting Elements From an Oblique Cone

representation of such planes. The subsequent articles apply these principles
to actual problems.

Elements are cut from any cone by planes which pass through the vertex
of the cone and intersect (or are tangent to) the base of the cone. Figure
18–12(a) shows in pictorial form the cutting plane OXY which intersects
the cone in the elements 1 and 2. Note that line XY of the cutting plane lies
in the base plane of the cone. Figure 18–12(b) shows this same relationship
in two views. Also shown is a plane OWZ which, being tangent to the cone,[2]
contains the single element 3.

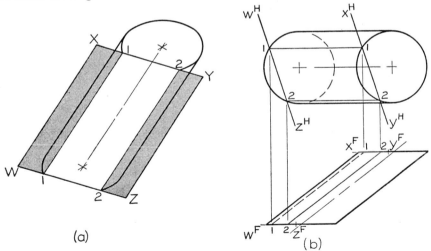

Fig. 18–13. Plane Cutting Elements From an Oblique Cylinder

[2] Art. 15.2.

Elements are cut from any cylinder by planes which pass parallel to the axis of the cylinder and intersect or are tangent to the cylinder. Figure 18–13 shows first in pictorial form and then in multiview projection the cutting plane $XYZW$, which intersects the cylinder in the elements 1 and 2.

The introduction of a plane that cuts elements from a cone or a cylinder is a convenient method for finding the points in which a line pierces a conical or cylindrical surface, Fig. 18–14. If lines are drawn from the vertex of the cone, Fig. 18–14(a), and intersecting given line AB at any two convenient points such as P and B, a cutting plane is formed. The intersection XY of this plane with the base plane of the cone establishes elements 1 and 2 of the cone, which in turn intersect AB at piercing points M and N.

A similar procedure is employed in Fig. 18–14(b) to find the points in which line AB pierces the cylindrical surface. In this case the cutting plane is established by introducing two lines parallel to the axis of the cylinder and intersecting line AB.

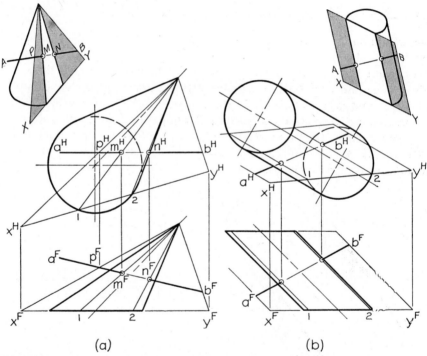

(a)   (b)

Fig. 18–14.   Piercing Points of Line and Cone and Line and Cylinder

18.9   INTERSECTION OF OBLIQUE CONE AND CYLINDER

To obtain the intersection of the oblique cone and cylinder of Fig. 18–15, oblique cutting planes are used which cut elements from both the cone and cylinder. The cutting planes must pass through the vertex of the cone to cut elements from the cone; the same cutting planes must also pass parallel to the axis of the cylinder in order to cut elements from the cylinder.

To secure the type of cutting plane that will accomplish these objectives, a line VS, Fig. 18–15(a) and (b), is drawn through the vertex of the cone

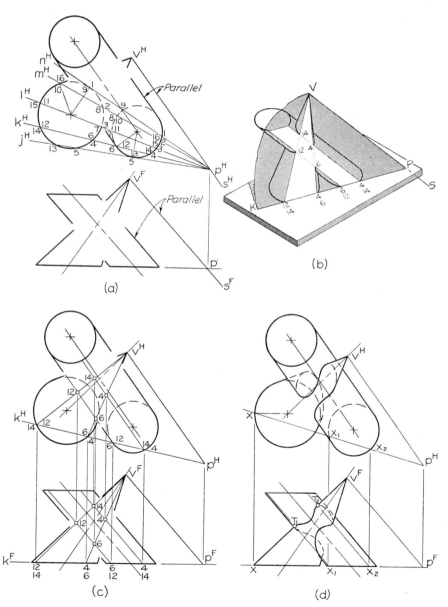

Fig. 18–15. Intersection of Oblique Cone and Cylinder

and parallel to the axis of the cylinder. Any plane containing this line and intersecting the cone and cylinder will cut elements from each. These elements, being in the same cutting plane, must intersect in points common to the cylindrical and conical surfaces. Thus the points are points on the curve of intersection.

The next step in the construction is therefore to establish the cutting planes and the corresponding elements. Point P on line VS is the intersection of this line with the plane of the bases. Line VP together with any horizontal line emanating from point P and intersecting the bases represent a plane which cuts elements from the cone and cylinder. The pictorial, Fig. 18–15(b), shows one cutting plane and the four points secured by the intersecting elements thus obtained.

Planes VPN and VPJ of Fig. 18–15(a) are called *limiting* planes. Each is tangent to one surface and cuts through (is *secant* to) the other surface. Any plane outside the narrow segment of space between these limiting planes is of no value to the construction since it cannot contact both surfaces.

A numbering system for the elements and the resulting points on the curve has been developed for any combination of cylinders and cones when the type of cutting plane shown is used to find the intersection.

The system and its properties follow:

1. In Fig. 18–15(a) the limiting planes and an appropriate number of intermediate planes are established. Point number 1 is assigned to any point where the horizontal line of any one of the cutting planes crosses either base outline. Other points on the same base are numbered consecutively, either clockwise or counterclockwise, except

2. When a secant limiting plane is reached, the order is reversed, and the numbers are continued around in the other direction.

3. The numbering is continued until every point on the first base has two numbers, except the secant points which have only one.

4. The second base is numbered, following the same rules; it is necessary that numbers 1 and 2 are assigned to lines of the same planes as on the first base. This procedure results in like numbers appearing on the bases for each cutting plane, this fact serving as a check on proper numbering.

5. The elements of each surface are then drawn, and the intersections of the like-numbered elements noted. Each point is identified by a single number corresponding to the intersecting elements. As an example, Fig. 18–15(c) shows the single cutting plane given in the pictorial together with the resulting elements and points.

6. After all points are located, a preliminary curve is drawn consecutively from point 1 to point 2, then through 3, 4, etc.

7. Intermediate cutting planes are added where needed to assure an

accurate curve. In particular the exact locations of points on extreme elements are found in each view. At each such point the curve is tangent to the extreme element. The locations of some of these tangent points may be obtained by the strategic location of the original cutting planes as shown in Fig. 18–15(a), or by a subsequent addition of one or more intermediate cutting planes as illustrated at (d).

8. The visibility of the portion of the curve extending between any two successive tangent points is determined by a test of the visibility of any point on that segment of the curve. *A point on the curve is visible only if that point is established by two elements which are each visible in their respective surfaces.* The four points on the curve in Fig. 18–15(c) are all visible points in both views since these points lie on visible elements of both forms in the top view and again in the front view. Points 6 and 12 in the top view, being located on the extreme elements of the cylinder in that view, represent the tangent points at which the curve in this problem changes visibility. The final curve is drawn as shown at (d).

The line of intersection will always be a single continuous curve where one limiting plane is tangent to the first form and the other limiting plane is tangent to the second. Two separate curves result when the two limiting planes are tangent to the same form as shown in Fig. 18–16. This illustration is discussed in Art. 18.10, following. If a limiting plane is tangent to both bases, the result according to the numbering system is two curves with a point in common.

18.10 INTERSECTION OF TWO OBLIQUE CONES—BASES IN SAME PLANE

To cut elements from each of two intersecting cones, the cutting planes must pass through the vertex of each cone. If in Fig. 18–16 a line V_1V_2 is drawn, each of the cutting planes must contain this line. The given pictorial shows one of these planes cutting from the cones elements 5 and 13, the intersections of which locate the correspondingly numbered points on the required intersection. Point P, the intersection of line V_1V_2 with the plane of the bases of the cones, is used as in Fig. 18–15 in establishing the cutting planes. The remaining construction and numbering is performed as explained in Art. 18.9. In Fig. 18–16 the two limiting planes are tangent to the same surface. The results is therefore two separate curves, one being established by points 1 through 8 and the other by points 9 through 16.

For the special case in which the vertices of the two cones are at the same elevation, the line through the vertices may be regarded as intersecting the base plane at infinity. The lines of intersection of the cutting planes with the base plane are then parallel to the line through the vertices.

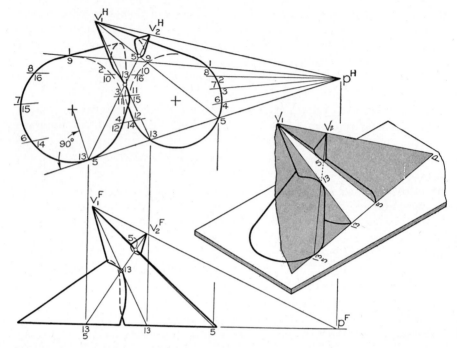

Fig. 18–16.   Intersection of Oblique Cones—Bases in Same Plane

18.11   INTERSECTION OF TWO CONES—BASES IN NONPARALLEL PLANES

To cut elements from both the given cones, the cutting planes must pass through the vertices of the given cones. Thus in Fig. 18–17, line V_1V_2 is drawn as in the preceding example. In this case, however, line V_1V_2 intersects the base planes in separate points P_1 and P_2. A partial left-side view showing the circular shape of the base of one cone is added to provide a means of transferring points on this base from one view to another.

In the multiview illustration, cutting plane P_1P_2B is shown in detail. This plane is first drawn in the top view locating elements 2,10 and 8,16 on cone V_1. Line P_1B of this same plane is added to the side view by use of transfer distances D and D_1. The intersection of this line with the circular base of cone V_2 locates the elements 2′,8′ and 16′,10′ for this cone. After these elements of both cones are located in the top and front views, the intersections of the correspondingly numbered elements are noted. Other cutting planes are added as shown. As is evident in the top view, limiting planes

P_1P_2A and P_1P_2E are both tangent to cone V_1. Hence there are two separate curves of intersection as shown.

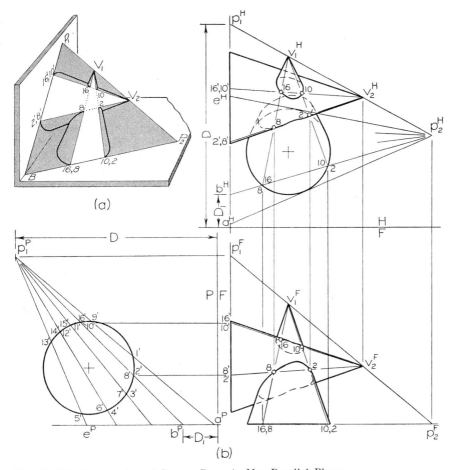

(a)

(b)

Fig. 18–17. Intersection of Cones—Bases in Non-Parallel Planes

18.12 INTERSECTION OF OBLIQUE CYLINDERS—BASES IN SAME PLANE

In order to cut elements from both of two intersecting cylinders, the cutting planes must pass parallel to the axis of each cylinder. Since each cutting plane must be parallel to these two axes, it follows that the cutting planes will be parallel to each other. If in Fig. 18–18 a plane OX_1Y_1 is passed through any point O and parallel to the axes of the two given cylinders,[3] a plane is thus established to which the cutting planes must be parallel.

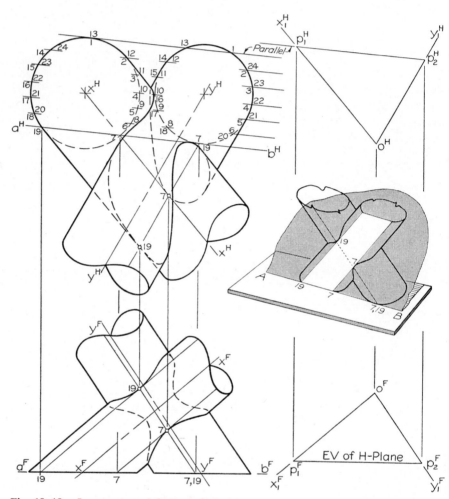

Fig. 18–18.   Intersection of Oblique Cylinders

The lines of intersection of the cutting planes with the horizontal base plane must therefore be parallel to a line of intersection such as P_1P_2 of a horizontal plane and plane OX_1Y_1. Thus the cutting planes are represented by drawing lines in the top view which intersect the bases and are parallel to $p_1{}^H p_2{}^H$. Their intersections with the bases of the cylinders locate the result-

---

[3] See Art. 9.3.

ing cut elements. Cutting plane *AB* is shown in detail in the pictorial and in both views of the multiview drawing, together with the resulting elements and intersection points 7 and 19. This plane, being a limiting plane, produces only two points on the intersection. Other points are obtained similarly to produce the complete intersection as shown.

18.13 LINE TANGENT TO CURVE OF INTERSECTION

A line tangent to a curved surface lies on a plane tangent to the surface. A line tangent to the curve of intersection of two curved surfaces is tangent to both surfaces. Therefore, a line tangent to a curve of intersection at a chosen point is the line of intersection of the two tangent planes containing the particular point.

Figure 18–19 is a reproduction of Fig. 18–15(d). Let it be required to construct a line tangent to the curve of intersection at point 14. The plane tangent to the cone and containing point 14 is represented by element 14 of the cone and line *AB* tangent to the base of the cone. The plane tangent to the cylinder and containing point 14 is represented by element 14 of the cylinder and line *XY* tangent to the base of the cylinder.[4] Lines *AB* and *XY*

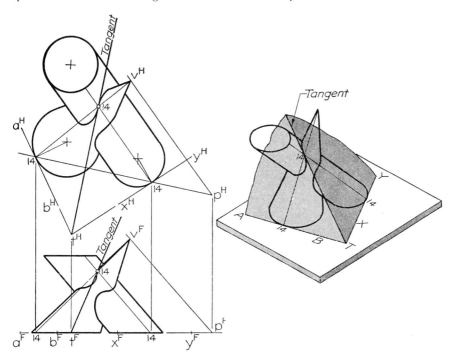

Fig. 18–19. Line Tangent to Curve of Intersection

---

[4] See Arts. 15.2 and 15.3.

are both in the base plane and hence intersect at point T. This point and point 14 of the curve are common to the two tangent planes, and thus the line joining them is tangent to both surfaces at point 14 of the curve of intersection. As a rough visual check, when such constructions are properly performed, the resulting line will appear tangent to the curve. If the line seems to cross rather than lie along the local portion of the curve, the construction is probably incorrect.

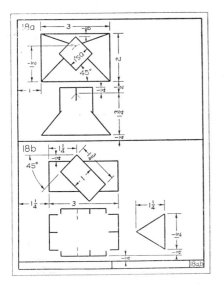

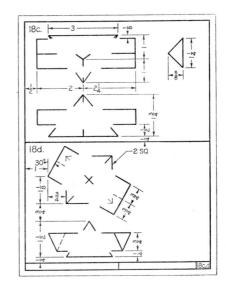

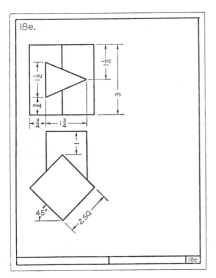

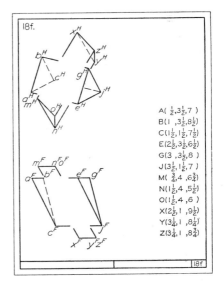

A($\frac{1}{2}$,$3\frac{1}{2}$,7)
B(1 ,$3\frac{1}{2}$,$8\frac{1}{2}$)
C(1$\frac{1}{2}$,1$\frac{1}{2}$,$7\frac{1}{2}$)
E(2$\frac{1}{2}$,$3\frac{1}{2}$,$6\frac{1}{2}$)
G(3 ,$3\frac{1}{2}$,8)
J(3$\frac{1}{2}$,1$\frac{1}{2}$,7)
M($\frac{3}{4}$,4 ,$6\frac{3}{4}$)
N(1$\frac{1}{2}$,4 ,$5\frac{1}{2}$)
O(1$\frac{1}{2}$,4 ,6)
X(2$\frac{1}{2}$,1 ,$9\frac{1}{2}$)
Y(3$\frac{1}{4}$,1 ,$8\frac{1}{4}$)
Z(3$\frac{1}{4}$,1 ,$8\frac{3}{4}$)

18a. Show the intersection of the prism and pyramid.

18b. Show the intersection of the two prisms.

18c, d. Locate the intersection of the prism and pyramid.

18e. Add a right-side view showing the intersection of the prisms.

18f. Use the auxiliary-view method to obtain the intersection of the two prisms. Show complete visibility.

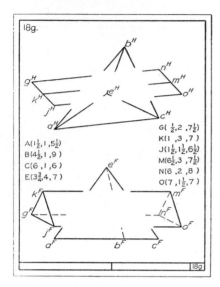

18g.

$G(\frac{1}{2},2,7\frac{1}{2})$
$K(1,3,7)$
$J(1\frac{1}{2},1\frac{1}{2},6\frac{1}{2})$
$M(6\frac{1}{2},3,7\frac{1}{2})$
$N(6,2,8)$
$O(7,1\frac{1}{2},7)$

$A(1\frac{1}{2},1,5\frac{1}{2})$
$B(4\frac{1}{2},1,9)$
$C(6,1,6)$
$E(3\frac{3}{4},4,7)$

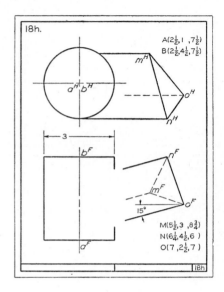

18h.

$A(2\frac{1}{2},1,7\frac{1}{2})$
$B(2\frac{1}{2},4\frac{1}{2},7\frac{1}{2})$

$15°$

$M(5\frac{1}{2},3,8\frac{3}{4})$
$N(6\frac{1}{4},4\frac{1}{2},6)$
$O(7,2\frac{1}{2},7)$

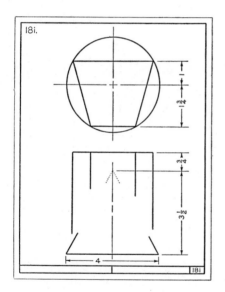

18i.

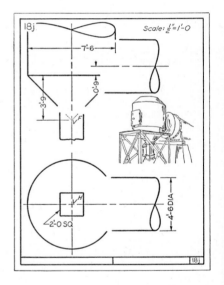

18j.   Scale: $\frac{1}{2}''=1'-0$

18g. Show the intersection of the prism and the pyramid.

18h. Show the intersection of the prism and the cylinder.

18i. Show the intersection of the prism and the cone.

18j. Find the intersection of the cone and the square outlet tube, and the intersection of the horizontal cylinder and the vertical cylinder and cone.

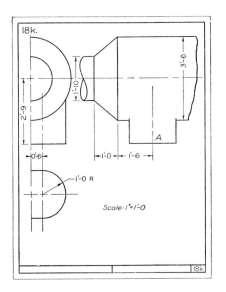

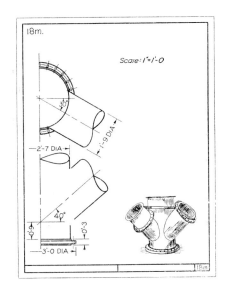

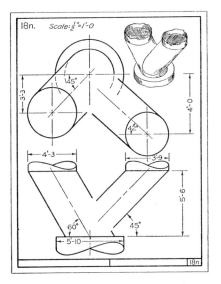

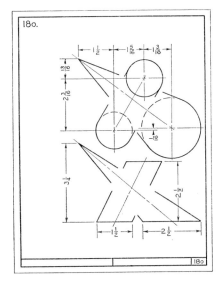

18k. Lay out the development for a 6-in. wide reinforcing collar for the intersection of outlet A with the 3½-ft diameter main. Complete the views. Neglect thickness.

18m. Show the line of intersection between the vertical and lateral pipes. Small details for which dimensions are not given may be approximated or omitted.

18n. Complete the front and top views of the oblique cylindrical ducts, showing their line of intersection. The axes do *not* intersect.

18o. Complete the views of the intersecting forms.

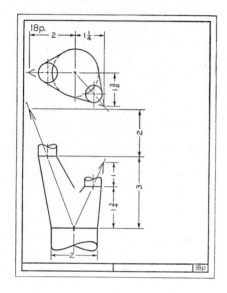

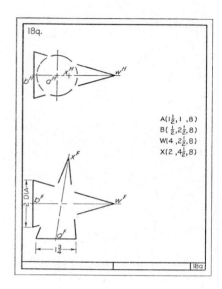

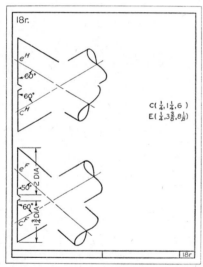

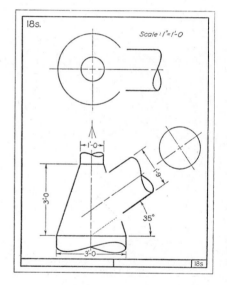

18p. Complete the views of the branches of the Y dust-collector fitting.

18q. Complete the front and top views of the intersecting cones.

18r. Complete the front and top views of the intersecting oblique cylinders.

18s. Find the intersection of the inverted funnel and cylindrical duct, using only the front and top views.

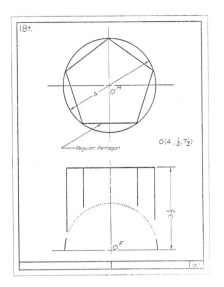

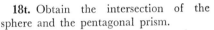

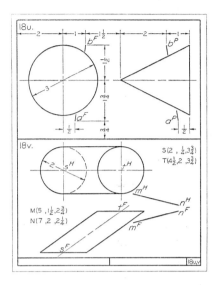

18t. Obtain the intersection of the sphere and the pentagonal prism.

18u. Using only the given views, determine the intersection of line *AB* and the cone.

18v. Using only the given views, determine the intersection of line *MN* and the cylinder.

18w. Indicate whether the following statements are true or false. If assigned, prepare written explanations or sketches to justify the answers.

(a) The lines of intersection of two prisms form either one or two closed figures.

(b) If two spheres intersect, the intersection is a circle.

(c) A plane through the vertex of a cone may intersect the cone in two elements.

(d) A single plane cannot cut elements from each of two cones unless the cones have a common vertex.

(e) In determining intersections by the use of cutting planes, it is essential that the cutting planes appear edgewise in one of the given views.

SHADES AND SHADOWS

CHAPTER 19

THE ARCHITECT AND ENGINEER frequently employ shades and shadows to help produce an illusion of depth in a drawing which of necessity is made on a plane surface. In the field of production illustration in particular, the technique of shading is used to promote realism and advertising appeal. This technique applied to an architect's *rendering* presents to the prospective

Fig. 19-1. Shadow Study—40,000 Gallon "Watersphere," Tam O' Shanter Golf Club, Chicago

252

client a picture emulating and often surpassing the effect of a photograph. The United States Government Patent Office in its directive to patent draftsmen specifies that patent drawings should include a shading technique for both edges and surfaces.[1] Although several methods exist for finding exact or approximate shades and shadows, the discussion in this text will be confined to a single approach utilizing the principles of descriptive geometry.

19.1   SHADE, SHADOW, AND UMBRA

Shade is that surface area of a geometric form from which direct light is excluded by the form itself, Fig. 19–2.

Shadow is that surface area of a geometric form from which direct light is excluded by a second intervening form. Many physical objects are composed of several geometric forms. For purposes of distinction between shade and shadow, the above definitions are applied to the various forms independently.

Umbra is that portion of space from which direct light is excluded.

As Professor Eliot Tozer has frequently cautioned students, the phrase, "Standing in the shade of the old apple tree," should more correctly be stated, "Standing in the *umbra* of the old apple tree" or "Standing *on* the *shadow* of the old apple tree."

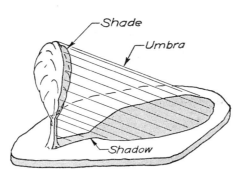

Fig. 19–2.   Shade, Shadow, and Umbra

19.2   LIGHT SOURCE AND DIRECTION

Although any source of light may be used as a basis for establishing shade and shadow, it is conventional to employ a distant source such as the sun, since the rays may then be considered parallel. In addition these parallel rays are assumed to have the direction of the diagonal of a cube extending from the upper left to the lower right, Fig. 19–3(a). This direction is particularly convenient because the resulting principal views of this diagonal are at 45° with horizontal on the paper, Fig. 19–3(b).

---

[1] Guide for Patent Draftsmen, Commissioner of Patents, Washington, D. C.

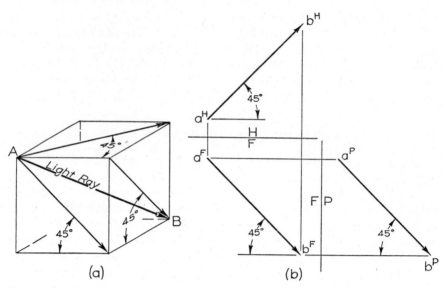

Fig. 19–3.   Conventional Light Ray Direction

19.3 SHADOW OF A PRISM

The shadow cast by the prism of Fig. 19–4 is determined by locating the shadows of the corners of the prism. The shadow of a point is the intersection of the light ray from the point with the surface on which the shadow is cast.

As an example, the shadow of point A is found by introducing the conventional light ray AX which is then extended to point S, its intersection with the horizontal plane on which the prism rests. The shadows of points C and E are found by the same method. Since points B and G are in the given horizontal plane, they coincide with their shadows. The shadows of the edges of the prism are then represented by the lines connecting the shadows of the corners. Note that the shadow on a horizontal plane of any vertical edge falls along the 45° ray in the top view.

While in this illustration the theoretical shadows of the undesignated edges are also indicated (in phantom form), they are of course not necessary, since only the outline of a shadow is actually observed.[2]

19.4 SHADE AND SHADOW OF A PYRAMID AND WALL

In Fig. 19–5 the shadow of the wall is similar to that of the prism in the preceding example. The shadow of the pyramid falls partly on the ground and partly on the front face of the wall. To secure the shadow on the ground, the wall is temporarily considered removed. The light ray through apex A is

---

[2] A shadow obtained by this method is an *oblique projection*, Art. 20.3.

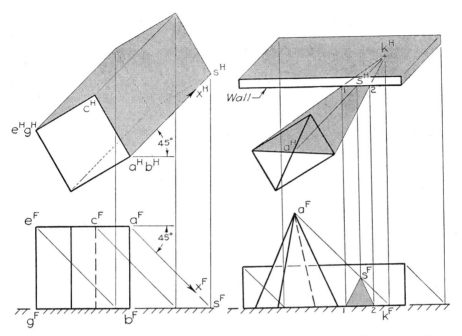

Fig. 19–4. Shadow of a Prism   **Fig. 19–5.** Shade and Shadow of Pyramid and Wall

introduced, and its intersection with the ground, point K, is established. Since the base of the pyramid rests on the ground, the required shadow extends from point K to the base corners. With the wall considered replaced, this ground shadow terminates at the front face of the wall as shown in the top view, leaving the shadow of the pyramid incomplete. The remaining portion of the shadow falls on the frontal wall face. To secure this portion, the intersection S of the ray from A with the front face of the wall is found. Points S, 1, and 2 are projected to the front view to complete the outline of this portion of the shadow. The two back faces of the pyramid are in shade as indicated in the top view.

19.5   SHADE AND SHADOW OF OBJECT COMPOSED OF CYLINDERS

The shadow of a circle cast on a plane to which it is parallel is a true circle of the same diameter. Thus the shadows of the various bases of the cylinders of Fig. 19–6 appear as circles in the top view. Point 5 is the center of the circular shadow of the upper base of the cap, and point 6 is the center of the shadow on the ground of the lower base of the cap. Point 7 is the center of that portion of the shadow of this same lower base that falls on surface A.

Point 8 is the center of the shadow of surface *A* on the ground. The corresponding circles together with the tangent lines representing the shadows of extreme elements are drawn as shown to complete this portion of the shadow.

The lower base of the cap casts a portion of its shadow on the cylindrical support column. The curved outline of this shadow is established by finding the shadows 1, 2, 3, and 4 of appropriate points of the lower base.

The shade areas appearing in the front view are established by locating the elements along which light rays are tangent to the cylinders.

19.6   SHADE AND SHADOW OF CONE AND PRISM

The shadow of the prism of Fig. 19–7 is cast on the ground as shown. Part of the shadow of the cone falls on the ground and part on the upper surface *B* of the prism. To obtain the portion that falls on the ground, the prism is temporarily considered removed, and the lateral surface of the cone is extended to the ground as shown. To find the portion that falls on surface *B*, surface *B* is extended to secure the imaginary shadow, point 2, of the cone apex. The shadow together with the shade area as shown complete the solution.

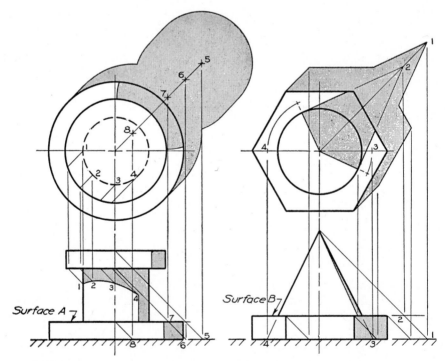

Fig. 19–6. Shade and Shadow of Cylindrical Forms

Fig. 19–7. Shade and Shadow of Cone and Prism

19.7   SHADE AND SHADOW OF SHELF AND SUPPORT

The shelf and support of Fig. 19–8 is an illustration of a shadow problem involving a front and left-side view. Although no new fundamentals are presented in this solution, the direction of the light rays in the left-side view should be noted. Of interest in this problem is the fact that the shadow falls partly on different surfaces of the object itself and partly on the frontal wall.

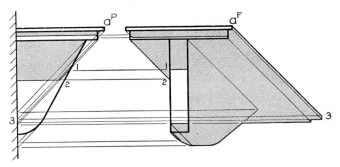

Fig. 19–8.   Shade and Shadow of Shelf and Support

19.8   SHADOW OF CHIMNEY ON INCLINED ROOF PLANES

To find a shadow on an oblique or inclined plane in which the edge view is not given, the two-view piercing-point method is used to secure the intersection of the light rays with this type of surface. As an example, the shadow

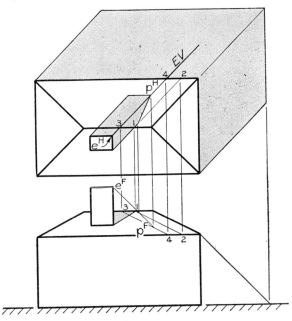

Fig. 19–9.   Shadow of Prism on Inclined Plane

of point E, Fig. 19–9, is obtained by passing a vertical cutting plane through the top view of the ray from E. This cutting plane intersects the rear roof plane in the line 3,4. The intersection of the light ray and the front view of line 3,4 locates the required shadow, point P. Other points are obtained as indicated to complete the solution. Note in the front view that only the visible shadow is shown.

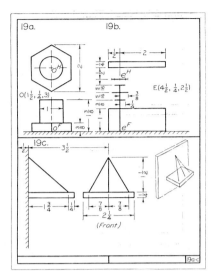

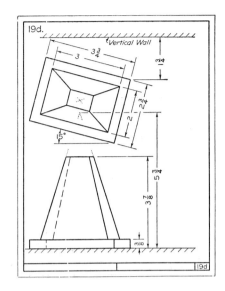

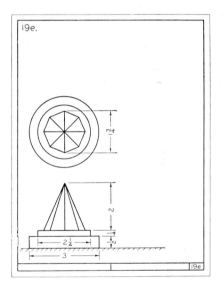

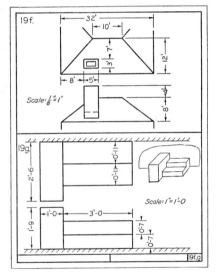

19a. Find the shade and shadow of the cylinder and hexagonal prism.

19b. Determine the shadow of the antenna and wall.

19c. Show the shadow of the canopy.

19d. Determine the complete shade and shadow.

19e. Determine the shade and shadow of the octagonal pyramid and the cylindrical base.

19f. Determine the shadow of the chimney on the inclined roof planes.

19g. Show the shadow of the wall and steps.

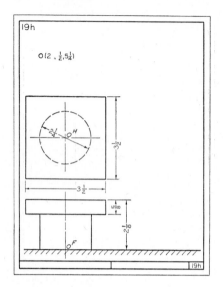

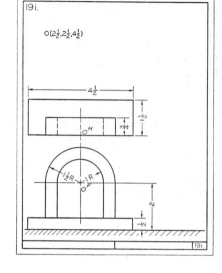

19h. Determine the complete visible shade and shadow of the prism and cylinder.

19i. Determine the shade and shadow of the archway and base.

19j. Indicate whether the following statements are true or false. If assigned, prepare written explanations or sketches to justify the answers.

(a) The shadow of a vertical line on a frontal wall is a vertical line.

(b) The shadow of a horizontal circle on a frontal wall is a circle.

(c) The shadow of a line on two parallel planes is two parallel lines.

(d) A top view always shows the true area of a shadow.

(e) A roof sloping at 30° and with no overhang does not by itself cast a shadow.

(f) The shadow of a frontal circle on a frontal wall is a circle.

(g) The shadow of a line is always longer than the line itself.

(h) The shadow of a circle may be a straight line.

CHAPTER 20

PICTORIAL
PROJECTIONS

In Chapter 1 it was pointed out that multiview projection is the only completely exact method of representing complex space relations; that is, the only direct method for laying out and measuring on paper all the true distances and angles involved in a space or three-dimensional problem. If the engineer is to convey information by this method, the recipient of the information must of course understand or be able to "read" multiview drawings. Since, however, the general public and many technicians are not trained in this subject, the various types of pictorial drawings occupy an important sector of the field of graphical communication. As was mentioned, it is difficult and sometimes impossible to supply in a pictorial drawing the complete technical information necessary in the manufacture of an article. The layman, however, does not normally need all the details but merely the general appearance and method of operation of the product. For such a description a pictorial drawing is usually satisfactory. The engineer should therefore be familiar with the more widely used types of pictorial drawing and the principles of projection used in their construction. Since an extensive treatment of this subject is beyond the scope of this book, only a few types of pictorial construction employing descriptive geometry principles are discussed here.

20.1   ISOMETRIC PROJECTION AND DRAWING

If an object is so placed that its principal faces are oblique to a plane of projection, and orthographic projection is employed, the resulting view is an *axonometric* projection. This construction may be performed by successive auxiliary views by assuming an oblique line of sight such as *AB* in Fig. 20–1(a) and constructing the secondary auxiliary view which shows arrow *AB* as a point. If as in this case the line of sight *AB* is assumed in the position of a diagonal of a cube, the principal edges of the object become foreshortened in the same proportion (about 82 per cent of true length). The

261

projections of three concurrent principal edges such as OX, OY, and OZ fall 120° apart in the secondary auxiliary view. This particular axonometric projection is therefore called *isometric* (uniformly measured) projection. The hidden edges are omitted in pictorial projection unless absolutely necessary for clarity.

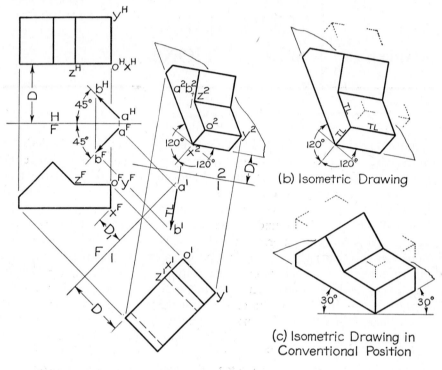

(b) Isometric Drawing

(c) Isometric Drawing in Conventional Position

(a) Isometric Projection

Fig. 20–1.   Isometric Projection and Drawing

Since in isometric projection the principal edges are drawn to the same scale, there is no change in the *proportions* if the edges are drawn true length and 120° apart as in Fig. 20–1 (b). This is, of course, not a true projection, but the fact that it is oversize is not usually obvious until it is placed side by side with a full-size multiview drawing or the actual object. A pictorial drawing thus constructed is called an isometric *drawing* to distinguish it from the true projection. Since no auxiliary views are needed, an isometric drawing may be constructed directly with the usual drafting equipment and is hence a very popular type of pictorial drawing. The true isometric projection is rarely used. For convenience and a more natural position, an isometric drawing is usually constructed with one set of principal edges vertical on the paper, as in Fig. 20–1 (c).

20.2   DIMETRIC AND TRIMETRIC PROJECTION

If a draftsman is required to produce many pictorial drawings, he eventually encounters objects for which isometric drawing is unsuitable. One common fault occurs in the representation of 45° angles. Under certain circumstances surfaces at 45° with horizontal, Fig. 20–1, appear in edge view in an isometric, detracting from the pictorial effect. Under these conditions a change in the position of the line of sight AB, Fig. 20–2, improves the representation. In this illustration the top view of the line of sight was not shifted from the position given in Fig. 20–1(a). The result in the secondary auxiliary view is that edges OY and OZ are foreshortened to the same degree, while edge OX is foreshortened to a lesser degree. Hence *two* different scales are needed to measure these edges directly in the pictorial view, and this type of projection is called *dimetric*.

If the position of $a^H b^H$ is also changed, the result in general will be a

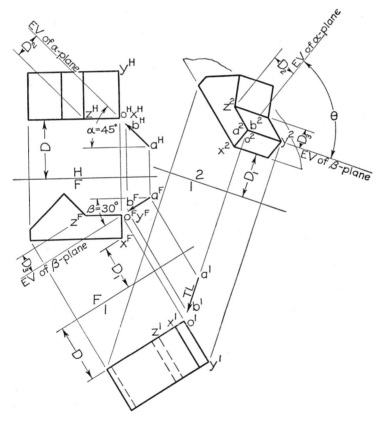

Fig. 20–2.   Dimetric Projection

trimetric projection, since unless angles α and β again become equal, the principal edges such as OX, OY, and OZ will be foreshortened at *three* different scales in the pictorial or secondary auxiliary view.

The construction shown in Fig. 20–2 is not, however, a practical method for constructing dimetrics, since the primary auxiliary view is useless as far as the end product is concerned. The construction for a complicated object is thus too long and tedious for extensive use in practice. Further study of Fig. 20–2 suggests a method of eliminating the primary auxiliary view.

If an edge-view reference plane, the α-plane, is introduced, coinciding with $a^H b^H$ as shown, and if another edge-view reference plane, the β-plane, is introduced, coinciding with $a^F b^F$, line-of-sight AB is a segment of the line of intersection of the two reference planes. The secondary auxiliary view, which shows AB as a point, thus shows both the α-plane and the β-plane in edge view, from which any point of the object may be established by its two perpendicular distances from the reference planes. These distances are available in the given views as exemplified by distances D_2 and D_3 for point Z. Thus, if the angle θ between the α- and β-planes can be established, the dimetric projection may be drawn without using a primary auxiliary view.

In Fig. 20–3(a) only the three principal edges OX, OY, and OZ together with the α- and β-planes are reproduced. In the dimetric construction, Fig. 20–3(b), the α-plane is drawn vertical for convenience, and point O is assumed on it at any desired location. In (a) a frontal line OF of any random length is drawn perpendicular to AB (extended) at point O. Since line ABO appears as a point in (b), line OF must appear true length. Distance D

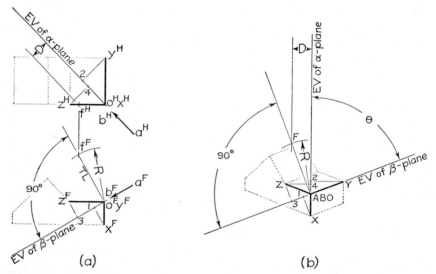

Fig. 20–3.   Elimination of the Primary Auxiliary View in Dimetric Projection

and radius R are then used as indicated to locate line OF in the dimetric. In (a) it is apparent that the β-plane is also perpendicular to line OF. Hence in (b) the β-plane is located accordingly, perpendicular to OF in this con-struction. Points X, Y, Z and the remaining points of the object may now be established by their respective distances from the α- and β-planes to complete the dimetric projection.

If convenient, given views may be thumb-tacked or otherwise fastened at their respective angles with the α- and β-planes in the dimetric projection, Fig. 20–4. The dimetric itself is then drawn by projecting parallel to the reference planes from points of the given views instead of by transferring distance with dividers.

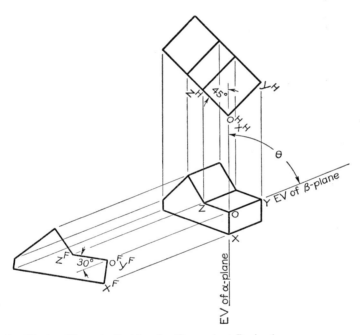

Fig. 20–4.　Placing Views in Position for Convenient Projection

20.3　OBLIQUE PROJECTION

Certain types of objects, particularly those involving a number of circular forms, are often more easily drawn by *oblique* projection than by other methods. In oblique projection it is customary to place the object with a principal face parallel to the plane of projection (the picture plane), just as in multiview projection. The projection lines are not, however, drawn per-pendicular to the picture plane but at a suitable angle other than 90°.

In Fig. 20–5 an object is shown with its circular front face lying in a frontal picture plane. Regardless of the direction of projection to the picture plane, the projections of points on the frontal face, such as points X and Y, coincide with the points themselves. The pictorial axes OX and OY thus remain horizontal and vertical, respectively, and the true circular shape of the front face is retained. This is the principal advantage of oblique projection, for in other projections, such as axonometric, a circle ordinarily projects as an ellipse.

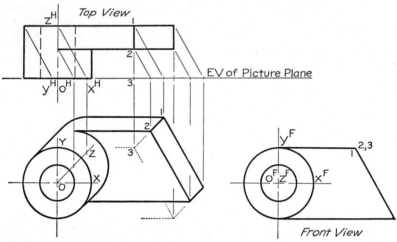

Fig. 20–5. Oblique Projection

Since any direction may be chosen for projection to the picture plane, it is possible to establish the third principal axis OZ, the so-called *receding* axis, at any angle with horizontal in the oblique projection and at any length. Naturally, convenient receding angles such as 45°, 30°, or 60° are usually employed. If the direction of projection in the top view is chosen so as to combine with the selected angle of the receding axis in such a manner as to cause the receding axis to appear at the same scale as the other axes, the result is called a *cavalier* projection. If the angles are so combined as to produce a receding axis at one-half the scale of the others, the projection is called *cabinet*. Other scales may also be established, but scales for the receding axis greater than the scales of the other axes are not used in practice because the resulting projection does not appear natural.

Other points of the object in Fig. 20–5 are projected to the picture plane in lines parallel to the projection line for point Z. The given front view serves to establish heights for those points and edges which are *in the picture plane*. Other edges perpendicular to but not intersecting the picture plane, such as edge 1–2, may be extended forward to pierce the picture plane. Edge 1–2 extends to point 3, and the height of point 3 is established by projection horizontally from the front view. The direction of line 1,2 in the pictorial is thus along a construction line extending from point 3 parallel to axis OZ. Points 1 and 2 are then located on this construction line as shown.

In the completed oblique projection it is apparent that not only is the front face in true shape but all surfaces parallel to the front face appear in true shape, with angles, lengths, and circular arcs preserved. On the other hand, angles and other shapes in receding surfaces are distorted in a fashion similar to axonometric projection.

20.4 APPROXIMATE ELLIPSES

Since the circle is a widely used geometric form, its representation in pictorial projections is a frequently encountered problem. A circle lying in any of the principal faces of an object projects as a true ellipse in an axonometric projection. A similar situation is encountered when a circular form lies in one of the receding surfaces in an oblique projection. Of course any curve may be plotted in a pictorial drawing by finding the projections of a series of points on the curve, just as the projection of any other point of the object is found. This is somewhat tedious, however, and it is common practice to approximate an ellipse whenever practicable.

In isometric drawing or projection, in certain surfaces in a dimetric projection, and in the receding surfaces in a cavalier projection, a square circumscribed about a circle, with the sides of the square parallel to the principal edges of the object, projects as an equilateral parallelogram or rhombus, Fig. 20–6(a). If the four perpendicular bisectors of the sides of a rhombus are drawn, Fig. 20–6(b), they meet at the four points 1, 2, 3, and 4. Points 1 and 2 are used as the centers of arcs of radius R, Fig. 20–6(c), and points 3 and 4 are used as the centers of arcs of radius r. The arcs thus drawn are tangent to each other and to the sides of the rhombus at the mid-points of the sides. The resulting oval, while not an ellipse, is a satisfactory approximation in most cases. This method is possible only when the enclosing parallelogram has equal sides. When the adjacent sides are drawn to different scales, the perpendicular bisectors meet at points which are not equidistant from

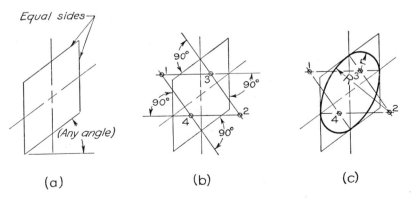

Fig. 20–6. Four-Center Approximate Ellipse

these sides, and arcs drawn with these points as centers cannot be made tangent to two sides. In such cases the curve must be plotted or some other method for producing an ellipse must be employed.

20.5 PERSPECTIVE OR CENTRAL PROJECTION

Axonometric and oblique projections are widely used in pictorial work because of their relative ease of construction. They do not and cannot, however, represent an object in a completely natural manner. In both methods, as well as in ordinary multiview projection, the projection lines from the object to the picture plane are parallel. In nature, projection lines are actually *visual rays* extending from an object to the eye of the observer. In order for these rays to be parallel, the observer must be at an infinite distance from the object. Since this is not the situation in normal viewing, such projections can at best only roughly simulate a true picture of an object. *Perspective* projection takes into consideration the fact that an observer in nature is at some finite or measurable distance from any object he sees. While the methods of construction employ descriptive geometry or multiview methods, the resulting projection closely approximates an actual optical image.

Figure 20–7 shows the basic arrangement in space for perspective projection. The T-square is the object viewed. The eye of the observer is at an established point SP, the *station point*. The visual rays are represented by lines drawn from the station point through the various points of the T-square. If a picture plane is introduced, the visual rays pierce it at points which are then the perspective projections of the respective points of the T-square. Lines properly joining the piercing points complete the perspective projection on the particular picture plane. It is evident that on picture plane 1,

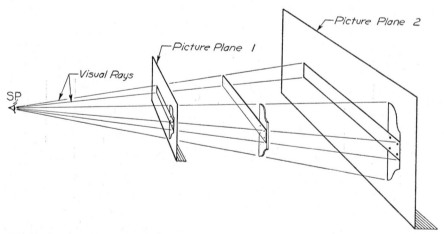

Fig. 20–7. Perspective Projection

which is between the observer and the object, the perspective projection is smaller than the object. On picture plane 2 the perspective projection is larger than the object. On a picture plane behind the observer (to the left of SP) the perspective projection would be inverted as in a real image formed by a lens.

20.6 PERSPECTIVE CONSTRUCTION BY MULTIVIEW PROJECTION OF PIERCING POINTS

The basic construction for perspective projection is shown in multiview form in Fig. 20–8. A frontal picture plane is employed and appears in edge view in the plan and right-side views. The plan view of the object is turned so that an observer at the given station point may see clearly two of the vertical faces of the object. It should be noted that the plan view is an ordinary top view placed or fastened in a revolved position, and that the resulting side view is a special view of the revolved object, an objectionable feature of the construction which will be eliminated later.

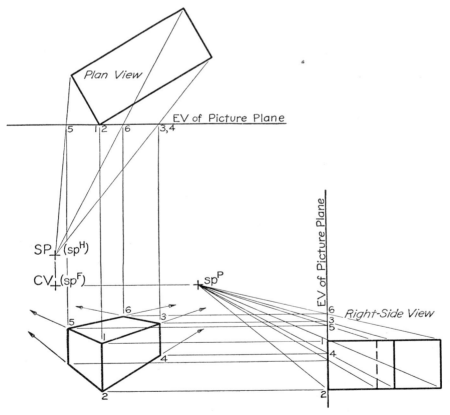

Fig. 20–8.   Construction of a Perspective by Multiview Projection of Piercing Points

The visual rays are now drawn from SP to the points of the object in the plan and side views. Their piercing points with the picture plane (for example, points 1, 2, 3, and 4) are projected to the front view. When all the visible piercing points are located, they are connected with lines representing the edges of the object to complete the perspective projection.

Several important fundamentals of perspective projection are revealed by a careful study of Fig. 20-8:

1. *Lines parallel to the picture plane remain parallel to their original positions in the perspective projection.* Note, for example, lines 1,2 and 3,4.

2. *Lines in the picture plane* (such as 1,2) *appear true length in the perspective projection,* as well as parallel to their original positions.

3. *All lines parallel to each other but not parallel to the picture plane converge to a common point in the perspective projection.* If extended, lines 1,3 and 2,4 intersect at some point to the right of the perspective in Fig. 20-8. As will be seen later, line 5,6 intersects 1,3 and 2,4 *at the same point* in the perspective projection.

20.7   TWO-POINT AND ONE-POINT PERSPECTIVES

The geometry of the construction in Fig. 20-8 is such that the intersection or *vanishing point* of lines in the perspective is at *eye level* (level with sp^F) if the edges they represent are horizontal.[1] In the terminology of perspective projection, sp^F is called the *center of vision,* CV, since sp^F coincides with the central point toward which the observer is looking. The picture plane is perpendicular to the visual ray through the center of vision.

Figure 20-9 illustrates perspectives in which the vanishing points are actually shown. To produce the perspective in Fig. 20-9(a), the *steps* were placed with the vertical edges parallel to, and the horizontal edges inclined to, the picture plane. In the perspective the vertical edges remain vertical and the horizontal edges converge to two vanishing points. Thus the per-

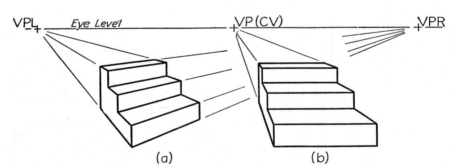

Fig. 20-9.   Two-Point and One-Point Perspectives

---

[1] The actual construction for vanishing points is explained in Art. 20.8, following.

spective is called *two-point perspective*. If there were inclined or oblique lines present, they would have still other vanishing points. The term *two-point* refers to the number of vanishing points of *principal edges* only.

For Fig. 20–9(b) the steps were placed with two sets of principal edges, the vertical edges and one set of horizontal edges, parallel to the picture plane. These sets of parallel lines remain parallel in the perspective, and only the second or receding set of horizontal edges have their perspective projections converging to a vanishing point. This is therefore called *one-point perspective*. The vanishing point coincides with the center of vision.

20.8 CONSTRUCTION FOR VANISHING POINTS

As was pointed out in Art. 20.5, the perspective of a point is the point at which the visual ray from SP to the point pierces the picture plane. This is illustrated again in Fig. 20–10. If a construction line through points A and B of the building is extended an infinite distance, the visual ray to the infinitely distant point on AB is parallel to AB. The piercing point of this visual ray in the picture plane, point VPR (vanishing point to right), is thus the perspective of the infinitely distant point. Since the same visual ray is also parallel to several other lines on the building, the single point VPR is the perspective of infinitely distant points on all these parallel lines and is thus

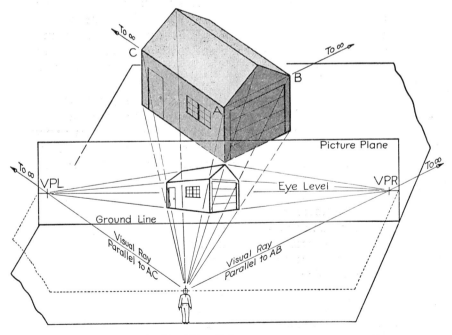

Fig. 20–10. Construction for Vanishing Points

the vanishing point of these lines. In similar fashion, the visual ray parallel to the other set of horizontal principal lines of the building, of which AC is a member, pierces the picture plane at VPL (vanishing point to left), which is the vanishing point of this second set of principal edges. It is evident that, since the two visual rays are horizontal in space, VPL and VPR are at the same height as SP, which is at eye level as described previously.

A third visual ray, parallel to the vertical lines of the building, would not pierce the picture plane at all, proving that these lines have no vanishing point and thus must be parallel in the perspective. This is then another two-point perspective as expected from the arrangement of object and picture plane.

20.9 CONSTRUCTION OF A TWO-POINT PERSPECTIVE

In Fig. 20–11(a) the construction for vanishing points discussed in the preceding article is performed in multiview form. The point labeled SP, it must be remembered, is the top or plan view of the station point. The visual rays parallel to the horizontal edges of the block pierce the picture plane in points which appear in the plan view as points vpl^H and vpr^H. The points labeled VPL and VPR are the *front views* of these piercing points which are at eye level, the *horizon*. The location of the horizon must be known therefore before the perspective can be constructed. Since the perspective itself is merely the front view of the pattern formed by the piercing points of the visual rays to the object, VPL and VPR are the two vanishing points to be used in the construction of the perspective. The beginner must take special care to avoid being confused by the overlapping top and perspective (front) views. This arrangement is customary because of the space saved.

With the vanishing points established, construction of the perspective can be started, Fig. 20–11(b). The forward or leading vertical edge 1,2 of the object has been placed in the picture plane and thus is its own perspective (like edge 1,2 in Fig. 20–8). This line is therefore true length in the perspective and is drawn directly below the corresponding corner of the plan view at its true height with respect to the horizon. It is convenient to place an available elevation view, in this case the right elevation (right-side view), at this given height with respect to the horizon so that the T-square may be used to transfer height dimensions as shown for edge 1,2.

Construction lines containing the horizontal edges extending from point 1 are now drawn to the corresponding vanishing points. The piercing points 3 and 4 of visual rays to the other ends of these horizontal edges are determined in the top view and projected to the front view as shown to establish points 3 and 4 of the perspective. Point 5 is now located by a visual ray and projection to edge 1,3 in the perspective. From point 5 a line is drawn toward VPR, and point 6 is located on this line by a vertical projection line from

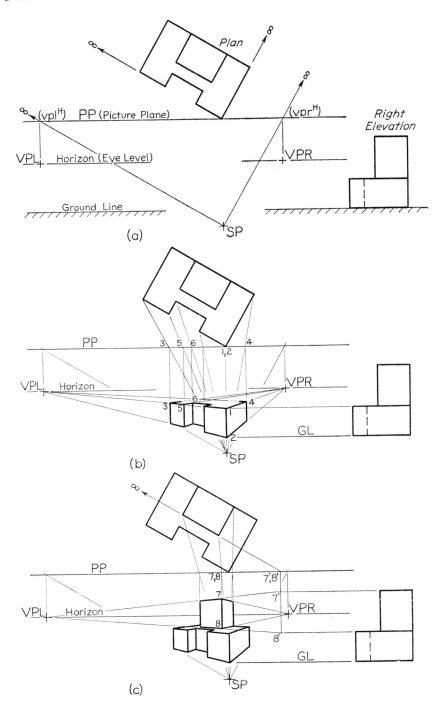

Fig. 20–11. Construction of a Two-Point Perspective

the piercing point of the visual ray for the corresponding point in the plan view. These procedures are repeated for other points until the perspective of the base of the object is completed.

When an object is so placed that its leading edge is not in the picture plane, the perspective of the leading edge is neither in true length nor at true height. This is the situation for the prismatic upper portion of the given object of Fig. 20–11. To locate the perspective of the leading edge of this prism, its vertical front surface is imagined to be extended to intersect the picture plane in line 7′,8′, Fig. 20–11(c). Since points 7′ and 8′ are in the picture plane, and since the lines extended to locate them are horizontal in space, points 7′ and 8′ must be at true height in the perspective. Thus they are located as shown by projection from the given side view. Construction lines representing the infinitely long extensions of the corresponding edges of the object may now be drawn in the perspective from points 7′ and 8′ to VPL. Points 7 and 8 are then located on these construction lines by projection from the piercing points of the corresponding visual rays obtained in the plan view. With the leading edge 7,8 of the prism located, the remainder of the perspective is completed in the same manner as the first portion.

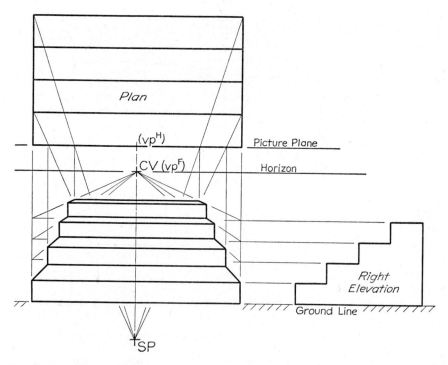

Fig. 20–12. Construction of a One-Point Perspective

20.10 CONSTRUCTION OF A ONE-POINT PERSPECTIVE

As stated in Art. 20.7, if an object is placed with two sets of principal edges parallel to the picture plane, only the third set of principal edges has a vanishing point. When a visual ray is drawn parallel to this third set of edges, Fig. 20–12, the vanishing point turns out to be the center of vision, CV. From this stage the perspective construction is the same as in two-point perspective.

One-point perspectives are popular for showing interiors and long, receding vistas. For instance, see Fig. 20–13, which is a one-point perspective except for minor discrepancies introduced by the optics of photography.

Fig. 20–13. One-Point Perspective—Courtesy Taylor Engineering and Manufacturing Co., Allentown, Pa.

20.11 CURVES IN PERSPECTIVE

By the methods explained in Art. 20.9, the perspective of any given point can be located. The construction of the perspective of a curve is merely repetition of this fundamental construction to locate a sufficient number of desirably spaced points so that a smooth curve may be drawn through them.

In Fig. 20–14 the straight-line portions of the perspective are located as before. A series of points is then introduced on the circular view of the larger arc, and their corresponding plan views are located by transfer distances such as D. Now, if horizontal construction lines are drawn through these points on the front surface of the object and extended to pierce the picture plane, the piercing points are at true height in the perspective. The perspectives of the construction lines then extend from the piercing points to VPL. The points themselves are located on the construction lines through the use of visual rays in the usual way. Points on the smaller arc are established in similar fashion.

The foregoing procedure could be repeated to locate points on the visible portion of the rear arc, but it is simpler to draw the elements of the cylindrical surface, in the plan and in the perspective, through the numbered points previously established. The points on the rear arc are then points on these elements and may be found directly by drawing visual rays to the points in the plan view and projecting from the piercing points of the rays.

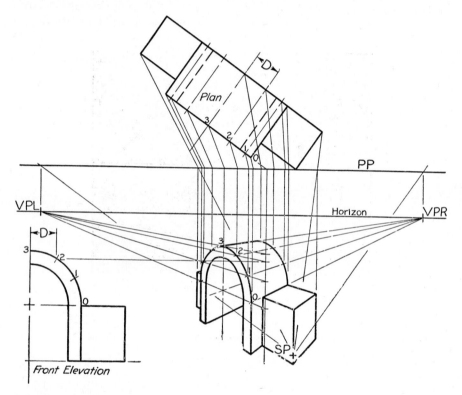

Fig. 20–14. Curves in Perspective

20.12   THREE-POINT PERSPECTIVE

If an object is placed so that none of its principal edges are parallel to the picture plane, there will be three principal vanishing points. The construction becomes somewhat more involved, so that three-point perspective is not widely used. It is effective, however, for realistic illustration of tall structures and for bird's-eye views where the heights of the objects are to be emphasized.

As an illustration, Fig. 20–15, a simple rectangular prism is drawn in three-point perspective. Given the front and top views of the prism and station point, Fig. 20–15(a), and given that the observer is looking toward the center C of the prism, an auxiliary view showing ray SP–C in true length also shows the picture plane in edge view and perpendicular to sp^1–c^1. Since the vanishing point of a line is the perspective of an infinitely distant point

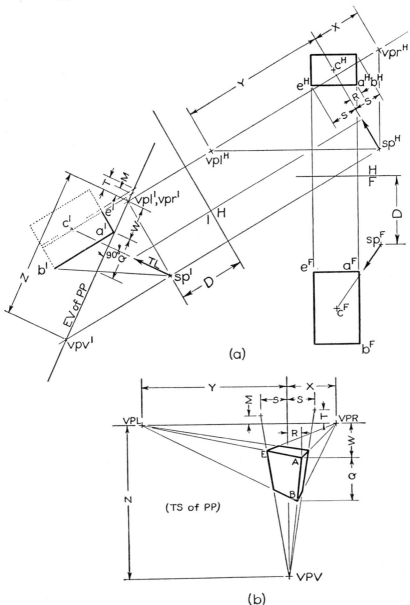

(a)

(b)

Fig. 20–15. Three-Point Perspective

on the line, visual rays are drawn parallel to the edges of the prism in the top and auxiliary views. Their piercing points with the picture plane are located in the auxiliary and top views and are transferred to Fig. 20–15(b) by means of distances X, Y, and Z. Figure 20–15(b) is to be a true-size view of the picture plane (and perspective), but its position on the paper is more natural if it is constructed with line VPL–VPR horizontal than if it is projected from view 1 as a secondary auxiliary view.

Point A of the prism is in the picture plane and is located in the perspective by transfer of distances R and W. The three edges meeting at A then lie along the construction lines from A to the three vanishing points. The ray from sp^1 to b^1 pierces the picture plane at a distance Q below a^1. This distance then locates B in the perspective.

As an illustration of another method of locating the perspective of a point not in the picture plane, the prism edge through e^1 is extended and pierces the picture plane at a distance M from vpl^1–vpr^1. This piercing point is transferred to the perspective by means of distance M, and distance S obtained in the top view. The extended edge of the prism then appears in the perspective as the line from this piercing point to VPV. Its intersections with the lines from A and B to VPL determine the end points of the edge of the prism through E. Repetition of these methods completes the perspective.

Of course, if the entire auxiliary view of the object is drawn as indicated in phantom, the method is objectionable for representing a complicated structure. If the object is composed principally of horizontal and vertical lines, however, the entire auxiliary view need not be completed. The piercing points of extended vertical edges may be located instead by projection from the top view to the picture plane in view 1.

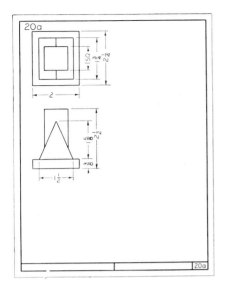

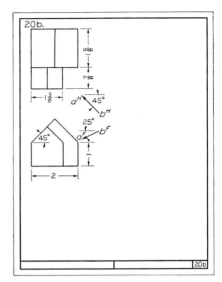

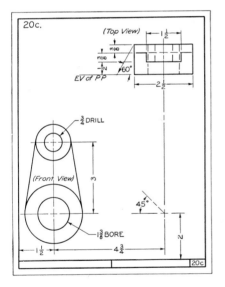

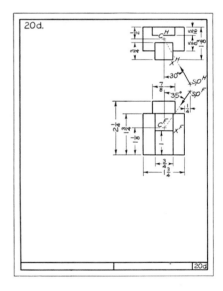

20a. Draw an isometric projection of the given object.

20b. Using the given layout, draw a dimetric projection.

20c. Construct an oblique projection as indicated.

20d. Using the given layout, draw a three-point perspective. Point C is the center of vision. The arrow indicates the direction of sight. Pass the picture plane through point X.

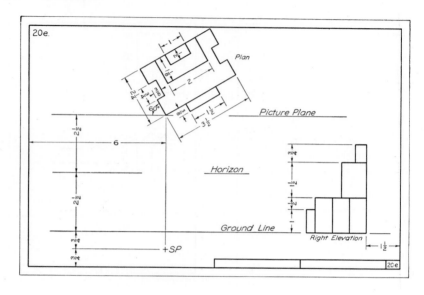

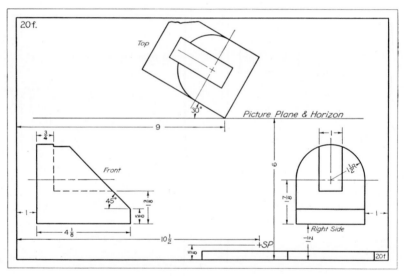

20e. Show the perspective of the *office building* outline.

20f. Draw the perspective of the *slide block*. The front view may be deleted.

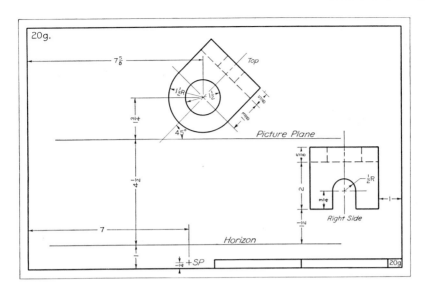

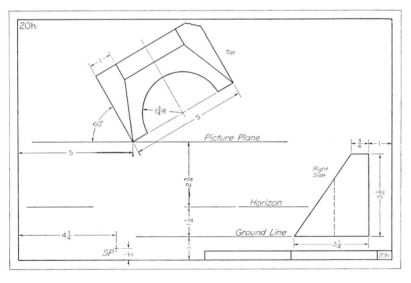

20g. Construct the perspective of the *guide collar.*

20h. Draw the perspective of the *abutment.*

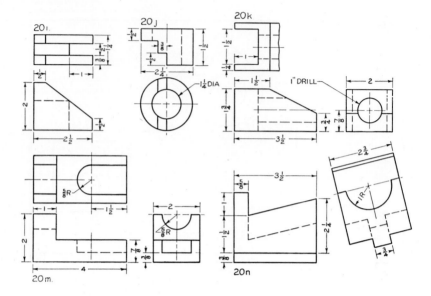

20i–n. Draw axonometric, oblique, or perspective projections as assigned.

20o. Indicate whether the following statements are true or false. If assigned, prepare written explanations or sketches to justify the answers.

(a) Hidden lines are usually omitted from pictorial drawings.

(b) An isometric projection is a form of orthographic projection.

(c) A true ellipse can be drawn by the four-center method.

(d) A circle can appear in its true shape in a perspective pictorial.

(e) In two-point perspective not more than two vanishing points are ever desirable.

(f) On a perspective drawing a line can project longer or shorter than its true length.

(g) The perspective projection of a straight line is always a single straight line.

(h) In three-point perspective all vertical lines converge to a single vanishing point.

CHAPTER 21 | CONICS

THE INTERSECTIONS OF planes and right-circular cones produce the more common plane curves or *conic sections,* namely, the *circle, ellipse, parabola,* and *hyperbola.* When a plane is perpendicular to the axis of a right-circular cone, the section is a circle. An ellipse is formed when the plane intersects every element of the cone and is not perpendicular to the axis. If the cutting plane is passed parallel to an element of the cone, the section is a parabola. The hyperbola is formed when the plane cuts both *nappes*[1] of a conical surface.

21.1 THE ELLIPSE

In Fig. 21–1, the intersection of a plane and a right circular cone is shown. The plane is placed so as to cut each and every element of the cone. The introduction of a series of horizontal cutting planes permits the establishment of points on the ellipse in the auxiliary view. The *foci* are determined by the projections of the centers of two spheres inscribed in the cone and tangent to the cutting plane. The *directrices* are projected to the auxiliary view as the lines of intersection between the given cutting plane and the horizontal planes through the tangent circles of the spheres and cone.

The ellipse may be defined as the locus of points in a plane whose distances from a fixed point (either of the foci) are in constant ratio, less than unity, to their distances from a fixed line (the corresponding directrix). Note the procedure used to locate point K on the ellipse.

Another definition of the ellipse describes it as the path of a point moving in a plane in such a manner that the sum of its distances from two fixed points (the foci) is constant and equal to the longest dimension of the ellipse. This definition is utilized in the pin-and-string method given in most general mechanical drawing texts.[2]

---

[1] See Appendix III.2.
[2] For still other methods of constructing an ellipse, see Appendix II.

The tangent to an ellipse at a given point such as G on the ellipse, Fig. 21–1, bisects the angle formed by the two *focal radii* through the given point

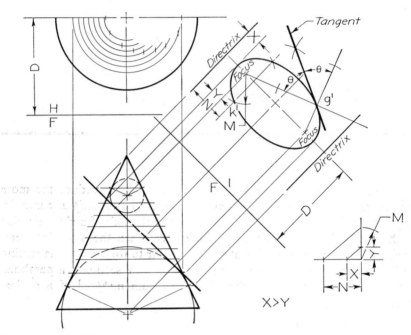

Fig. 21–1. The Ellipse

21.2   THE PARABOLA

A parabola is formed when the cutting plane is parallel to an element of the right-circular cone, Fig. 21–2. The line of intersection between the cone and cutting plane is determined by a series of horizontal cutting planes and is shown in true size in the auxiliary view. The focus is the projection of the center of a sphere inscribed in the cone and tangent to the cutting plane. The directrix is the line of intersection between the cutting plane and a horizontal plane passed through the circle of tangency of the inscribed sphere and cone. The axis of the parabola is the projection of the axis of the cone.

The parabola may also be described as the path of a point moving in a plane so that its distance from a given point (the focus) is always equal to its distance from a given straight line (the directrix). Point K in the auxiliary view illustrates application of this principle in constructing the parabola.

The tangent to a parabola through a given point bisects the angle formed by a focal radius and a diameter (a perpendicular to the directrix) through the given point. Figure 21–2 shows the tangent through a point P.

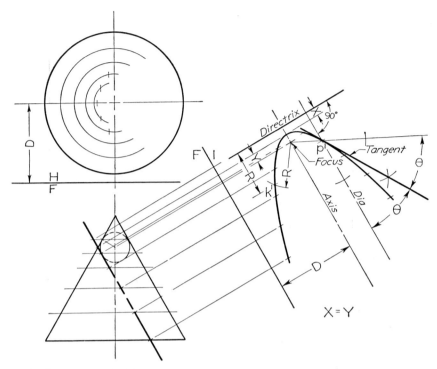

Fig. 21–2. The Parabola

21.3 THE HYPERBOLA

Figure 21–3 shows a hyperbola, which is composed of the intersections of the cutting plane with both nappes of the conical surface. For convenience, the cutting plane has been passed parallel to the axis. The focus for each nappe is the projected center of the sphere inscribed in the corresponding nappe of the cone and tangent to the cutting plane. The directrices are the lines of intersection between the cutting plane and planes passed through the circles of tangency of the spheres and the nappes of the cone. The *asymptotes* are the projections of the extreme elements of the nappes. They are the lines to which the curves would thoeretically be tangent at an infinite distance.

The hyperbola may also be described as the path of a point moving in a plane in such manner that the difference of its distances from two fixed points (the foci) is constant and equal to distance *AB*. This principle, used in Fig. 21–3 to locate points *G* and *H,* is applied for as many points as desired to draw the complete hyperbola.

The tangent at a given point on a hyperbola bisects the angle formed by the two focal radii which intersect at the given point. The construction for the tangent at point P illustrates this procedure.

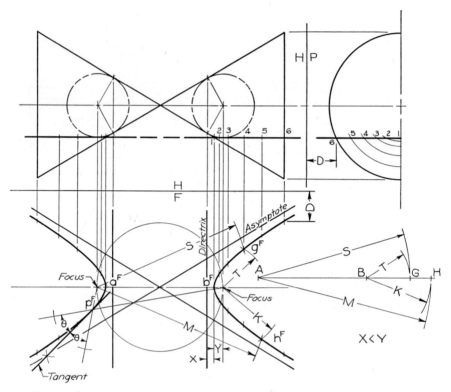

Fig. 21–3.   The Hyperbola

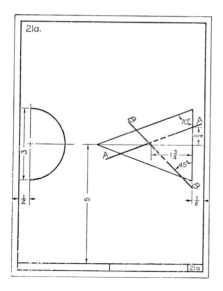

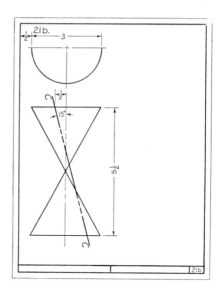

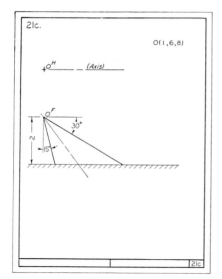

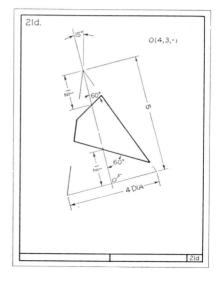

21a. Plot and name the curves produced by cuts *AA* and *BB*. Show the foci and directrices and construct tangent lines at assigned points.

21b. Plot and identify the curves of intersection of cutting plane *CC* with both nappes of the conical surface. Locate the foci and asymptotes.

21c. Show the true-size view of the ground area illuminated by the right-circular conical beam of a floodlight at point *O*. Calculate the area illuminated. [Area of ellipse $= \dfrac{\pi}{4}$ (major axis × minor axis)]

21d. Draw the views that show the true sizes of the bases of the given portion of a right-circular cone.

CHAPTER 22 | MAP PROJECTION

ALTHOUGH THE SHAPE of the earth closely approaches an ellipsoid, for an introductory study of map-making the shape may be considered spherical. The characteristics of the surface of the earth are best portrayed on the familiar spherical globe found in geography classrooms. But since the globe is impractical for many uses, other methods have been devised for representing the earth's surface. These methods all involve laying out the earth's surface on a single plane. This, then, is a development problem; and if a sphere were theoretically developable, an accurate representation would be possible. Since this is not the case, approximate methods are used. Although some accuracy is lost in these approximations, there are unique inherent advantages that for many uses make them more valuable than the globe.

The most fundamental principle of cartography (map-making) is the establishment of a coordinate system on the earth's surface to which any point can be related. The most frequently used set of coordinates is the *parallel-meridian* system. In this system there are 90 parallels of *latitude* between the equator and each pole. Figure 22–1 shows the 45° North

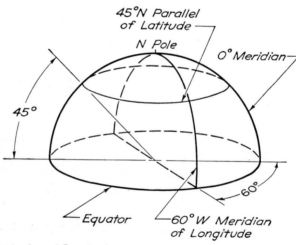

Fig. 22–1. Latitude and Longitude

288

parallel of latitude. The other set of coordinates consists of 180 great circles radiating from the pole at equal angles and dividing the parallels into 360 degrees of *longitude*. Figure 22–1 shows the 60° West meridian of longitude. It is customary to reckon longitude east and west from a prime (zero) meridian up to 180 degrees. The meridian through Greenwich, England, is used by almost all countries except France as the prime meridian. This system of coordinates provides a framework upon which the position for each spot on the earth's surface may be located according to its known latitude and longitude.

22.1　REPRESENTATION OF EARTH'S SURFACE

The earth's surface may be approximately represented by projection on a plane or on a developable geometric shape such as a cylinder or cone, Fig. 22–2. The projectors used may be either parallel or converging.

Since the earth is essentially flat for limited areas, no problem exists in providing satisfactory maps for such areas. It is for relatively large areas that many types of maps have been devised in an attempt to minimize distortion.

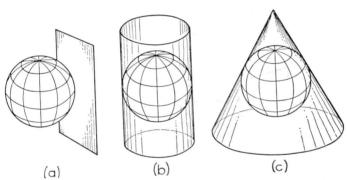

(a)　　　　　(b)　　　　　(c)

Fig. 22–2.　Types of Developable Surfaces on Which the Surface of a Globe May Be Projected

22.2　PROJECTION ON A TANGENT PLANE

If the earth's axis is inclined and the surface is projected orthographically to a plane as shown in Fig. 22–3, the resulting map has a pictorial effect that makes it particularly useful for many elementary textbook illustrations.

In *gnomonic* projection the projection lines emanate from the center of the sphere. Figure 22–4 shows a *polar gnomonic projection* with projection lines radiating from the center to a plane tangent at the North pole. The principal advantage of gnomonic projection is the fact that all great circles are projected as straight lines, a property of particular value in navigation

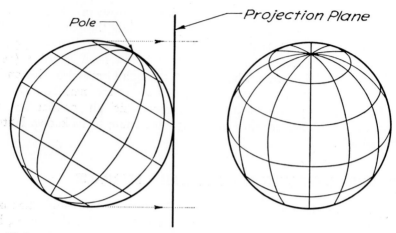

Fig. 22–3. Orthographic Projection

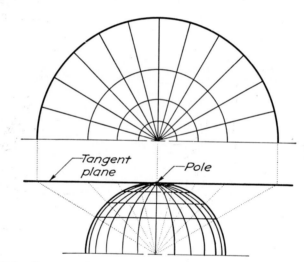

Fig. 22–4. Polar-Gnomonic Projection

since the shortest distance between two points on the earth's surface lies along a great circle.

Most maps in common use are not obtained by such geometrical means as previously introduced but are nongeometrical variations of these types. For instance, the map of Fig. 22–5 is one in which the gnomonic projection is altered so that the distances between parallels are equal. Thus measurements made radially from the pole are true distances on the earth's surface. Distances measured in other directions, however, are not true.

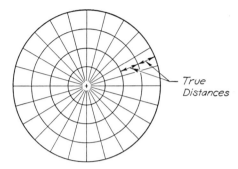

Fig. 22–5. Non-Geometrical Polar Map

22.3 PROJECTION ON A CONE

The surface of the earth may be projected on a tangent cone, resulting in the geometrically produced map of Fig. 22–6. Here the parallels are projected as concentric circles and the meridians as converging straight lines. The parallel in contact with the enveloping cone is projected true and is called the *standard parallel*. Other features of the earth are not projected true, with the distortions increasing in proportion to the distance from the standard parallel. To avoid undue distortion the area projected on the cone is limited to that included between the 0° and 60° parallels.

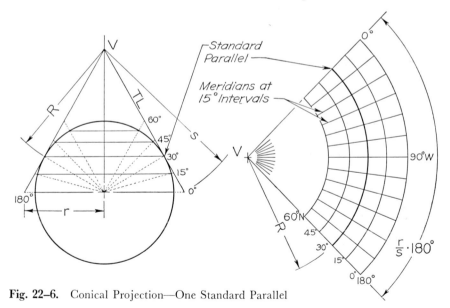

Fig. 22–6. Conical Projection—One Standard Parallel

For practical use a nongeometrical variation of this conical projection has been developed, Fig. 22–7. A standard parallel is used as before, along which true distances are laid off. In contrast to the theoretical projection, here the parallels are spaced at true distances. Again the number of parallels is limited to avoid increasing scale variations.

Projection on a cone passed through the earth as shown in Fig. 22–8 results in two standard parallels. In this method a somewhat greater area may be projected without objectionable scale variation. For practical use this projection is altered so that the parallels are evenly spaced.

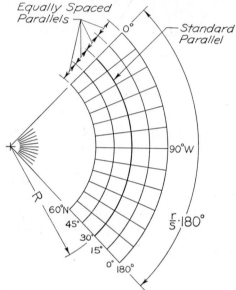

Fig. 22–7.   Non-Geometrical Conical Map

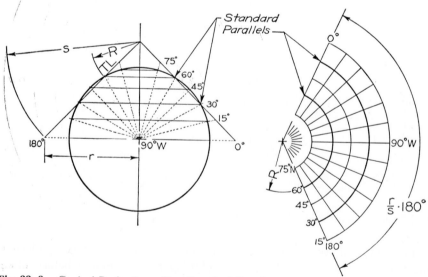

Fig. 22–8.   Conical Projection—Two Standard Parallels

Another nongeometrical variation of conical projection is the *polyconic map*, Fig. 22–9. This map is an alteration of the zone method [1] of a sphere development.

In the polyconic map the parallels appear as nonconcentric circles, the radii of which are the slant heights of the corresponding tangent cones of Fig. 22–9(a). The spacing of the parallels is controlled by the straight central meridian which is drawn to true scale, Fig. 22–9(b). The points at which the meridians cross the parallels are located by setting off along each parallel the corresponding distances between the meridians. These distances may be approximated by transfer of the chordal distances such as X from the top view, or by the rectified-arc method of Appendix II.11. Alternatively, the total angle through which each parallel extends may be calculated in the same way as in the development of a right-circular cone, Art. 17.4. The parallel is then subdivided to correspond to the number of meridians included. The meridians passing through these points are curved lines. The scale along the meridians increases as the distance from the central meridian increases. Thus the polyconic map has but little scale distortion near the central meridian but rapidly increasing distortion at the east and west extremes.

The polyconic map is well known in the United States since it has had considerable use by the U. S. Coast and Geodetic Survey.

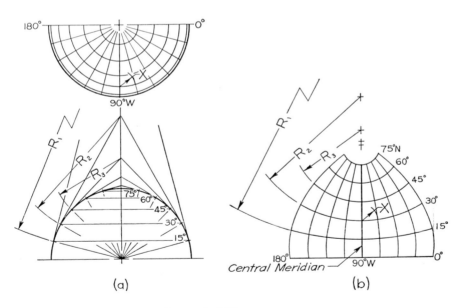

Fig. 22–9.   Polyconic—Non-Geometrical Map

_____
[1] See Art. 17.13, Example 3.

22.4   CYLINDRICAL PROJECTION

A cylindrical surface is another developable form on which the earth's surface may be projected to secure a geometrically produced map. Figure 22–10 shows a cylindrical projection in which the projectors emanate from the center of the sphere. On the development of the cylindrical surface both the parallels and meridians are produced as straight lines. The equator is projected at its true scale, but other parallels have a scale distortion which increases in relation to the distance from the equator.

Variations may be obtained in cylindrical projections by the use of ortho-graphic projection or by the use of a cylindrical form that cuts through the sphere in about the same manner as the cone of Fig. 22–8.

The most popular and useful nongeometric variation of cylindrical pro-jection is the Mercator map, Fig. 22–11. Here the scale of the meridians is increased in the same proportion as the scale of the parallels. Thus at any point on the map the scale is the same in every direction, but areas are con-siderably exaggerated for the extreme north and south latitudes. An advan-tage in navigation is the fact that a constant compass bearing appears as a straight line (a *rhumb* line) on this map.

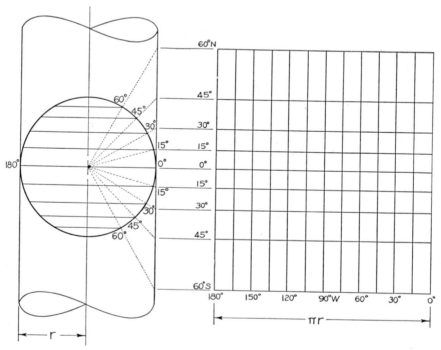

Fig. 22–10.   Geometrical Cylindrical Projection

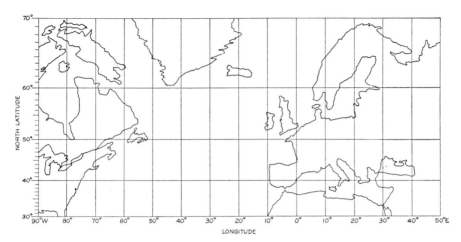

Fig. 22–11. A Mercator Map

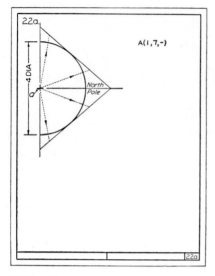

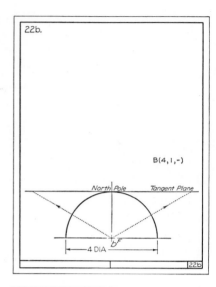

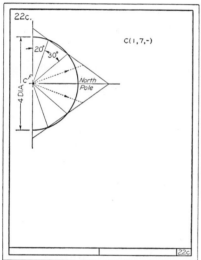

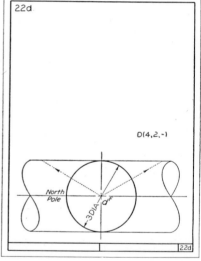

In each of the following problems locate points on the map as assigned by the instructor.

22a. Project as indicated the surface of the earth on a cone tangent at the 40° parallel and construct the map. Show the parallels at 10° intervals from 10° to 70° and the meridians at 10° intervals from 0° to 180° W.

22b. Draw the polar-gnomonic projection showing the parallels at 10° intervals from the pole to the 30° N parallel. Show meridians at 10° intervals. Show the great circle course between two assigned points.

22c. Project as indicated the surface of the earth on the cone. On the map show the parallels at 10° intervals from the equator to 70° N. Show the meridians at 10° intervals.

22d. Project as indicated the surface of the earth on the cylinder. On the map show the parallels at 10° intervals from 60° N to 60° S and the meridians at 10° intervals from 0° to 180° W.

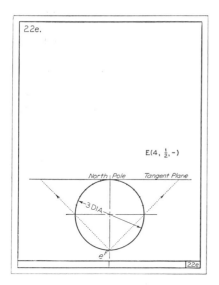

22e.

E(4, ½, -)

North Pole   Tangent Plane

3 DIA

e^F

22e

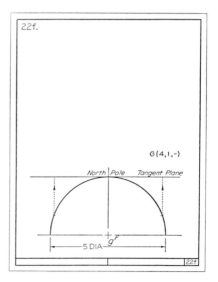

22f.

G(4,1,-)

North Pole   Tangent Plane

5 DIA   g^F

22f

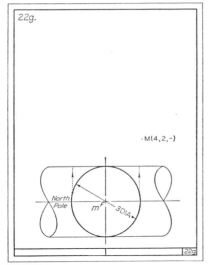

22g.

·M(4,2,-)

North Pole   m^F   3DIA

22g

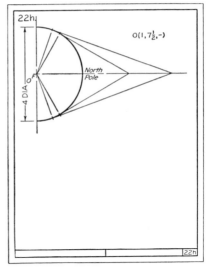

22h.

O(1,7½,-)

4 DIA   o^F   North Pole

22h

22e. Project as indicated the surface of the earth on the given tangent plane. Show the parallels at 15° intervals in the northern hemisphere. Show the meridians at 15° intervals.

22f. Project orthographically the surface of the earth on the tangent plane. Show the parallels at 10° intervals from 20° N to the North Pole. Show the meridians at 10° intervals.

22g. Project as indicated the surface of the earth on the cylinder. On the map show the parallels at 15° intervals from 75° N to 75° S. Show the meridians at 15° intervals from 0° to 180° W or as assigned.

22h. Using the given layout as started, construct a polyconic map with the parallels at 10° intervals from 20° N to 70° N. Show the meridians at 10° intervals from 0° to 180° W.

22i. Indicate whether the following statements are true or false. If assigned, prepare written explanations or sketches to justify the answers.

(a) On the earth's surface all meridians pass through the poles.

(b) On the earth's surface the parallels of latitude are great circles.

(c) New York is east of the zero meridian.

(d) On a Mercator map the length of the equator is the only line that appears true length.

(e) Neither the North nor South Pole can be represented on a Mercator map.

(f) A rhumb line is a constant bearing line.

(g) Any great circle appears as a straight line on a gnomonic projection.

(h) The polyconic projection provides a true representation of the earth's surface.

(i) In conic projection only one or two meridians are true length.

(j) The Cartesian coordinate system is normally used to identify the location of points on the earth's surface.

CHAPTER 23 | SPHERICAL TRIANGLES

THREE GREAT CIRCLES of the sphere of Fig. 23–1(a) intersect to form the *spherical triangle ABC*. This triangle together with the radial lines to the vertices form the *spherical pyramid OABC*, Fig. 23–1(a) and (b). The subsequent discussion is concerned with the relationships that exist between the parts of this pyramid.

Side *BC* is measured by the plane angle *BOC;* side *AC* is measured by the plane angle *COA;* and side *BA* is measured by the plane angle *BOA. The sum of the sides of a spherical triangle is less than 360°.*

The angle at *B* of the spherical triangle is measured by the dihedral angle formed by the intersecting faces *BOA* and *BOC*, the angle at *C* by the dihedral angle between faces *COB* and *COA*, and the angle at *A* by the dihedral angle between faces *AOB* and *AOC. The sum of the dihedral angles of a spherical triangle is greater than 180° and less than 540°.*

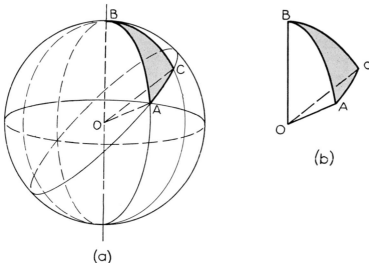

(a)

(b)

Fig. 23–1. Spherical Triangle and Spherical Pyramid

The following study of spherical triangles provides the basic theory for the solutions of problems in astronomy and navigation.

23.1 SOLUTION OF SPHERICAL TRIANGLE, THREE SIDES GIVEN

Let it be given that in a spherical pyramid $OABC$, side $BC = 40°$, side $BA = 60°$, and side $CA = 35°$. Let it be required to draw the front and top views of the pyramid and to solve for the angles of the spherical triangle.

The front and top views of any conveniently-sized sphere are drawn, Fig. 23–2. For simplicity of solution, face OBC is placed in a frontal plane. Being frontal, side BC is laid off at its given angle of $40°$ in the front view. In this position $b^F c^F$ appears as a true circular arc. Point c^H is located by projection.

With OB as an axis, face BOA is assumed revolved into this same frontal plane, and the given angle of $60°$ for BA is set off as indicated. About OC as

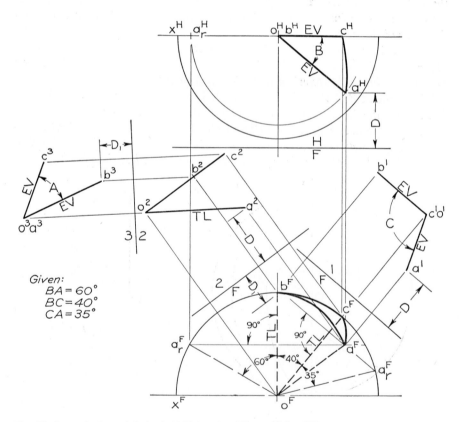

Fig. 23–2. Solution of Spherical Triangle—Three Sides Given

an axis, face COA is revolved into this same frontal plane, and the given angle of $35°$ for CA is set off. The front view at this stage is thus a development of the faces of the spherical pyramid. The actual front views of points O, B, and C coincide with these same points of the development. In the top view these three points are also in their correct positions. To complete the views of the actual pyramid, only point A needs to be located. The front view of A is secured by counter-revolution about the true-length axes of revolution $o^F b^F$ and $o^F c^F$. These paths of revolution, which appear perpendicular to the true-length axes, intersect to locate a^F. The path of revolution about the vertical axis OB appears as a true arc in the top view as shown. The intersection of this arc with a projector from a^F locates a^H. To aid visualization, the views of the spherical pyramid are completed by drawing the views of the great circle arcs $a^H c^H$, $b^F a^F$, and $a^F c^F$. These elliptical curves are not, however, necessary for the solution.

Angle B of the spherical triangle, which is measured by the included dihedral angle at B, is measured in the top view, since the intersecting planes of this angle both appear edgewise in this view. Angle C is obtained in auxiliary view 1, for which the direction of sight is along the true-length line of intersection $o^F c^F$. Since the line of intersection of planes BOA and OAC is oblique, successive auxiliary views 2 and 3 are used to produce edge views of these planes. In view 3 angle A is measured as shown, completing the solution.

23.2   SOLUTION OF SPHERICAL TRIANGLE, TWO SIDES AND INCLUDED ANGLE GIVEN

In a spherical pyramid $OABC$ let it be given that side $BA = 42°$, side $BC = 60°$, and angle $B = 50°$. Let it be required to draw the front and top views of the pyramid and solve for the remaining side and angles. A sphere of convenient size is drawn, Fig. 23–3, and plane BOC is placed in a frontal plane as shown, using the given $60°$ angle for side BC. Plane OBA is revolved into this same frontal plane about OB as an axis, utilizing the length $BA = 42°$ as given. In the top view the dihedral angle B is laid off at its given angle of $50°$, since the line of intersection OB of the planes appears as a point in this view. Point A is then counter-revolved. This path of revolution appears as a circular arc in the top view, and its intersection with the edgewise view of plane OBA locates a^H. The path of revolution appears perpendicular to the axis $o^F b^F$ in the front view. The intersection of this path in the front view with a vertical projector from a^H locates a^F. As in the previous example, angle C is obtained by use of the single auxiliary view 1; angle A is found by use of the successive auxiliary views 2 and 3. Side CA is obtained by the revolution of plane COA into the frontal plane about CO as an axis.

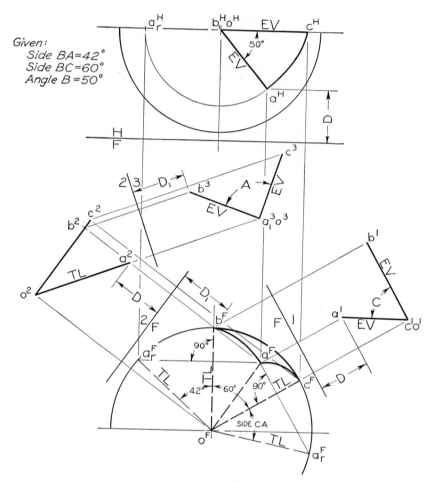

Fig. 23–3. Solution of Spherical Triangle—Two Sides and Included Angle Given

23.3 SOLUTION OF SPHERICAL TRIANGLE THREE ANGLES GIVEN—POLAR TRIANGLE METHOD

The *poles* of a great circle are the two end points of that diameter of the sphere which is perpendicular to the plane of the great circle. Six poles exist for the three great circles of a spherical triangle ABC. These poles can be joined to form eight spherical triangles. The *polar triangle*, however, is that triangle for which: pole B_1 is that pole of AC which falls on the same side of AC as does B; pole C_1 is that pole of BA which falls on the same side of BA as does C; and pole A, is that pole of BC which falls on the same side of BC as does A.

The polar triangle provides a means for solving a spherical triangle indirectly. For example a spherical triangle with the three angles given can be transformed into a problem of the related polar triangle with the three sides known. The solution of this polar triangle problem also provides the solution of the given triangle.

The following relationships are of particular importance:

1. *If a second triangle is the polar of a first, the first triangle is also the polar of the second.*

2. *An angle of a spherical triangle is the supplement of the opposite side of its polar triangle.*

This latter relationship can be explained by the following: Fig. 23–4 shows a given true dihedral angle X between two great circle planes of a spherical triangle. The plane angle at Y is produced by the perpendiculars used to obtain the poles of these great circles. It can be seen that angle Y is the supplement of angle X. Angle Y is the side of the polar triangle opposite to angle X of the given triangle.

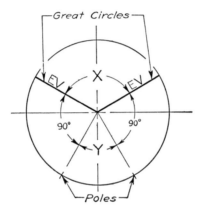

Fig. 23–4.   Poles of Great Circles

Thus a problem in which the three angles of a spherical triangle are given can be solved by means of its polar triangle.

PROBLEM:

Given:

$$\text{Angle } A = 120°$$
$$\text{Angle } B = 130°$$
$$\text{Angle } C = 125°$$

The sides of the related polar triangle are the supplements of the given angles.

$$\text{Side } B_1 C_1 = 180° - 120° = 60°$$
$$\text{Side } A_1 C_1 = 180° - 130° = 50°$$
$$\text{Side } A_1 B_1 = 180° - 125° = 55°$$

This polar triangle, having its three sides known, may be solved by the method of Art. 23.1. Then, in turn, the sides of the given spherical triangle can be computed, since they are supplementary to the angles of the polar triangle.

Figure 23–5 shows the polar triangle $A_1B_1C_1$, the views of which are found as explained in the foregoing. Vertices A and C of the given triangle are formed by drawing perpendiculars 2 and 3 to the great circle planes OB_1C_1 and OB_1A_1, which appear edgewise in the top view. Auxiliary view 1 is added to secure an edge view of the great circle plane OC_1A_1. Vertex B is found by drawing the perpendicular 4 to the edge-view plane OC_1A_1 as shown. When the vertices A, B, and C are located in each of the given views,

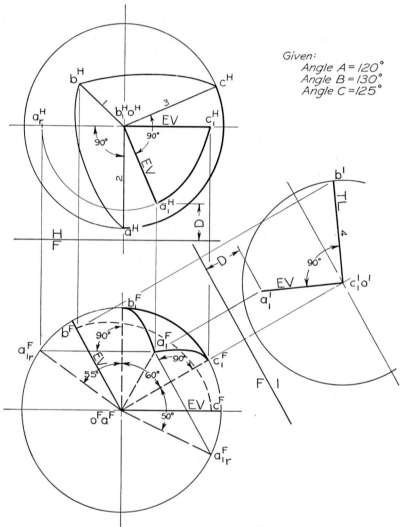

Fig. 23–5. Solution of Spherical Triangle, Three Angles Given—Polar Triangle Method

the views of the spherical triangle are completed as shown, the great circle lines being represented here for visualization purposes. The sides of the spherical triangle may now be solved as in previous examples (not shown here). As pointed out in the preceding paragraph, it is simpler to solve the polar triangle and then calculate the sides of the given spherical triangle.

23.4 NAVIGATION PROBLEM

On the surface of the earth, the shortest distance between two points is along the great circle containing the points. If the earth is assumed to be a perfect sphere, problems involving a great circle distance may be solved by the use of a spherical triangle.

Given point C, latitude 15° N, longitude 20° E, and point A, latitude 40° N, longitude 115° W, let it be required to solve for the distance between them.

Point B in the solution, Fig. 23–6, is regarded as the North Pole for convenience. Plane OBC is placed in the frontal plane through the pole, so that point C is located directly by using the angle of latitude 15° as given. Plane OBA is assumed to be revolved into the frontal plane about OB as an axis. For this revolved position, the given 40° angle of latitude is used to locate a_r^F.

The dihedral angle between planes OBC and OBA is equal to the difference in longitude of points A and C. Point C is 20° east of the prime meridian and A is 115° west of the prime meridian; thus the included angle between the two locations is 115° + 20°, or 135°. This angle is laid off as shown in the top view. Point A_r is counter-revolved to locate A as shown. Plane OCA is revolved about OC as an axis to secure an angular measurement of the required distance AC. Since 1° of arc is approximately equal to 60 nautical miles on the earth's surface, the great circle distance is obtained by multiplying the angle COA by 60.[1]

Since a great circle course would necessitate a constantly changing bearing, an exact great circle course is impractical. However, this shortest distance course can be approached by traveling a series of constant bearing courses called rhumb lines [2] which approximate the great circle. The initial rhumb-line bearing is equal to the dihedral angle between plane OBA and OCA. This angle θ is secured in auxiliary view 3 and is specified as N 47° (azimuth bearing). The final bearing is equal to the supplement of the dihedral angle between planes OCA and OBC. This angle is obtained in auxiliary view 1 and is specified as N 144°. Of interest is the fact that the course traveled is initially a northeasterly direction and is finally southeasterly.

---

[1] One nautical mile equals 6080 ft as compared with the statute mile of 5280 ft.
[2] Art. 22.4.

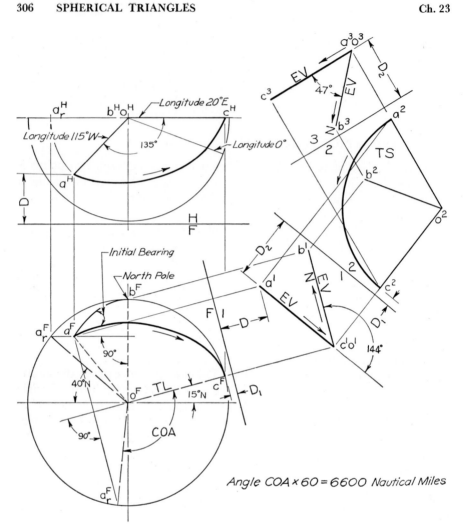

Fig. 23–6. Navigation Problem

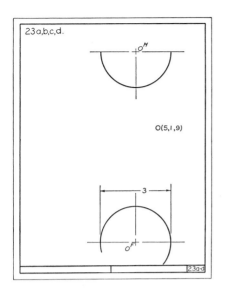

23a,b,c,d.

O(5,1,9)

3

23a-d

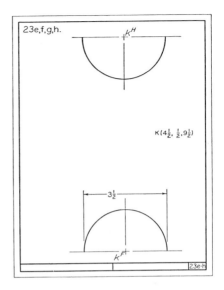

23e,f,g,h.

K(4½, ½,9½)

3½

23e-h

23a. Given that side $BC = 35°$, side $CA = 45°$, and side $BA = 65°$, solve for the angles A, B, and C of the spherical triangle ABC.

23b. Given that side $BC = 40°$, side $BA = 30°$, and angle $B = 60°$, solve for side CA and angles A and C.

23c. Given that side $BC = 30°$, angle $B = 50°$, and angle $C = 120°$, solve for angle A and sides BA and CA.

23d. Given that angle $A = 130°$, angle $B = 110°$, and angle $C = 130°$, solve for sides BC, CA, and BA.

23e. Given: point C, lat. 45° N, long. 10° W; and point A, lat. 40° N, long. 80° W. Determine the great-circle distance between the two points and plot the course in the given views.

23f. Given: point C, lat. 60° N, long. 20° E; point A, lat. 20° N, long. 115° W. Determine the great-circle distance between the two points and plot the course in the given views.

23g. Given: point C, lat. 45° N, long. 40° E; point A, lat. 0°, long. 100° W. Determine the great-circle distance from

A to C and the initial and final bearings.

23h. Given: point C, lat. 40° N, long. 30° W; point A, lat. 30° N, long. 115° E. Determine the great-circle distance from A to C and plot the course in the given views. Find the initial and final bearings.

23i. Indicate whether the following statements are true or false. If assigned, prepare written explanations or sketches to justify the answers.

(a) The sides of a spherical triangle are portions of great circles.

(b) The sum of the sides of a spherical triangle is equal to 180°.

(c) The shortest distance between two points along the earth's surface lies along a great circle through the points.

(d) The center of a great circle is always the center of the sphere.

(e) One degree of arc of a great circle is approximately equal to 60 nautical miles on the earth's surface.

(f) Only one great circle can be passed through two points on the earth's surface.

| REVIEW

In Chapters 1 through 23 the material was organized in a logical order for development of student understanding. Fundamental constructions were not introduced until needed. For example, primary auxiliary views were discussed in Chapter 2, but the introduction of successive auxiliary views was deferred until Chapter 5. Since there are a great many fundamental principles and constructions involving primary auxiliary views, it was felt that there was no need for burdening the student with successive auxiliary views until he had applied extensively to actual problems the principles of primary auxiliary-view constructions. But now that the student has almost completed his course in descriptive geometry, he should be aware of the fact that the really basic principles of the subject are few in number—that the majority of the topics covered are actually applications of these fundamentals to specific problems. This review chapter is *not* therefore an outline of the text but is an attempt to summarize and correlate in concise form the basic principles studied.

For ease in reading, back references are not given. It is expected that the student will use the index in the back of this book if he needs to refresh his memory on the details of a particular construction.

24.1 CONSTRUCTION OF ADDITIONAL VIEWS

In the early chapters several examples of the steps performed in the construction of additional views were discussed. These steps were worded in a general way because, as the student probably now realizes, the same procedure is used for the construction of *any* additional view of an object when two adjacent views are given.

It is perhaps the most important fundamental of descriptive geometry that if two points are established in adjacent views, their spatial relationship is thereby established. Hence information is available for the construction of any additional view of these two points. It may be that in a particular case the true spatial relationship of two points may not be so readily observed as in other cases. For example, if the front and top views of a profile line are given, the relative positions of the end points in space are more easily seen after a side view is added. Nevertheless, with only the front and top views *given*—implying that every point is shown and identified—all pertinent information about their relative positions is *available*.

Thus, with two adjacent views of an object given, any other views desired may be constructed. The procedure for constructing additional views adjacent to one of the given views is always the same. It is illustrated in Fig. 24–1, which is discussed in the following four steps.

Views 1 and 2 are assumed to be given. It is required that a third view be constructed adjacent to view 2.

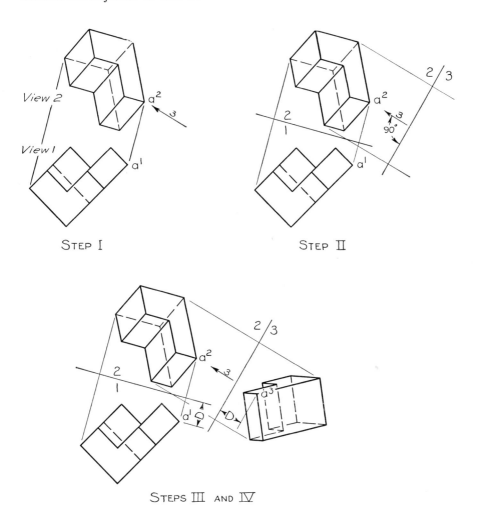

Fig. 24–1. Constructing an Additional View with Two Adjacent Views Given

Step 1.   Establish the line of sight for the desired information.

It might be said that this statement encompasses a large part of the understanding of descriptive geometry. The remaining steps 2, 3, and 4 become routine after a short period of application, so that the solution of almost any problem in reality reduces to the selection of the proper line of sight. In Fig. 24–1 the line of sight indicated by the arrow marked 3 is employed to make this illustration general and does not produce a particularly useful view 3. Article 24.2 reviews the general principles of establishing lines of sight in particular problems.

Step 2.   Introduce the necessary folding lines.

One folding line 1/2 is always perpendicular to the projection lines joining the given views. The second folding line 2/3 is always perpendicular to the line of sight for the desired additional view and is drawn at any convenient distance from the given view to which the required view is adjacent.

Step 3.   Transfer distances to the new view.

In Fig. 24–1 the additional view 3 is drawn adjacent to view 2. Hence a distance such as D for point a^1 is obtained in view 1 and is set off in view 3 along the projection line from a^2 to view 3.

Step 4.   Determine the visibility and complete the view.

24.2   THE FOUR FUNDAMENTAL USES OF VIEWS

Under Step 1 in Art. 24.1 it was stated that selection of the proper lines of sight is of basic importance in the solution of descriptive geometry problems. While a seemingly infinite variety of problems may be encountered in practice, each problem can be reduced to one or a combination of only four projected views. These are listed in Table 1, together with the corresponding positions for the lines of sight and a few frequently encountered applications.

Table 1. Uses of Additional Views

Use	Position of Line of Sight		Typical Applications
	In space	*On multiview drawing*	
1. True length of line (TL)	Perpendicular to line	Perpendicular to any view of the line or directed toward a point view of the line	(1) Prerequisite to Use 2 (2) Slope or grade (3) Angle between line and principal plane
2. Point view of line	Parallel to line	Parallel to true-length view of line	(1) In connection with Use 3 (2) Distance between line and point (3) Distance between line and another line
3. Edge view of plane (EV)	Parallel to plane	Parallel to true-length view of line in plane or directed toward a true-size view of the plane	(1) Prerequisite to Use 4 (2) Angle between two planes (3) Distance from point to plane, line perpendicular to plane
4. Normal or true-size view of plane (TS)	Perpendicular to plane	Perpendicular to edge view of plane	(1) Area of plane figure (2) Angle between intersecting lines (3) Other plane geometry constructions

A drawing employing the four uses listed in Table 1 is shown in Fig. 24–2. Examples of information obtained in the auxiliary views are:

View 1. True length of edge AB (use 1) and angle between AB and frontal plane (θ_F).
True size of surface $ABCE$ (use 4).

View 2. Point view of line AB (use 2).
Angle between surfaces $ABCE$ and $ABGK$ (use 3).

View 3. Point views of lines AK and BG (use 2) and angle between surface $ABGK$ and horizontal plane (use 3).

View 4. True size of surface $ABGK$ (use 4).

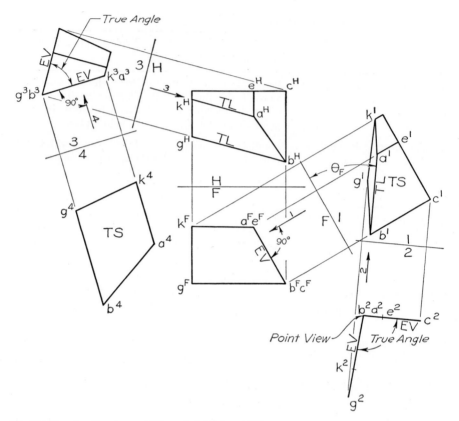

Fig. 24–2.   Applications of Uses of Additional Views

24.3   PROJECTIVE AND NONPROJECTIVE PROPERTIES

Relationships between lines and planes which are evident in their ortho-graphic projections are called *projective properties*.

Parallelism. If two lines are parallel, they appear parallel in any view (except in those views in which they coincide or appear as points).

If two lines are parallel in two views, the lines are parallel in space (unless the views are parallel to the projection lines between them, in which case the lines may or may not be parallel in space).

Perpendicularity. If two lines are perpendicular, they appear perpendicu-lar in any view showing at least one of these lines in true length (unless one of the lines shows as a point). In a view in which neither of two perpendicu-lar lines appears in true length, the lines will not appear perpendicular in the view.

If a line is perpendicular to a plane, it is perpendicular to all lines in the plane. Consequently a line perpendicular to a plane appears perpendicular to any true-length view of a line in the plane. A line perpendicular to a plane also must appear perpendicular to any edge view of the plane.

Points on Lines, Lines in Planes. If a point is on a line, the views of the point must lie on the repective views of the line.

If two lines intersect, they have a point in common; and in any two adjacent views, the two views of the point of intersection must lie on a common projection line.

If a line is in a plane, it must either intersect or be parallel to any other line in the plane, and these properties are retained as the lines are projected from view to view.

Proportional Division. Views of a series of points along a line segment divide the corresponding views of the line segment in the same proportions as the points divide the line segment. Thus the mid-point of a line appears as the mid-point in any view of the line.

On the other hand the views of a series of lines dividing a plane angle do *not* necessarily divide in the same proportion the corresponding views of the angle except where the angle appears in true size. For example, except in a true-size view, a view of the true bisector of an angle does *not* necessarily bisect the corresponding view of the angle.

24.4 EXAMPLE PROBLEMS

Example Problem 1:   True Size by Triangulation

GIVEN:

Triangle *ABC* represented by its front and top views, Fig. 24–3(a).

REQUIRED:

Construct the true size of the triangle without using auxiliary views.

ANALYSIS:

From plane geometry any triangle can be reproduced if the lengths of the three sides are known.

GRAPHIC SOLUTION:

Since no auxiliary views are permitted, the revolution method is used for finding the true lengths, Fig. 24–3(a). At (b) one of the edges, say *BC*, is drawn to length. Intersecting arcs of radii equal to *AB* and *AC* are drawn with *B* and *C* as respective centers to determine point *A*.

This method is used extensively in the development of surfaces by *triangulation* and by the *radial-line method*. It may also be used to reproduce polygons of more than three sides by dividing them into triangles by means of diagonals.

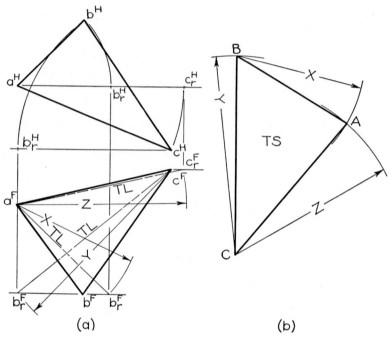

Fig. 24–3.   Example Problem 1: True Size by Triangulation

Example Problem 2:   Intersection and Development of Cylinders

GIVEN:

Front and top views of two intersecting right-circular cylinders, Fig. 24–4.

REQUIRED:

Plot the line of intersection and develop the surfaces of the cylinders, showing the line of intersection.

ANALYSIS:

A series of frontal cutting planes will be parallel to the axes of both cylinders and will cut elements from their surfaces.

GRAPHIC SOLUTION:

Partial auxiliary view 1 showing the inclined cylinder in its true circular form is added to facilitate the location of elements. The frontal cutting planes appear in this view as lines parallel to folding line $F/1$. They are drawn through equally spaced points 1 to 7 for convenience. Elements 1 to 7 are then located in the top view, in which their piercing points with the surface of the vertical cylinder are apparent. By projection, the front views of these piercing points are located and the front view of the intersection is completed.

Since the cylinders and their intersection are symmetrical about a center line, half-developments are sufficient. For accuracy in development the half-circumferences of the cylinders are calculated by $\pi D/2$ and $\pi d/2$. These distances are laid out to scale

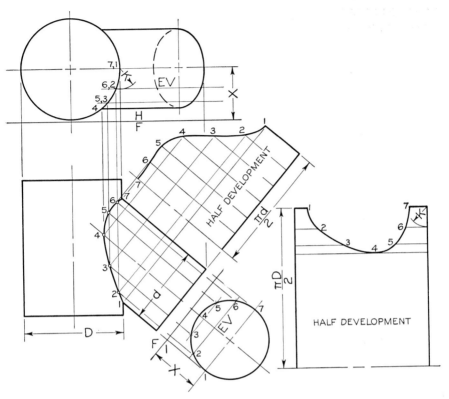

Fig. 24–4. Example Problem 2: Intersection and Development of Cylinders

and are divided into parts corresponding to the divisions of the circular views. For the larger cylinder, the elements containing the intersection points are located by chordal distances such as K. While theoretically these distances are too short, the error is slight and does not accumulate to an objectionable extent when the number of successive divisions is small, as in this case. The end points and intersection points on the elements are now located in the developments as shown to complete the problem.

Example Problem 3: Location of Reflected Light Ray

GIVEN:

Front and top views of a light ray GK and the plane $ABCE$ of a mirror, Fig. 24–5(a).

REQUIRED:

Locate the reflected ray without using auxiliary views.

ANALYSIS:

The *image* of point G is an imaginary point located on the opposite side of the mirror from point G and the same distance from the mirror. The direction of the reflected ray is determined by the image of point G and the intersection or piercing point of ray GK and plane $ABCE$. See the diagram in Fig. 24–5(b).

GRAPHIC SOLUTION:

Line GG_1 is constructed perpendicular to plane $ABCE$ by drawing its top view perpendicular to true-length view $c^H e^H$ and its front view perpendicular to true-length view $c^F f^F$. (Line CF is a frontal line added to the plane for this purpose.) The piercing point P of line GG_1 and plane $ABCE$ is then located by the two-view method. Length d of $g^F p^F$ is set off from p^F to locate g_1^F, thus making segments GP and PG_1 equal. The top view g_1^H is located by projection, or it could be located by transfer of the distance between g^H and p^H. Point G_1 is thus the image of point G.

Piercing point Q of ray GK (extended) and plane $ABCE$ is then located by the two-view method. The required reflected ray QS is the extension of the line G_1 to Q.

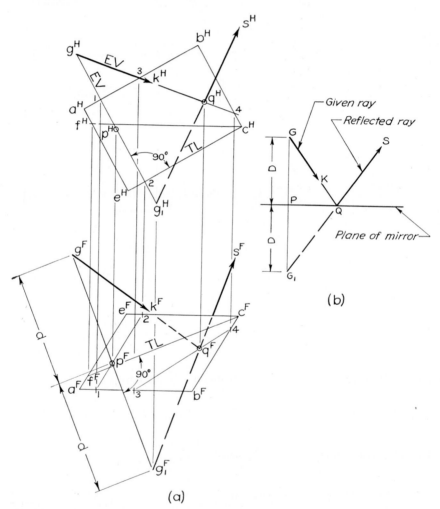

(b)

(a)

Fig. 24–5. Example Problem 3: Location of Reflected Light Ray

Example Problem 4:　Resultant and Resolution of Vectors

GIVEN:

The front and top views of plane $MNOP$ and of concurrent vectors AB and AC, point A being in plane $MNOP$, Fig. 24–6.

REQUIRED:

Find the resultant of the vectors and its magnitude. Locate the component (of the resultant) which acts normal to plane $MNOP$.

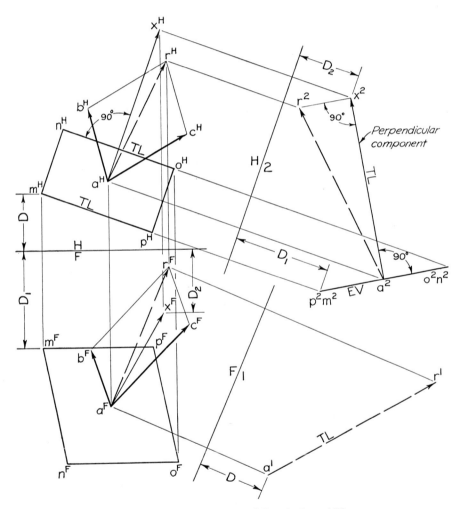

Fig. 24–6.　Example Problem 4: Resultant and Resolution of Vectors

ANALYSIS:

The resultant may be found in the given views by application of the *parallelogram of forces*. Its magnitude is its true length measured at the given scale. If the given plane is shown in edge view, any vector acting perpendicular to the plane must appear perpendicular to this edge view and in true length. The resultant may then be resolved into a component along this perpendicular (plus a component along the plane).

GRAPHIC SOLUTION:

Lines are drawn through points B and C parallel respectively to vectors AC and AB. These intersect at point R and diagonal AR is the required resultant. Its true length is found in auxiliary view 1.

Since lines MP and NO are in true length in the top view, it is convenient to obtain an edge view of plane $MNOP$ by projection from the top view as shown. Resultant AR is also projected to this auxiliary view and is resolved as required into component a^2x^2 acting perpendicular to plane $MNOP$. Since a^2x^2 is true length, the top view a^Hx^H is parallel to folding line $H/2$, and x^H is located by projection. The front view of AX is then established by projection from a^Hx^H and transfer of distance D_2 from the auxiliary view.

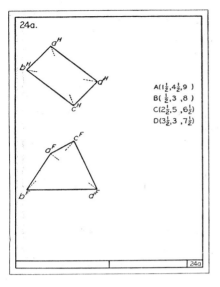

24a.

$A(1\frac{1}{2}, 4\frac{1}{2}, 9)$
$B(\frac{1}{2}, 3, 8)$
$C(2\frac{1}{2}, 5, 6\frac{1}{2})$
$D(3\frac{1}{2}, 3, 7\frac{1}{2})$

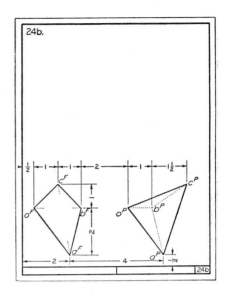

24b.

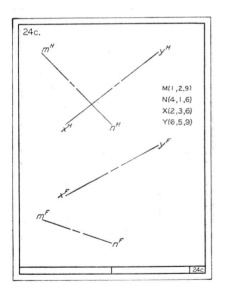

24c.

$M(1, 2, 9)$
$N(4, 1, 6)$
$X(2, 3, 6)$
$Y(6, 5, 9)$

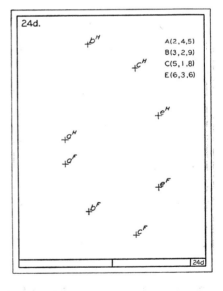

24d.

$A(2, 4, 5)$
$B(3, 2, 9)$
$C(5, 1, 8)$
$E(6, 3, 6)$

24a. Complete the visibility of the tetrahedron. Determine the true size of the angle formed by planes ABC and ACD. Show the true size of face ABC.

24b. Complete the visibility of the given pyramid. Find the true length and views of the altitude with O as the vertex. Show the true size of the plane ABC.

24c. Using only the given views, find the true length and the views of the shortest connector between the given pipe center lines.

24d. Locate the center of a sphere that passes through the four given points. Determine the radius of the sphere.

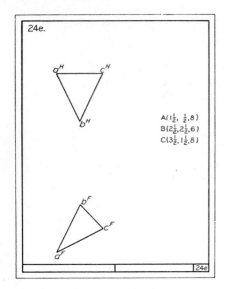

24e.

$A(1\frac{1}{2}, \frac{1}{2}, 8)$
$B(2\frac{1}{2}, 2\frac{1}{2}, 6)$
$C(3\frac{1}{2}, 1\frac{1}{2}, 8)$

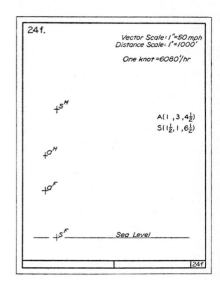

24f.

Vector Scale: $1''=50\,mph$
Distance Scale: $1''=1000'$

One knot = 6080'/hr

$A(1, 3, 4\frac{1}{2})$
$S(1\frac{1}{2}, 1, 6\frac{1}{2})$

Sea Level

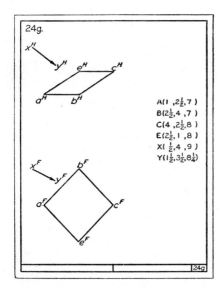

24g.

$A(1, 2\frac{1}{2}, 7)$
$B(2\frac{1}{2}, 4, 7)$
$C(4, 2\frac{1}{2}, 8)$
$E(2\frac{1}{2}, 1, 8)$
$X(\frac{1}{2}, 4, 9)$
$Y(1\frac{1}{2}, 3\frac{1}{2}, 8\frac{1}{4})$

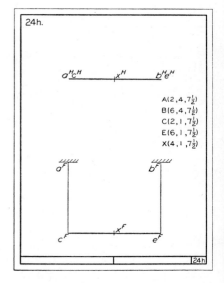

24h.

$A(2, 4, 7\frac{1}{2})$
$B(6, 4, 7\frac{1}{2})$
$C(2, 1, 7\frac{1}{2})$
$E(6, 1, 7\frac{1}{2})$
$X(4, 1, 7\frac{1}{2})$

24e. Show the views of a cube, one face of which lies in plane ABC with AB as a diagonal of this face of the cube.

24f. A ship at S is bearing N 75° at 30 knots. An airplane at A is bearing N 45° at 125 mph and is diving at a rate of 400 ft in 1000 ft. How close will the airplane come to the ship?

24g. Determine the true angle that light ray XY makes with the mirror surface $ABCE$. Show the views of the reflected ray and the true size of the mirror.

24h. Using only the given views, locate the new positions of the cross bar CE and its supporting cables AC and BE if the bar is revolved 75° clockwise about a vertical axis through point X.

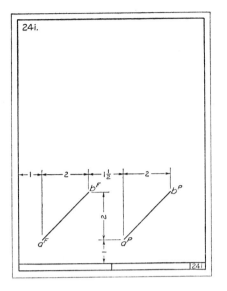

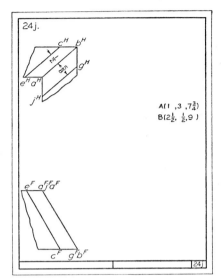

A(1 ,3 ,7¾)
B(2½, ½,9)

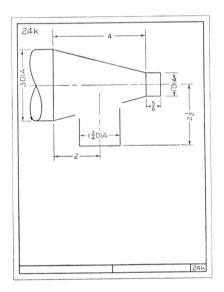

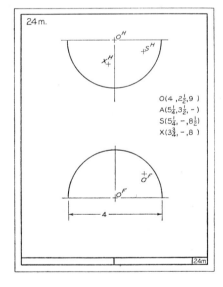

O(4 ,2½,9)
A(5¼,3½, -)
S(5¼, - ,8½)
X(3¾, - ,8)

24i. Pass a plane that contains line *AB* and makes an angle of 60° with a profile plane. Determine the angle that this plane makes with a horizontal plane.

24j. Determine the bend angle for the reinforcing plate *CEABJG*. Show the development of this plate.

24k. Using only the given view, con-struct the intersection of the conical and cylindrical ducts (sphere method). De-velop the surface of either or both as assigned, showing the intersection.

24m. Using only the given views, pass a plane tangent to the sphere at point *A*. Locate the gnomonic projections of points *S* and *X* on this tangent plane.

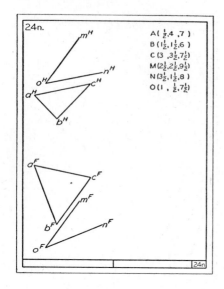

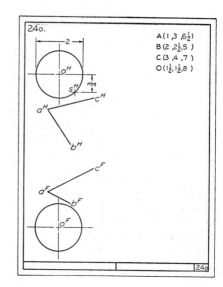

24n. Locate the views of the line in limited plane ABC that lies 2¼ in. from plane MON. Determine the bearing, grade, and true length of this line.

24o. (a) Determine the shortest distance from the surface of the sphere to plane ABC. (b) Point S lies on the surface of the sphere. Obtain the views of the orthographic projection of point S on the given plane.

24p. Prepare written statements and sketches (if assigned) explaining your answers to the following locus visualization questions:

(a) What is the locus of points at distance D_1 from a given plane and distance D_2 from a point?

(b) What is the locus of points equidistant from two parallel lines?

(c) What is the locus of points a fixed distance D from each of two skew lines?

(d) What is the locus of points equidistant from three points and lying in a given plane other than that of the three points?

(e) What is the locus of points equidistant from two points and from two intersecting lines?

(f) What is the locus of points 1 in. from a 3 in. diameter circle?

(g) What is the locus of points equidistant from two skew lines?

(h) What is the locus of points equidistant from four points no three of which lie in a straight line?

GRAPHICAL
ACCURACY

THE ACCURACY OF a graphic solution may be affected by many factors, several of the more important of which are discussed in the following material. In the interest of economy of time the engineer should realize that his graphical results can be no more significant than the original data. Then, too, if a problem is solved for which a large *safety factor* is introduced, the engineer, for economy of time and effort, needs only to maintain reasonable accuracy. With these considerations in mind the engineer can select a scale for his work that will help produce the desired accuracy, for it is the scale of the drawing that is perhaps the one factor that most drastically affects the accuracy. For instance an error of $\frac{1}{50}$ of an inch in 8 in. is an error of only $\frac{1}{4}$ of 1 per cent, while a similar error in 1 in. represents an error of 2 per cent. Thus it may be stated that the scale should be as large as can be conveniently handled with available drafting equipment.

I.1 DRAWING PAPER, EQUIPMENT, AND WORKING CONDITIONS

To assure best graphical accuracy, materials and working conditions should be carefully selected. A sharp, hard pencil should be used. A top quality paper or cloth that will retain its shape is essential; a metal surface may be used for best results. The drawing paper should be firmly attached to the board and left in the original position until the job is completed. Ideally, the temperature and humidity should be kept constant, since changes in these conditions may stretch or shrink the working surface. In lieu of this often impractical requirement, it is best to complete a particular construction in as short and continuous a working time as possible.

Top quality drafting instruments and other tools are needed to maintain accuracy. A small protractor should be used for only the roughest of work. If accurate angular measurements must be made, drafting machines or large vernier protractors are accurate tools for this purpose. In the absence

323

of such equipment an angular dimension may be laid off or measured by means of coordinates. For example, an angle of 38° 30′ can be established by using the tangent of the angle. The tangent of this angle is 0.7954, as found in the Table of Natural Tangents inside the back cover. As large a triangle as practicable is used to lay off this angle by means of its tangent, Fig. I–1. The adjacent side AC of the triangle is 10 units—any convenient unit such as 1 in. may be used. The length of side CB is then ten times the tangent of the desired angle, or 7.954 in. Actually, with the unaided eye a scale may be read only to an accuracy of approximately 0.01 in. Hence the side CB is set off with the scale to the nearest 0.01 in., or 7.95 in. as indicated.

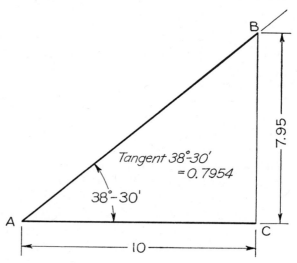

Fig. I–1.   Laying Out an Angle

I.2 DRAFTING PRACTICES

Although the student of descriptive geometry can be expected to exercise good drafting practices, it may be well to point out certain practices somewhat peculiar to this field. If, as in Fig. I–2, only the top view of point C on line AB is given, the front view of this point cannot be precisely located by direct projection because the projection line from c^H is too nearly parallel to $a^F b^F$. Point C can be located more accurately by use of an additional view as shown in Fig. I–2(a) or by means of revolution as illustrated in Fig. I–2(b).

In Fig. I–3 point K is in plane ABC. If either view of point K is given and it is required to locate the other view, the construction line through K and in the plane should be carefully chosen. For example, use of line 1,2 would probably introduce an error in a manner similar to that of Fig. I–2. It is better to draw the construction line through an established point of the

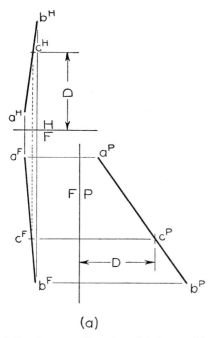

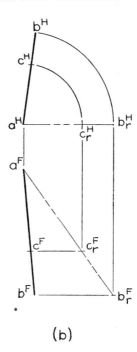

(a)   (b)

Fig. I–2.   Accurate Location of Point on Line

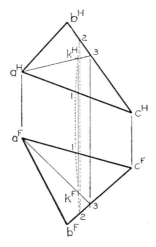

Fig. I–3.   Accurate Location of Point in Plane

plane and at a fairly large angle with the projection lines between the views. Thus use of construction line $A,3$ gives a more dependable result than use of line 1,2. In Fig. I–4 the top view of the horizontal line MH in plane MNO can be more accurately established by extending the plane to a point K, as shown, than by using the plane as given.

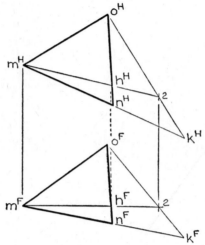

Fig. I–4. Accurate Location of Line in Plane

Figure I–5 illustrates another case in which location of a view of a point by projection to a given line is likely to be inaccurate. In this problem it is

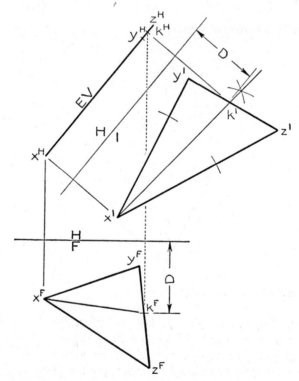

Fig. I–5. Accurate Location of Point by Transfer Distance

required to find the front and top views of the bisector of angle YXZ. The actual bisection is performed in the true-size auxiliary view, and the top view of point K on the bisector is readily found by projection. The front view of given line YZ is, however, nearly parallel to the vertical projection line from k^H. Thus it is preferable, for accuracy, to locate k^F by the transfer distance D available in the auxiliary view, rather than by intersecting $y^F z^F$ with the projection line from k^H.

When a line is established by locating two points of the line, the two points should not be too close together. It is physically impossible to draw a line precisely through two points, especially since *points* and *lines* in pencil or ink actually have diameters and widths in contrast to their theoretical definitions. Consequently it must be assumed that when an attempt is made to draw a line through a point, a certain amount of error will always be present. As an illustration, let it be required to draw a line through points A and B of Fig. I–6(a) and another line through points X and Y of Fig. I–6(b). For simplicity let it be assumed that the lines are actually drawn accurately through points A and X, and that inaccuracy is confined to the drawing of the lines through points B and Y, the errors being represented by the radii of the small circles. The angular error in the direction of a line thus drawn is obviously much greater when the points are relatively close together as in Fig. I–6(a). When this situation occurs in the solution of a problem, a third point on the required line should be secured if possible.

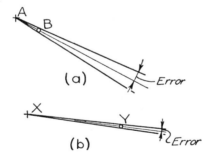

Fig. I–6. Line Located by Two Points

In the measurement of grade, Fig. I–7, the construction triangle should be as large as practicable. A scale error in measuring the distance labeled "rise" would be considerably less, percentage-wise, than a similar error in the measurement of distance Y.

Accumulative error is a frequent source of inaccuracy in drafting. If, for instance, dividers are used to step off a series of equal distances along a line, a seemingly insignificant error in the setting of the dividers may accumulate to an objectionable degree if the number of successive distances is large. This may be avoided if the over-all length of the line is known or can be calculated. This length may then be set off to scale and the divisions determined by the parallel-line method (Appendix II.1) or by trial with dividers. A similar situation arises when a series of dimensions are set off with a scale along a line. The scale should not be shifted for each dimension but should be left in one position for all settings, even though this may involve some mental arithmetic.

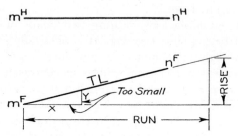

Fig. I–7. Measurement of Grade

GEOMETRIC
CONSTRUCTIONS

For quick reference a number of constructions frequently needed in the solution of descriptive geometry problems are given here. The methods shown are those which draftsmen prefer because of the rapidity and ease with which they are performed.

II.1 PARALLEL-LINE METHOD OF DIVISION OF LINE INTO SEGMENTS, FIG. II–1

Given line AB is to be divided into three equal parts. A scale is placed at any convenient angle with line AB and with its zero index at point A. Three equal divisions are marked and the third division point, point K, is connected by a construction line to point B. Lines are drawn through the intermediate points parallel to line BK. Their intersections with line AB establish the required divisions of AB.

The construction may be made somewhat more readily by first drawing a vertical (or horizontal) construction line through point B. The scale is then placed at such an angle that the third division point (K) falls on this

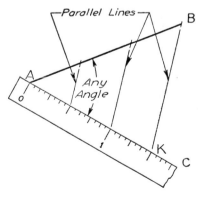

Fig. II–1. Parallel-Line Method of Division of Line into Segments

construction line. This makes the drawing of the intermediate construction lines more convenient.

II.2   CONSTRUCTION OF A SQUARE, GIVEN THE CENTER AND ONE CORNER, FIG. II–2

If point O is the center and point C the given corner, line OC is one-half of a diagonal. The complete diagonal is thus CB, with distance OB made equal to OC. The other diagonal is perpendicular to CB, and its end points are located by divider distances equal to OC or by drawing the circle with center at O and radius OC.

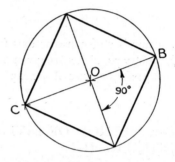

Fig. II–2.   Construction of a Square, Given the Center and One Corner

II.3   DRAWING A CIRCLE THROUGH THREE POINTS, FIG. II–3

If A, B, and C are given points on the required circle, lines AB and AC are chords of this circle. The perpendicular bisectors of these chords are

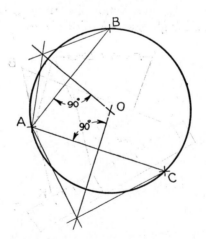

Fig. II–3.   Drawing a Circle Through Three Points

constructed by the draftsman's method of equi-angular lines, and they inter-sect at the center O of the required circle. The circle is then drawn with radius OA, OB, or OC.

II.4 TRANSFERRING A POLYGON, FIG. II–4

While several methods, including triangulation, may be used to transfer a polygon from one position to another, the method shown is probably the most accurate. Let it be required to transfer the polygon from the given position at (a) to the position at (b) with edge 1,2 given at (b).

Construction lines X_1 and X are drawn perpendicular to lines 1,2 in (a) and (b) at points 1 and 2, respectively. In (a), construction lines Y and Y_1 are drawn parallel to edge 1,2 from the remaining corners 3 and 4. The lengths of X and X_1 are then transferred from (a) to (b), and lines Y and Y_1 are drawn parallel to 1,2 in (b). The lengths of Y and Y_1 are transferred to locate corners 3 and 4 and the polygon is completed in (b).

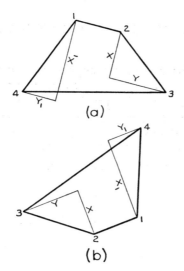

Fig. II–4.   Transferring a Polygon

II.5 CONSTRUCTION OF ELLIPSE BY CONCENTRIC CIRCLE METHOD, FIG. II–5

If the major axis XX_1 and the minor axis YY_1 are given, points on the ellipse may be located as follows: Two concentric circles are drawn with the given axes as diameters. Diameters such as 2,2 are then drawn, intersecting the smaller circle at points 1. Lines 2,P are drawn from points 2 parallel to minor axis YY_1. Other lines 1,P are drawn from points 1 parallel to major axis XX_1. These lines intersect the first lines at points P, which are points on the required ellipse. This process is repeated for other diameters until a sufficient number of points is secured to locate a smooth, accurate curve.

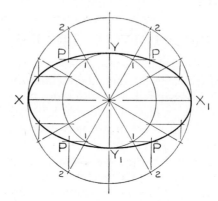

Fig. II–5.   Construction of Ellipse by Concentric Circle Method

II.6   CONSTRUCTION OF ELLIPSE BY TRAMMEL METHOD, FIG. II–6

This method is perhaps the most popular among draftsmen. Given the major and minor axes XX_1 and YY_1, a *trammel* is constructed by marking along a straight edge of a strip of paper the division points A, B and C spaced and arranged as shown. If the trammel is placed at any angle with points C and B in contact with the major and minor axes respectively, point A is a point on the ellipse. By repeated shifting of the trammel, any desired number of points may be found rapidly and easily.

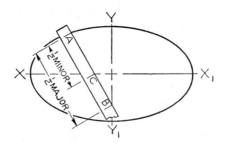

Fig. II–6.   Construction of Ellipse by Trammel Method

II.7   PARALLEL AND PERPENDICULAR LINES, FIG. II–7

With line AB given, a triangle is placed as shown in combination with the T-square or another triangle. Note that the side of the triangle *opposite* the 90° angle is placed in contact with the T-square. The two instruments are then moved as a unit until one leg of the triangle lies along the given line *AB*. With the T-square held firmly, the triangle may now be shifted along the T-square until this same leg is aligned with a given point such as *M*. Line *MN* drawn along this leg is parallel to line *AB*.

If instead, the triangle is moved until its *other* leg is aligned with a given point such as *O*, a line *OK* drawn along this leg is perpendicular to line *AB*.

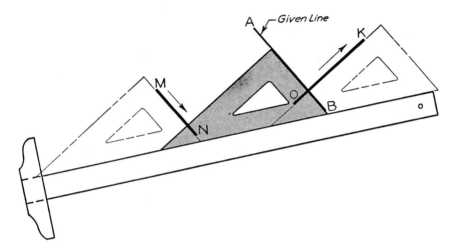

Fig. II–7.   Parallel and Perpendicular Lines

II.8   DRAWING A LINE TANGENT TO A CIRCLE FROM A POINT OUTSIDE THE CIRCLE, FIG. II–8

The perpendicularity construction discussed in Appendix II.7 is frequently employed in the construction of lines tangent to circles. In the illustration shown, the given point is point *A*. *A line tangent to a circle is perpendicular to the radius drawn to the point of tangency.*

The triangle and T-square are arranged as shown, with one leg of the triangle aligned with point *A* and tangent to the circle. The triangle is then moved along the T-square until its other leg passes through the center of the given circle. This leg then represents the radius perpendicular to the required tangent line, and the point of tangency *T* is thus located and is marked.

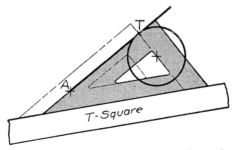

Fig. II–8.   Drawing a Line Tangent to a Circle From a Point Outside the Circle

With the triangle returned to its original position, the required tangent is drawn from A to T.

II.9   APPROXIMATE LOCATION OF A TANGENT TO A NONCIRCULAR CURVE, FIG. II–9

A tangent at given point T may be located accurately enough for many practical purposes by assuming that a small portion of the curve in the vicinity of point T is circular. Setting off small equal distances such as $\frac{1}{8}$ in. on both sides of T locates a chord AB to which the required tangent line is drawn parallel.

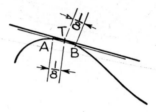

Fig. II–9.   Approximate Location of a Tangent to a Non-Circular Curve

II.10   DRAWING AN ARC TANGENT TO TWO STRAIGHT LINES, FIG. II–10

The given lines are AB and CD and the required radius is $\frac{5}{8}$ in. Centered at any convenient points such as X and Y, one on each line, construction arcs are drawn with the required radius of $\frac{5}{8}$ in. By the method of Appendix II.7, construction lines are drawn parallel respectively to the given lines and tangent to the arcs. The construction lines intersect at the required center O. Again using Appendix II.7, perpendiculars are extended from O to AB and to CD to locate points of tangency T_1 and T_2. The required arc is then drawn between these points.

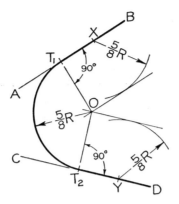

Fig. II–10.   Drawing an Arc Tangent to Two Straight Lines

II.11   APPROXIMATE RECTIFICATION OF AN ARC, FIG. II–11

The length of arc XY may be approximated by drawing line XQ tangent to arc XY at X and stepping off suitably small distances Y–1, 1–2, $\cdots$ 6–7, with dividers along the arc from Y toward X. When near X and without lifting the nearer divider point from the paper, the same number of distances is stepped off along XQ to establish Y_1. Length XY_1 will be reasonably near the length of arc XY_1, particularly if angle XOY is small. Larger angles may be divided into small equal parts for improved accuracy of this method.

The procedure may be reversed for establishing an arc approximately equal in length to a given line segment. The same general idea may also be used to set off approximately equal lengths along arcs of different radii.

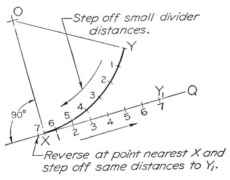

Fig. II–11.   Approximate Rectification of an Arc

CLASSIFICATION OF GEOMETRIC FORMS

APPENDIX III

FORMS FROM PLANE and solid geometry are reviewed here under three classifications: plane figures and forms composed of plane figures, single-curved surfaces, and double-curved and warped surfaces.

III.1 PLANE FIGURES AND POLYHEDRA, FIG. III–1

Polygons are plane figures bounded by straight sides. A *triangle* is a three-sided polygon and a *quadrilateral* is a four-sided polygon. *Squares* and *rectangles* are included among the quadrilaterals. The square is also one of the regular polygons, a regular polygon being any polygon with equal sides and equal interior angles.

Polyhedra are three-dimensional forms whose *faces* or surfaces are polygons, the most common examples being *pyramids* and *prisms*. A pyramid is a polyhedron with a *base* having three or more sides, and a corresponding number of *lateral faces* which are triangular and have a common point, the *vertex* or *apex* of the pyramid. A pyramid is commonly classified by the position of its principal center line or *axis* with respect to its base, plus the shape of its base, as "right square pyramid" or "oblique rectangular pyramid." The term *tetrahedron* means "four-faced," and this form could be described as an "oblique (or right) triangular pyramid."

Prisms are composed of two parallel and congruent polygons as bases, joined by lateral faces which are parallelograms. If the lateral faces (and edges) are perpendicular to the planes of the bases, the prism is a *right* prism. A *cube* is a special example of a right square prism.

Parallelepiped is a term assigned to prisms having parallelograms for bases and thus having three sets of parallel edges.

336

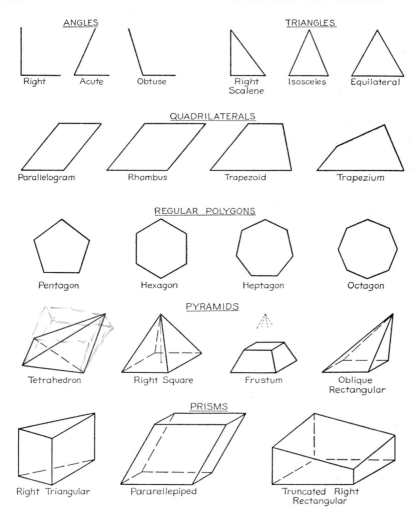

Fig. III–1. Plane Figures and Polyhedra

III.2 SINGLE-CURVED SURFACES, FIG. III–2

Single-curved surfaces are surfaces which may be *generated* by a straight line, the *generatrix*, moving in contact with a curve, the *directrix*, in such manner that any two successive positions of the generatrix either intersect or are parallel. The various positions of the generatrix are called *elements* of the surface. A single-curved surface is developable. It is a *ruled* surface, which term includes any surface which can be generated by a moving straight line.[1]

Cylinders. If the generatrix of a single-curved surface moves in such manner that it always remains parallel to its original position, the surface is called *cylindrical.* A cylinder is formed when a cylindrical surface is intersected by two cutting planes forming bases. Cylinders are classified according to the positions of their axes and the shapes of their *right sections* as "right circular," "oblique elliptical," "oblique parabolic."

Cones. If the generatrix of a single-curved surface moves so that it always passes through a fixed point, the vertex, the surface generated is *conical.* If the generatrix extends through the vertex, the conical surface consists of two portions called *nappes.* A cone consists of one nappe intersected by a cutting plane forming a base. Cones are classified in the same manner as cylinders.

Convolutes. If the directrix is a double-curved line (a curve whose points do not all lie in the same plane) and the generatrix is always tangent to the directrix, the surface generated is a *convolute.* It is a single-curved surface because any two consecutive elements (if reasonably close together) intersect and thus lie in the same plane.

The most common practical form of the convolute is the *helical convolute,* in which the directrix is a helix. In order to fulfill the requirement that the generatrix be tangent to the directrix, the elements of the helical convolute in the illustration shown are drawn at a true slope equal to the *helix angle.*

A convolute may also be generated as the *envelope* of a series of planes tangent to two curved lines which do not lie in the same plane. The line connecting the two points of tangency of any plane is an element of the surface. The *tangent-plane convolute* is represented by drawing a number of elements spaced around the two curves. A common form of this convolute occurs when two dissimilar curves, such as the circle and ellipse of the illustration in Fig. III–2 are connected with a smooth surface. Elements are located as follows: Any point such as *B* is selected on the circle. The tangent line at *B* is a frontal line, and the line tangent to the ellipse at the other end of the element through *B* is also a frontal line. Since these two frontal lines are in the same tangent plane, they are parallel. Hence the other end, point *A,* of the element through *B* is located by drawing a line tangent to the ellipse (by eye) and parallel to the line tangent at *B.* The point of tangency of this second line is the desired point *A,* and line *AB* is one element of the convolute.

---

[1] Other ruled surfaces are *warped surfaces* (Appendix III.3) and *planes.*

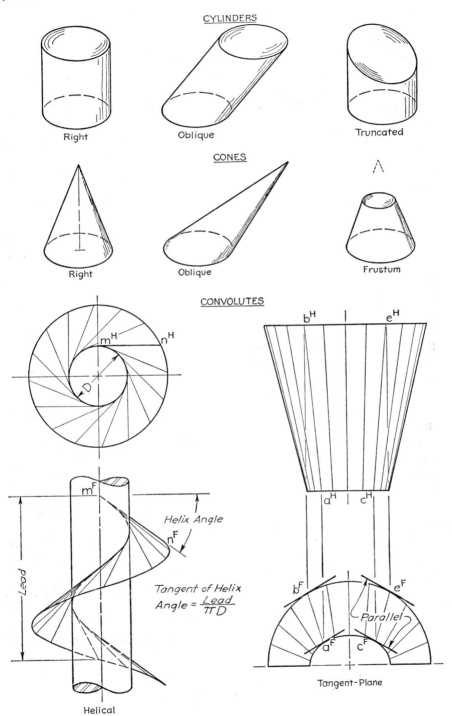

Fig. III–2. Single-Curved Surfaces

III.3 DOUBLE-CURVED AND WARPED SURFACES, FIG. III–3

A *double-curved surface* is a surface generated by a moving curved line and containing no straight-line elements. Double-curved surfaces are not developable but, in practice, are approximately developed by substituting small segments of developable surfaces for the double-curved surface.

The most common form of the double-curved surface is the *sphere,* generated by revolving a circle about one of its diameters.

The *torus* is formed when a circle is revolved in a circular path about an axis outside the circle but in the plane of the circle.

Oblate and *prolate* ellipsoids are generated by revolving ellipses about their minor and major axes, respectively.

A parabola revolved about its axis generates a *paraboloid,* and a hyperbola revolved about its axis generates a *hyperboloid.*

Warped surfaces are ruled surfaces in which no two successive positions of the straight-line generatrix either intersect or are parallel. Like double-curved surfaces they are not developable but are sometimes approximated in practice by substituting for them small portions of developable surfaces.

A common form of warped surface is the *helicoid,* in which the generatrix moves along two concentric helices and remains at a constant angle with the axis of the helices. Theoretrically the generatrix need not necessarily intersect the axis, but in practice it normally does. If the angle between the generatrix and the axis, angle θ in the illustration, is other than $90°$, the helicoid is called an *oblique helicoid.* The sloping sides of V- or Acme threads are examples of oblique helicoids. The right helicoid, used frequently in screw conveyors, is formed when the generatrix is perpendicular to the axis. An example is shown in Fig. 17–17.

An *hyperboloid of revolution* is generated by revolving a straight-line generatrix about an axis which is neither parallel to nor intersects the generatrix. In the illustration the generatrix could be either line *AB* or line *CE,* since these lines are in the same relative positions with respect to the axis except that they slope in opposite directions. The hyperboloid thus has two sets of straight-line elements and is a *double-ruled* surface.

The *cylindroid* is a warped surface generated by a straight line moving parallel to a plane director and in contact with two curves. In practice the curves are usually similar but lie in nonparallel planes.

The *hyperbolic paraboloid* is commonly used as a smooth transition between walls of different slopes. It is generated by a straight line moving parallel to a plane director and in contact with two straight-line directors which are skew lines. In the illustration the straight-line directors are lines *MN* and *XY,*

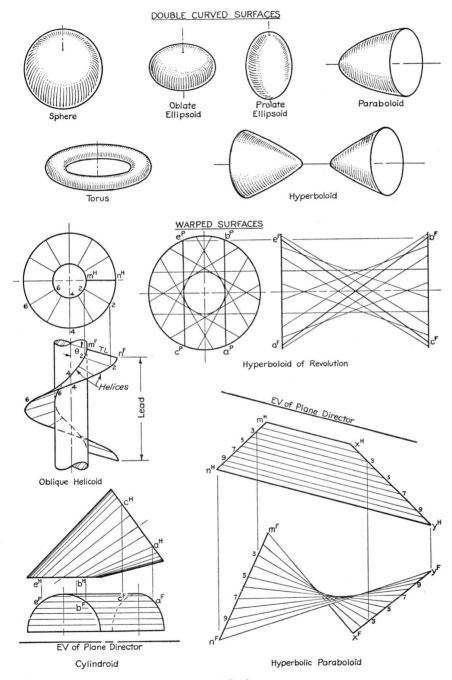

Fig. III–3. Double-Curved and Warped Surfaces

INDEX

INDEX

A

Accumulative error, 327
Accuracy, graphical, 323
Additional views, construction of, 64, 308
Adjacent views, 5
Analysis, space, 59
Angle
  accurate layout, 324
  between planes, 95–103
  dihedral, 95
  line and oblique plane, 129–135, 154
  line and principal plane, 42, 152
  plane and principal plane, 99
Apex, 336
Arc, rectification, 335
Arc tangent to lines, 334
Area, outcrop, 141
Arrangement of views, 5, 8
Asymptotes, 285
Auxiliary elevation, 22
Auxiliary views
  primary, 22
  secondary, 64
  successive, 64, 308
Axes, major and minor of ellipse, 73
Axonometric projection, 4, 261
Azimuth bearing, 46

B

Batter, 49
Bearing, 45
  azimuth, 46
  initial and final, 305
Bedding plane, 141
Bend allowance, 202
Buttock lines, 197

C

Cabinet projection, 266
Cartography, 288
Cavalier projection, 266
Center of vision, 270
Central projection, 268
Circle through three points, 330
Civil engineering problems, 136–148
Common perpendicular, 117
Concurrent vectors, 164–175, 317
Cones, 338
  development of, 205
Conical projection, 291
Conics, 283–287
Constructions, geometric, 329
Contour
  line, 137
  map, 138
Convolute, 338
Coordinate dimensions, 18
Coplanar vectors, 164
Counter revolution, 154
Curve plotting, 33, 73
Cut and fill, 144
Cylinder, 338
  development of, 210, 314
Cylindrical projection, 294
Cylindroid, 340

D

Datum plane, 137
Descriptive geometry, definition, 2
Development of
  cone, 205
  cylinder, 210, 314
  double-curved surface, 216
  helicoid, 218
  prism, 208

345

Development of (*Continued*)
  pyramid, 203
  sphere, 217
  transition piece, 214
  warped surface, 216
Developments, 201–225
  parallel-line, 202, 208
  radial-line, 202, 203
  triangulation, 202, 216
Dihedral angle, 95
Dimetric projection, 263
Dip, 140
Directrix, 283–286, 337
Distance, point to line, 68
Double-curved surface, 340
  development of, 216
Double-ruled surface, 340
Drafting practices (accuracy), 324
Drawing, multiview, 5
Dump lines, 144

E

Edge view of plane, 29, 69, 311
Elements, 236, 338
Elevation view, 22
Ellipse, 283
  approximate, 267
  construction of, 331, 332
  views of, 73
Ellipsoid, oblate and prolate, 340
Envelope, 338
Equilibrant, 164
Errors, accumulative, 327
Errors, graphical, 323

F

Fair surfaces, representation of, 197
Fault, 141
Fill and cut, 144
First-angle projection, 5
Focus, 283–286
Folding line, 10
Forces, 164
Forms, geometric, classification of, 336
Frame lines, 197
Frontal line, 37
  in plane, 59
Frontal plane, 5

G

Generatrix, 337
Geology, 140
Geometric
  constructions, 329–335
  forms, classification of, 336–341

Gnomonic projection, 289
Grade, 45, 327
Graphic solution, 1
Graphical accuracy, 323–328
Great circle, 299
Grid survey, 138

H

Helical convolute, 338
Helicoid, 340
  development of, 218
  oblique, 340
  right, 218
Helix angle, 338
Horizontal
  line, 40
  line in plane, 59
  plane, 5
  projection, 137
Hyperbola, 285
Hyperbolic paraboloid, 340
Hyperboloid, 340
  of revolution, 340

I

Intersection of
  cones, 234, 241, 242
  cylinder and cone, 232, 238
  cylinders, 231, 234, 243, 314
  line and plane, 80
  lines, 51
  plane and cone, 192
  plane and cylinder, 195
  plane and prism, 193
  plane and pyramid, 190
  plane and solids, 190–200
  plane and torus, 196
  planes, 88–94
  prism and cone, 229
  prism and pyramid, 228
  prisms, 227, 229
  surfaces, 226–251
    line tangent to, 245
    numbering system, 240
    sphere method, 234
    surfaces of revolution, 235
    visibility of, 241
Isometric
  drawing, 261
  projection, 261

L

Lateral face, 336
Latitude, 288
Layouts, problem, 17

Limiting planes, 240
Line(s), 37–55
  at given angles, 157
  contour, 137
  dump, 144
  fill, 144
  frontal, 37
  horizontal, 40
  horizontal, in plane, 59
  in planes, 56, 58, 325
  intersecting, 51
  non-intersecting, visibility, 15
  outcrop, 141
  parallel, 104
  parallel to plane, 108
  perpendicular, 111
  perpendicular to plane, 111, 116
  piercing point with plane, 80
  point dividing into ratio, 50
  point view, 66
  points on, 48
  principal, 37
  profile, 41
  profile in plane, 59
  projection on plane, 123
  segment, 37
  shortest horizontal, 121
  shortest specified grade, 122
  skew, 105, 117, 121, 122
  tangent to circle, 176, 333
  tangent to conic sections, 284–286
  tangent to curve of intersection, 245
  tangent to curved surface, 176
  tangent to plane curve, 334
  true length, 37, 42, 151, 311
  views of, 13
Line of sight, 9
Locus, 59
Longitude, 288

M

Map
  contour, 139
  projection, 288–298
  topographic, 137
Mercator map, 294
Meridian, 288
Mining and civil engineering problems,
  136–148
Motion, relative, 171
Multiview drawing, 4, 5

N

Nappe, 283, 285, 338
Nautical mile, 305
Navigation, 289, 294, 305

Non-coplanar vectors, 164
Non-intersecting lines, visibility of, 15
Normal view of plane, 29, 71, 311
  by revolution, 155
Notation, *inside front cover*, 18
Numbering system, intersection of surfaces,
  240

O

Oblate ellipsoid, 340
Oblique
  cylinder, 338
  helicoid, 340
  line, 42
  projection, 265
One-point perspective, 270, 275
Orthographic map projection, 289
Orthographic projection, 1–21, definition,
  4
Outcrop, 141

P

Parabola, 284
Paraboloid, 340
  hyperbolic, 340
Parallel of latitude, 288
Parallel line(s), 104
  construction of, 332
  development, 202, 208
  method of division, 329
Parallel planes, 106
Parallelepiped, 168, 336
Parallelism, 104–110, 312
Parallelogram of vectors, 164
Partial view, 30
Perpendicular
  common, 117
  lines, 111
  construction of, 332
Perpendicularity, 111–128, 312
Perspective projection, 2, 268
  curves, 275
  one-point, 270, 275
  two-point, 270–272
  three-point, 276
Pictorial projections, 261–282
Picture plane, 2
Piercing point of line and
  cone, 238
  cylinder, 138
  plane, 80–87
Pitch of roof, 49
Plan view, 269
Plane(s), 56–63
  angle between, 95–103
  at specified angle, 184

Plane(s) (*Continued*)
  definition, 56
  edge view, 69
  frontal, 5
  frontal line in, 58
  horizontal, 5
  horizontal line in, 59
  intersection of, 88–94
  normal view of, 29, 71, 155
  parallel, 106
  parallel to line, 108
  perpendicular to line, 113
  picture, 2
  points and lines in, 56
  profile, 7
  profile line in, 59
  projection, 2
  representation of, 56
  revolution of, 155
  tangencies, 176–189
  tangent to cone, 177
  tangent to cylinder, 179
  tangent to sphere, 181
  tangent to torus, 183
  true size and shape, 29, 71, 155, 311
Plotting curve, 33, 73
Point view of line, 66, 311
Points
  dividing line in ratio, 50
  in planes, 56, 324
  on lines, 48, 324
  views of, 12
Polar gnomonic projection, 289
Polar triangle, 302
Pole of a great circle, 302
Polyconic map, 293
Polygon, 336
  transfer of, 331
  vector, 164
Polyhedron, 336
Primary auxiliary views, 22–36
  definition, 22
Principal lines, 37
  in planes, 58
Principal planes, 22
Prism, 336
  development of, 208
Problem layouts, 17
Problems, *end of each chapter (see table of contents)*
Profile, 138
  line, 41
  line in plane, 59
  plane, 7
  section, 138
Projection(s), 2
  axonometric, 4, 261
  box, 8
  first-angle, 5
  horizontal, 137
  line on plane, 123
  map, 288
  orthographic, 4
  perspective, 2, 268
  pictorial, 261
  plane, 2
  third-angle, 7
Projective and non-projective properties, 312
Projector, 2
Prolate ellipsoid, 340
Pyramid, 336
  development of, 203
  right square, 101

Q

Quadrants, 5
Quadrilateral, 336

R

Radial-line developments, 202, 203
Rays, visual, 2
Rectification of arc, 335
Relative motion, 171
Resolution of vectors, 166, 169, 317
Resultant, 164, 167, 317
Review chapter, 308–322
Revolution, 149–163
  axis of, 149
  normal view of plane, 155
  true length, 151
Revolution of
  line, 150
  plane, 155
  point, 149
  solid, 156
Rhumb line, 294
Right
  cone, 339
  cylinder, 338
  helicoid, 340
  prism, 336
  pyramid, 336
  section, 208, 338
Ruled surface, 338

S

Secondary auxiliary views, 64
Shades and shadows, 252–260
  light source, 253
Shadows, 253
Single-curved surface, 337

Skew lines, 105, 117, 121, 122
Slope, 45, 49, 152
Solids, *see geometric forms*
Solution, graphic, 1
Space analysis, 59
Sphere, 340
  development of, 217
  method of intersection, 234
Spherical
  pyramid, 299
  triangles, 299–307
Square, construction of, 330
Station point, 2, 268
Steps in construction of additional view,
  22, 64, 308
Stratum, 140
Stretch-out line, 209
Strike, 140
Successive auxiliary views, 64–79, 308
Surface,
  double-curved, 340
  ruled, 338
  single-curved, 337
  warped, 340
Surfaces, intersections of, 226
Survey, grid, 138
Symbols on drawings, *flyleaf*

T

Table of natural tangents, *inside back
  cover*
Tangent
  line to conic section, 284–286
  line to intersection, 245
  planes, *see plane, tangent*
Tangents, natural table of, *inside back
  cover*
  use of, 324
Tetrahedron, 336
Third-angle projection, 7
Three-point perspective, 276
Topographic
  crest, 137
  map, 137
Torus, 340
Transition piece, 214
Triangulation, 202, 213, 313
Trimetric projection, 263
True length
  by revolution, 151
  diagram, 207, 214
  of line, 37, 42, 151, 311
True size and shape of plane, 29, 71, 155,
  311
  by revolution, 155

Truncated form, 33
Two-point perspective, 270

U

Umbra, 253
Uses of views, 76, 310

V

Vanishing points, 270
  construction for, 271
Vector polygon, 164
Vectors, 164, 317
Vein, 141
Velocity, 164, 170
Vertex, 336
View(s), 5
  adjacent, 5
  arrangement of, 5, 8
  basic, 8
  bottom, 8
  construction of additional, 22, 64, 308
  elevation, 22
  front, 5
  fundamental uses of, 76, 310
  left side, 8
  of line, 13
  of plane, edge, 29, 69
  of plane, normal, 29, 71
  of point, 12
  partial, 30
  primary auxiliary, 22
  profile, 7
  projected from
    front, 26
    side, 27
    top, 22
  rear, 8
  side, 7
  successive auxiliary, 64
  top, 5
Visibility, 14
  curve of intersection, 241
  non-intersecting lines, 15
  successive views, 16
Visual rays, 2, 268
Visualization, 9

W

Warped surface, 340
  development of, 216
Water lines, 197

TABLE OF NATURAL TANGENTS

Angle	Tangent	Angle	Tangent	Angle	Tangent	Angle	Tangent
0° 00′	0.0000	12° 00′	0.2126	24° 00′	0.4452	36° 00′	0.7265
15	.0044	15	.2171	15	.4505	15	.7332
30	.0087	30	.2217	30	.4557	30	.7400
45	.0131	45	.2263	45	.4610	45	.7467
1° 00′	.0174	13° 00′	.2309	25° 00′	.4663	37° 00′	.7535
15	.0218	15	.2355	15	.4716	15	.7604
30	.0262	30	.2401	30	.4770	30	.7673
45	.0305	45	.2447	45	.4823	45	.7743
2° 00′	.0349	14° 00′	.2493	26° 00′	.4877	38° 00′	.7813
15	.0393	15	.2540	15	.4931	15	.7883
30	.0437	30	.2586	30	.4986	30	.7954
45	.0480	45	.2633	45	.5040	45	.8026
3° 00′	.0524	15° 00′	.2679	27° 00′	.5095	39° 00′	.8098
15	.0568	15	.2726	15	.5150	15	.8170
30	.0612	30	.2773	30	.5206	30	.8243
45	.0655	45	.2820	45	.5251	45	.8317
4° 00′	.0699	16° 00′	.2867	28° 00′	.5317	40° 00′	.8391
15	.0743	15	.2915	15	.5373	15	.8466
30	.0787	30	.2962	30	.5430	30	.8541
45	.0831	45	.3010	45	.5486	45	.8617
5° 00′	.0875	17° 00′	.3057	29° 00′	.5543	41° 00′	.8693
15	.0919	15	.3105	15	.5600	15	.8770
30	.0963	30	.3153	30	.5658	30	.8847
45	.1007	45	.3201	45	.5715	45	.8925
6° 00′	.1045	18° 00′	.3249	30° 00′	.5773	42° 00′	.9004
15	.1095	15	.3297	15	.5832	15	.9083
30	.1139	30	.3346	30	.5890	30	.9163
45	.1184	45	.3394	45	.5949	45	.9244
7° 00′	.1228	19° 00′	.3443	31° 00′	.6009	43° 00′	.9325
15	.1272	15	.3492	15	.6068	15	.9407
30	.1316	30	.3541	30	.6128	30	.9490
45	.1361	45	.3590	45	.6188	45	.9573
8° 00′	.1405	20° 00′	.3640	32° 00′	.6249	44° 00′	.9657
15	.1450	15	.3689	15	.6309	15	.9742
30	.1494	30	.3739	30	.6371	30	.9827
45	.1539	45	.3789	45	.6432	45	.9913
9° 00′	.1584	21° 00′	.3839	33° 00′	.6494		
15	.1629	15	.3889	15	.6556		
30	.1673	30	.3939	30	.6619		
45	.1718	45	.3990	45	.6682		
10° 00′	.1763	22° 00′	.4040	34° 00′	.6745		
15	.1808	15	.4091	15	.6809		
30	.1853	30	.4142	30	.6873		
45	.1899	45	.4193	45	.6937		
11° 00′	.1944	23° 00′	.4245	35° 00′	.7002		
15	.1989	15	.4296	15	.7067		
30	.2034	30	.4348	30	.7133		
45	.2080	45	.4400	45	.7199		